Alert
Lifeguarding in Action

Acknowledgements

Alert: lifeguarding in action features the expertise and experience of lifeguards, aquatic administrators, facility managers and programmers, and professionals in a variety of fields including education, emergency medicine and law.

The author of the first edition of *Alert*, **Jocelyn Palm**, then national executive director of the Society, identified the need for an updated edition of her standard-setting text and initiated the work toward an expanded second edition. While the second edition introduces new content, *Alert* retains much of the material from the first edition, attesting to Jocelyn's insight, sound judgment, and understanding of lifeguarding principles.

This second edition of *Alert: lifeguarding in action* was prepared under the leadership and guidance of National Lifeguard Service Committee experts from across the country. This edition also includes **Frank Pia's** research on the Instinctive Drowning Response found in *On Drowning* and *Observations on the Drowning of Nonswimmers* and the factors leading to drownings in supervised areas which he authored in *The RID Factor as a Cause of Drownings* and outlined in *The World of Lifesaving*. **Richard Huint,** author of *Lifeguarding in the Waterparks*, developed the chapter on Waterpark Operation and Safety and the **World Waterpark Association** is acknowledged for "Safety Rules" from their publication, *Considerations for Operating Safety*.

Photojournalist **Victor Fisher,** whose work appears in books and magazines around the world, contributed many of the photographs. A lifeguard himself for seven years including four years with the Wasaga Beach Patrol in Ontario, Fisher says that by photographing lifeguards he still lives the life of a lifeguard vicariously through the images.

The Lifesaving Society thanks the many individuals who helped shape the content of this second edition. In particular the Society acknowledges the following people for their significant contributions throughout this book and thus to the standard of lifeguarding education in Canada:

Ed Bean
Steve Beerman
John Blaicher
Suzanne Bolduc
Frank Carlisle
Ann Carmichael
Kelvin Case
Barney Chanda
Patrick D'Almada
Mary Daniels
David Dumont
David Ferguson
Ron Ferguson
Andrew Fletcher
Frank Fowlie
Laura Grime
Raynald Hawkins
Vicky Hemming
Richard Huint
Brian Jones
Steve Jones
Sue Kanitz
Tony Kyle
Ross Leckie
Kelly Lendsay
Calum MacLeod
Wendy Mahony
G. Perry McLean
Kevin Minkhorst
Jacques Morissette
Gordon Olivant
Ted Paris
Larry Patterson
Alain Rabeau
John Rapp
Rob Richardson
James Saunders
Glenn Schultz
Michael Shane
Toby Snelgrove
Heather Straight
Ron Straight
Stuart Taylor
Michael Tremblay
Doug Trentowsky
Roy Warren
Brian Wynn
Mark Zonneveld

Foreword

Years ago, lifeguarding was a task assigned to good swimmers, often with no specific training. Then lifeguarding became the job of swimmers who had additional lifesaving credentials. Today, lifeguarding is a fascinating and important area of recreation administration, and an art and science of its own.

Lifeguards accept an enormous responsibility. They undertake to master principles and skills that are crucial to one of the greatest risk management challenges of organized recreation. Individuals who accept this responsibility are impressive. They assume attitudes and develop skills to ensure alert, vigilant and attentive service to the patrons they supervise. They learn about the burdens and pleasure of responsibility, knowledge that will serve them in many ways, beyond aquatics, for a lifetime.

The National Lifeguard Service (NLS) award was created in 1964 when the Royal Life Saving Society Canada (RLSSC), the National Council of the YMCA, the Society of Directors of Municipal Recreation of Ontario and the Water Safety Service of the Canadian Red Cross Society identifed the need for a standard-setting lifeguard training program. Today, the National Lifeguard award of the Lifesaving Society is recognized by employers and aquatic supervision legislation as "the standard" for lifeguard training.

The original lifeguard training text, *The Canadian Lifeguard Manual*, written by Richard Carlton and published by the Society in 1963, was the first publication to express a need for "special" training for lifeguards. After eight printings, the manual was replaced in 1974 by a new publication, *Alert: aquatic supervision in action*, written by Jocelyn Palm. *Alert* was a giant step forward for the definition of subject matter, and the development of the principles that shape lifeguard training today.

There are several reasons for the remarkable interest which has been shown in the successive drafts of this second edition. First, there is now a recognition of the importance of teaching lifeguards specific knowledge and skills, and it is recognized that *Alert* defines this standard. Second, drafts of the revised text have been widely circulated for critical review among lifeguards, educators, aquatic administrators and other professionals. This has made them aware of many fundamental ways in which this second edition differs from its predecessor. Building on the "your lifeguard cares" theme developed in the first edition, this second edition of *Alert* is characterized by an emphasis on accident prevention. This edition of *Alert* expands upon the technical skills and knowledge of lifesaving presented in *The Canadian Lifesaving Manual.*

Alert: lifeguarding in action reflects the original author's insight complemented by the experience of seventeen years in the evolution of lifeguarding principles and practice. We hope it meets your needs and stimulates your interest in the continuing development of lifeguarding.

Dr. Steve Beerman, President
Lifesaving Society

Contents

Chapter 1
Lifeguarding in Action

Chapter 2
Accident Prevention: Facility Analysis and Supervision

Chapter 3
Aquatic Emergencies: Recognition and Intervention

Chapter 4 Lifeguarding Skills and Procedures

Chapter 5 Waterfront and Surf Rescue

Chapter 6 Aquatic Emergency Care

Chapter 7 Public Relations and Public Education

Chapter 8 The Lifeguard and the Law

Chapter 9
Administration and Management

Chapter 10
Pre-Season and Inservice Lifeguard Training

Chapter 11 Swimming Pool Operation and Safety

Chapter 12 Surf and Waterfront Operation and Safety

Chapter 13 Waterpark Operation and Safety

Chapter 1

Lifeguarding in Action

Chapter Focus

A mature and professional attitude toward the role and responsibilities of the job is an essential characteristic of the effective lifeguard. The lifeguard's primary function is accident prevention. When prevention fails, the lifeguard is ready to respond as a rescue expert. This chapter explores the lifeguard's role and responsibilities and highlights the qualities required to do the job well.

Think About Yourself as a Lifeguard

- Picture yourself in a lifeguard uniform!
  - What is your job?
  - What do you do?
  - How do you do it?
- What are the chances of an accident?
  - How will you react in an emergency?
- Think about yourself and your lifeguard team members.
  - How will you work as a team?
  - What responsibilities do you have?
- What skills do you need?
  - What equipment do you use?
- Think about recreation.
  - Who goes to the pool or beach?
  - Why do they go?
  - When do they go?
- What do people enjoy doing in water?
  - How can you make it both safe and fun?
- Think about accidents.
  - How do you prevent them?
  - When should you act?
  - What makes prevention effective?

THE ROLE OF THE LIFEGUARD

Lifeguards are employed in a wide variety of organized aquatic environments including swimming pools, surf beaches, waterparks, and summer camps. Although there are variations in individual job descriptions, all lifeguards perform as accident preventers, rescuers, public relations officers, and administrators.

ACCIDENT PREVENTION

Since the primary task of a lifeguard is to prevent accidents, it is not surprising that as a lifeguard, you will spend most of your time engaged in accident prevention activities including controlling, directing, or influencing patron behaviour. Lifeguards must be knowledgeable about how aquatic accidents occur – when, where, why, and to whom – so that they have the understanding necessary to prevent them.

a) Prevention through facility analysis.

Lifeguards analyse both the physical characteristics and the operation of the aquatic facility, and the causes of accidents occurring in it, to identify hazards and to determine safety practices which will reduce or eliminate risks. Among other things, facility analysis and accident evaluation affect decisions about:

- the preparation and revision of safety rules
- numbers and locations of lifeguards
- the design of emergency procedures
- the type and location of lifeguard equipment
- facility operation and equipment maintenance

b) Prevention through education.

Lifeguards have a responsibility and opportunity to educate patrons and the community about the hazards and risks associated with aquatic activities and how to be "water smart." Lifeguards concern themselves with:

- communicating with patrons about how to use the facility safely
- preparing and posting facility rules
- opportunities to deliver educational messages to the community outside of the aquatic facility

c) Prevention through supervision.

To provide vigilant, attentive, and alert supervision of the patrons of the facility, lifeguards must master a variety of skills and techniques. These important supervision skills and knowledge include:

- positioning
- scanning
- victim recognition
- communication

Accident Prevention: Lifeguards prevent accidents.

RESCUE RESPONSE

Lifeguards, who train very hard to prepare for emergencies they hope will never happen, ensure their rescue capabilities through ongoing development of judgment, knowledge, skill, fitness, leadership, and teamwork.

a) Recognition of an emergency.

The ability to recognize trouble (even before it becomes life-threatening) is the foundation of effective lifeguarding.

b) Intervention in an emergency.

Lifeguards must be very good problem solvers and decision makers. Improvement in these skills as well as in specific rescue techniques results from participation in simulated emergency situations and experience with real emergencies. The experienced lifeguard is an invaluable resource for the education of new lifeguards and a source of information which leads to the development of new and improved lifeguarding techniques.

Lifeguards act as both leaders and team members, assuming a share of individual responsibility and supporting other team members in their tasks. Good communication skills become important.

c) **Lifeguarding skill, knowledge, and fitness.**

Lifeguards have a range of rescue techniques from the basic to the advanced.

Lifeguards continuously assess the needs of an emergency situation as it unfolds. Changes in rescue procedure can become necessary and the lifeguard must be able to draw instantly on an understanding of alternative skills, techniques, and procedures and adapt them to the demands of the situation.

Rescue skills are not confined to swimming accidents or deck, sauna, and shower incidents. Lifeguards who may become involved in small craft emergencies while working at a waterfront will be required to understand navigation, distress signals, and emergency repairs for example.

Physical and mental fitness are prerequisites for effective lifeguarding. Lifeguards can be called upon to perform a demanding physical rescue at any time and under a variety of environmental circumstances. Mental and physical fitness are needed to sustain vigilant, attentive, and alert supervision.

Rescue Response: Lifeguards perform rescues.

PUBLIC RELATIONS

Demonstrated concern for people is essential in achieving good public relations. The lifeguard's challenge is to maximize patrons' fun while minimizing their risk of injury.

Positive public relations stems from the attitude that patrons are guests in the aquatic facility – not inmates. "Your lifeguard cares" is an appropriate theme underlying successful public relations, and one which should be demonstrated in every comment and evident in every action of a lifeguard. Good public relations results in positive patron attitudes and behaviour.

Lifeguards have to work to overcome the attitude that lifeguard supervision inhibits fun. The goal should be to persuade patrons to see the lifeguard as someone who is professional, approachable, and eager to help rather than someone who interferes with enjoyment.

Public Relations: Lifeguards are public relations officers.

ADMINISTRATION

Every lifeguard is an administrator with some responsibility for organizing time and reports, and sometimes people and events. Reports of attendance, weather conditions, water quality and temperature, accidents, and rule infractions are data for future reference. Such reports are also critical in implementing changes which will both improve lifeguarding and prevent accidents. For example, peak attendance periods may require different staffing arrangements.

Administration: Lifeguards are administrators.

THE LIFEGUARD'S RESPONSIBILITIES

Lifeguards accept one of the major responsibilities in organized aquatics – a professional responsibility for the safety of others. Ultimately this includes the duty to respond in an aquatic emergency.

TO THE PUBLIC

The public who use the facility for recreation and pleasure are entitled to and expect a safe and happy experience. The lifeguard has both an ethical and a legal duty to provide patrons with a high level of concern and a high standard of care for their safety. At the same time, the lifeguard is expected to facilitate this safe, enjoyable aquatic experience.

TO FELLOW LIFEGUARDS

A lifeguard places trust in fellow lifeguard team members. Thus each lifeguard has a responsibility to maintain this trust by maintaining adequate skill, knowledge, and fitness levels and demonstrating a concern for personal and lifeguard team development.

TO THE EMPLOYER

In accepting the job, the lifeguard accepts the objectives, duties, and responsibilities stated by the employer.

TO ONE'S SELF

A lifeguard's education and skill improvement never stops. Ongoing practice and refinement of personal lifeguarding skills is essential. Lifeguarding techniques are revised periodically, new equipment is developed, changes in the structural features of aquatic facilities require reassessment of rules, emergency procedures, and educational practices. A commitment to excellence is crucial to a rewarding and fulfilling career as a lifeguard.

THE NATIONAL LIFEGUARD SERVICE

The National Lifeguard Service (NLS) was launched in 1964 in response to a need recognized by aquatic specialists for a comprehensive and national lifeguard education standard. Today, the Lifesaving Society certifies over 25,000 National Lifeguards annually in Canada.

THE NLS PROGRAM

The NLS training program offers comprehensive lifeguard training in four options – Pool, Waterfront, Surf, and Waterpark. The minimum 40-hour training course presents common core material plus specific training in one of the four options.

NLS courses are organized and delivered through municipal recreation departments, YMCAs, colleges and universities, boards of education, and summer camps. Individuals with NLS certification are recognized by provincial government regulations and standards as lifeguards qualified to supervise public swimming pools.

While NLS training is certainly concerned with the development of skills and knowledge, it also concerns itself with personal attitudes and values. Service, professionalism, and a commitment to excellence are three key values which NLS education attempts to instill.

NLS: CANADA'S LIFEGUARD STANDARD

The founders of the National Lifeguard Service envisioned a definitive, national standard for professional lifeguards in Canada – a single standard accessible to all employers. Today, the National Lifeguard certification is that and more.

Your National Lifeguard certification is backed by the authoritative expertise of the Lifesaving Society supported by an NLS Advisory Committee – the Canadian Armed Forces, Canadian Parks and Recreation Association, Canadian Association of Health and Physical Education and Recreation, Canadian Red Cross Society, the National YMCA and the RCMP.

The integrity of Canada's National Lifeguard certification is also assured through the national and global network of technical and medical expertise tapped by the Lifesaving Society's worldwide reach – the Society teaches swimming, lifesaving and water safety in over 60 countries, and represents Canada in the International Life Saving Federation and the Commonwealth Royal Life Saving Society. (Your National Lifeguard certification is recognized by the International Life Saving Federation.)

The National Lifeguard certification represents the definitive performance requirements and evaluation criteria for Canada's lifeguards based on the Society's research into drowning and water-related injuries, rescue techniques and equipment. This, combined with the knowledge and experience gained from the Society's participation in drowning inquests and court cases over the past 40 years, means the National Lifeguard program is regularly reviewed and authoritatively revised.

On a practical level, the single NLS standard means all guards are immediately "on the same page" when it comes to preventing and responding to incidents as a member of a team.

The single NLS standard means employers know instantly what your National Lifeguard card stands for and who stands behind it. Employers can be confident that NLS is accepted by governments and the courts as the reasonable standard for lifeguarding. Employers also know that the NLS standard is supported by the Lifesaving Society's safety management services – aquatic safety audits, expert witness consultation, aquatic safety standards, and interpretation of provincial regulations. Importantly, employers know that the Society is prepared to assist in cases of catastrophic injury or fatality.

TEST YOURSELF

1. *Describe some of the traditional ways a lifeguard is portrayed in the media (films, TV, magazines). Are these portrayals accurate?*
2. *Interview at least one non-swimmer to find out what he or she thinks a lifeguard's job is like. If you learn that misconceptions exist about the professional lifeguard's job, suggest three things you personally could do to help change these misconceptions.*
3. *Commission or make a poster that would help the public better understand your role as a lifeguard. Post it in a place where the public will see it.*
4. *Make a contract with a fellow lifeguard, your instructor, or a friend. In your contract specify what practical steps you will take to make patrons feel more welcome at your facility. For example, "I will smile at twenty people as they come through the door," or "I will say 'Good afternoon' to five swimmers I haven't met before." Carry out your contract and report back to your partner to discuss your experiences.*

Chapter 2

Accident Prevention: Facility Analysis and Supervision

Chapter Focus

Lifeguard education is directed at training lifeguards to become experts at both preventing accidents and responding to them. To be effective, the lifeguard must develop sensitivity to the dangers and safety hazards resulting from the facility's environmental and physical characteristics, as well as from patron activity. The lifeguard must be attuned to the ebb and flow of risk arising from the behaviours and varying abilities of the people being supervised. At all times, the lifeguard must be vigilant, attentive, and alert.

This chapter outlines the lifeguarding skills, systems, and procedures necessary to ensure effective safety supervision.

Think About the Meaning of "Alert"

On a hot summer afternoon, a young boy slips away from his parents, enters the water, and suddenly finds himself over his head. He is a non-swimmer. A struggle for survival begins. Even though three lifeguards are on duty, the boy might eventually drown.

The eyes of the first lifeguard pass over the young boy, who appears to be playing. The second lifeguard, who normally patrols this area on foot, is performing maintenance duties at the time. The third lifeguard is engaged in an extended conversation with a patron.

The young boy, wide-eyed and silent, slips below the surface as the first lifeguard begins a return sweep of the area.

FACILITY ANALYSIS

ASSESSING HAZARDS AND RISK

Lifeguards must be continuously alert for hazards that pose a risk to the safety of patrons. Some of these hazards are environmental such as tides, rips, or weather which can change quickly. Other hazards arise from the number of patrons and from patron behaviours or activities. Some arise from the physical characteristics of the facility itself (e.g., slopes and drop-offs).

Identification of dangers affects decisions about how to cover the area, the number of lifeguards required, positioning, and equipment needed.

a) Determine risks.

Determine hazards by analysing the facility design, potential failures of equipment and people, and environmental factors (wind, temperature, precipitation). Among other things, consider:

- deep, shallow, slope, and drop-off areas
- entry and exits points
- structures and equipment
- condition of the water and impact of weather conditions
- tides, currents, rips, holes
- signage
- potential blind spots
- number of patrons

Daily inspection of equipment and facility structures is an essential part of a lifeguard's routine. Check for items such as loose ladders, projecting bolts, worn lines, knots in rescue lines.

b) Eliminate risks.

For example, move competitive swimming starting blocks from the shallow end to the deep end, and remove them altogether when they are not in use for competition.

Note problems in writing in the daily report and check that the individuals responsible have also noted the problem and arranged for correction. Close the area when a problem which could cause an injury is not corrected.

Wordless signage conveys important messages to ALL patrons.

c) Control risks.

Regulate activity through:

- Rules for the activities.
- The physical set up of the waterfront or beach area including boundaries of supervised areas and the location of rescue equipment and rescue craft.
- Staff enforcement of acceptable behaviour.

Lifeguards often make suggestions to change the way the public use a facility. When a facility opens for the first time, unanticipated problems arise in spite of excellent planning. Note frequently occurring minor accidents or near-accidents, identify the problem, and suggest a change for the better. When crowds are using the facility, alter rules, traffic patterns, or the use of toys and play equipment if necessary.

DEVELOPING FACILITY RULES

Facility rules are designed to reduce and control risks. Safety rules are vital in preventing accidents. Rules should be:

a) Fair and realistic.

Because people come to aquatic facilities for fun and recreation, there should be as few rules as reasonably possible. Positive guidelines are often the most effective; for example, "Walk on deck areas", or "Dive only at the deep end", or "One person on the slide at a time." Sometimes a "Do Not" rule is needed, such as "No diving into shallow water."

The rules should be appropriate for the facility. In view of the variety of aquatic environments (leisure pools, wave pools, waterparks, surf beaches, and waterfronts), no standard set of rules can apply universally. Consult government regulations or standards for specific requirements in your area.

b) Specific.

Each facility's rules should outline the acceptable standard of behaviour in that particular setting so that swimmers understand what is expected without continuous interference from lifeguards. If there is a unique piece of play equipment or a special design in a pool, the rules determine how that item will be safely used. Once a new facility is in use for a time, these specific rules will evolve when unanticipated hazards emerge as problems or when anticipated difficulties do not occur. The appropriate rule is then determined to minimize risks to the users.

c) Easily understood.

Rules should be easy to interpret. The people using the facility must be able to read the written rules. The more cosmopolitan the population, the greater the number of languages required. Alternatively, universal symbols and signs provide instant recognition of a rule. Even children understand that a red slash through a sign means the activity is prohibited; that a green border permits an activity; and that yellow is a warning or caution.

Patrons are more likely to accept and abide by a rule if they understand the reason for it. Where possible, include the reason in the rule. For example, "Please walk. Decks are slippery when wet."

d) Posted.

Rules should be posted in several conspicuous locations where they can be seen by all. In some provinces, legislation dictates certain specific rules and where they are to be posted. In addition, there exists in law a "duty to warn" users of dangers. Facilities must provide a warning of hazards and ways to avoid these hazards.

RULES FOR POOLS

Each facility should evaluate and prepare the minimum number or required rules suitable for the specific characteristics of the pool and its use. The following sample rules are typical in swimming pools:

- Please shower before entering the pool.
- Please use only plastic containers. Glass may break causing injury to bare feet.
- Persons with communicable diseases: colds, open sores, nasal, eye, or ear discharge, are not permitted to use the pool.
- Floors and decks are slippery when wet. Please walk.
- Please respect the comfort and safety of others.
- Children must be accompanied by an adult, or be at least seven years old and taller than the height marker*.
- Please dive only in the three metre deep area. Diving into shallow water is dangerous.
- Please – one on the diving board at a time.

  * Height markers equal shallow water depth plus 15 cm.

See *Leisure and Flotation Accessories, Diving Boards, Hot Tubs and Whirlpools* in Chapter 2 for guidance on rules. See *Checklist for Developing Waterpark Safety Rules* in Chapter 13.

Children shorter than the height symbol on the wall at pool entrance must be accompanied by an adult.

RULES FOR BEACHES

Each beach area has rules for maintaining health and safety; some are specific to a particular waterfront situation, others apply generally to most beaches. Consider the following when establishing beach rules.

❑ **Glass containers**

Broken glass presents a serious danger to unsuspecting beach-goers when it is buried in sand or grass.

❑ **Animals**

Urine and animal droppings on a beach present health hazards as well as unpleasant odours. Animals tend to be unpredictable in a crowd and may disturb or be a threat to patrons. (Seeing-eye dogs accompanying seeing-impaired persons are an exception.)

❑ **Games**

Designate a separate area for games. In congested areas, discourage potentially hazardous activities such as baseball, frisbee, and volleyball: missed throws can cause injury and running players can collide with other patrons. Ban dangerous activities such as tossing people in blankets.

❑ **Vehicles**

Permit only emergency vehicles approved by lifeguards, and post signs to keep vehicles clear of emergency access routes. Designate a launch area for vehicles which are necessary for launching or beaching boats.

❑ **Fires and barbecues**

Open fires are dangerous in congested areas and un-extinguished coals and embers present a hazard to bare feet. Barbecues can be knocked over easily. Encourage patrons to use the grills and barbecues (if any) provided by the facility in areas away from the main crowd and buildings.

Ask patrons to extinguish fires with water before abandoning them, or provide sand-filled receptacles for hot coals. Burying fires in the sand offers the possibility for injuries on still-burning embers or sharp pieces of wood.

❑ **Littering**

Provide an adequate supply of refuse containers and encourage patrons to use them.

❑ **Swimming, scuba diving, boardsailing, boating, fishing**

Separate these activities by area. Scuba instruction, boardsailing, and boats interfere with swimmers, each posing its own hazards. Sails of beached boats or sailboards obstruct lifeguards' scanning. Unskilled sailors can seriously injure swimmers with their equipment.

❑ **Vandalism**

Encourage patrons to stay clear of safety equipment including lifeguard towers, paddleboards, rescue boats, and personal rescue equipment. Post signs to discourage inappropriate use of rescue equipment which must be ready for instant use.

❑ **Water buffer zone**

At large waterfronts, establish and mark with buoys, a buffer zone between the outside limits of swimming and the inside limits of boating or boardsailing.

Close these water areas to all activity to allow closer supervision of the swimmers. Lifeguards can use the buffer zone to patrol in boats or on paddleboards.

❑ **Alcohol**

Legislation in most municipalities prohibits the consumption of alcoholic beverages in a public place. Persons under the influence of alcohol or drugs often are a nuisance to other patrons and a distraction to lifeguards. Because inebriated swimmers suffer poor judgment, poor physical coordination, and frequently experience difficulties in the water, they are a risk both to themselves and to other patrons.

❑ **Diving or jumping from a height**

Prohibit diving or jumping from a height where underwater hazards exist and when safe supervision cannot be assured. The risk is greater when piers, wharfs, and seawalls are situated close to boating lanes.

See *Leisure and Flotation Accessories* and *Diving Boards* in Chapter 2 for guidance on rules.

SAFETY SUPERVISION

NUMBER OF LIFEGUARDS

Minimum lifeguard-to-bather ratios are frequently prescribed by provincial government regulations or standards. This means that it is unlawful to operate with fewer lifeguards than required by the regulations. However, to ensure the safety of patrons, more lifeguards could be required than are prescribed by law. Important additional factors which must be considered are:

- size and configuration of the facility
- number of patrons
- age or ability/disability of patrons
- type of patron activity
- danger areas

- equipment in use (e.g., toys, slides)
- public education and public relations requirements
- other tasks required of lifeguards
- indoor or outdoor operation
- type of program(s) offered
- budget allocated

Refer to provincial or local regulations or standards concerning the number of lifeguards. Contact the Royal Life Saving Society Canada for further guidance if necessary.

See *Single Lifeguard Situations* in Chapter 4.

POSITIONING OF LIFEGUARDS

The objective in making decisions about where and how lifeguards are positioned is to ensure effective supervision of the entire facility. Consider the following factors:

- The number of lifeguards on duty.
- The number of patrons and their behaviour or activities.
- The ability of the lifeguards to see patrons, danger areas, other guards, the bottom of the pool.
- The ability of the lifeguards to respond efficiently in an aquatic emergency.
- The size and shape of the facility being supervised.
- The desire to have as many perspectives as possible on any given zone or area (ideally, a mix of mobile, stationary, and elevated positions on all sides of the area).

The following outlines the various strategies which are used – often in combination – to achieve effective safety supervision.

a) Zones.

The three basic approaches to the supervision of swimming areas are:

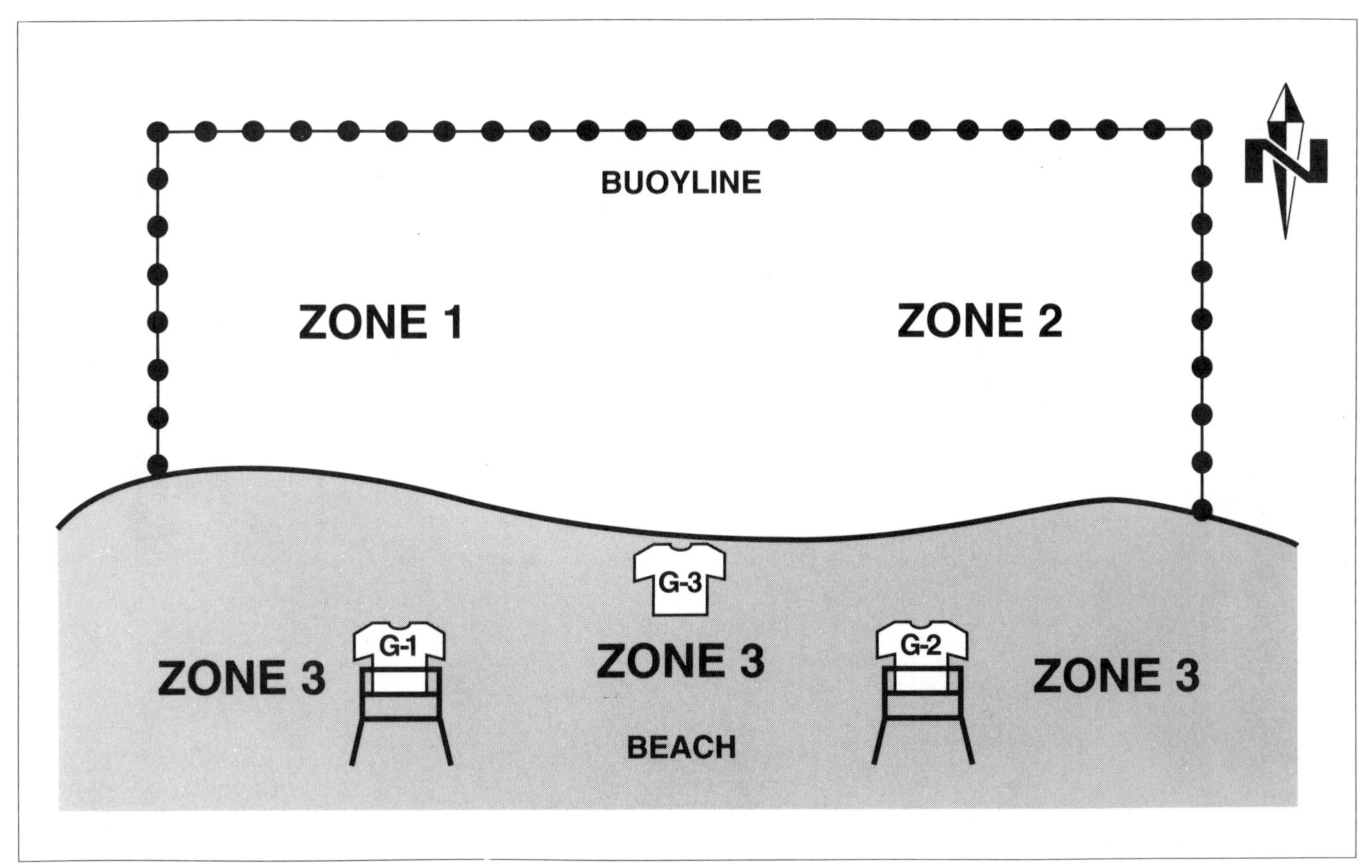

Zone Coverage

Lifeguard G1, positioned on tower, is responsible for Zone 1 (west half of the water area, from shoreline to just beyond buoyline)". Lifeguard G2, positioned on tower is responsible for Zone 2 (east half of water area, from shoreline to just beyond buoyline). Lifeguard G3, walking shoreline and beach, is responsible for Zone 3 (shoreline and beach).

- intensive coverage of specific zones
- extensive coverage of the entire swimming area
- combinations of intensive and extensive coverage

In an intensive coverage approach, the aquatic facility is divided into zones with each lifeguard responsible for a designated zone. In an extensive coverage approach, the entire swimming area is considered one big zone with all lifeguards responsible for its supervision.

Intensive or zone coverage is used where at least two, but usually three or more lifeguards are responsible for the swimming area. This approach is frequently used at pools and waterparks where multiple attractions and a high density of patrons result in an increased number of lifeguards on duty. The intensive approach may also be used at waterfronts which include a beach, rafts, docks and leisure accessories. Overlapping adjoining zone boundaries eliminates the risk of "dead zones" (unsupervised areas) which one lifeguard might assume another lifeguard is watching.

Extensive or global coverage is used where only one or two lifeguards are responsible for the entire swimming area. This approach might be used at a pool when there is a small number of swimmers and only one lifeguard on duty. The global approach is used at waterfronts where large areas of beach are covered by only one or two lifeguards from a single tower. Frequently, this approach is used along with a central back-up system. Lifeguards responsible for a long stretch of beach and water, signal the headquarters which dispatches additional staff and equipment in an emergency.

At many facilities, particularly larger facilities or those with unusual shapes, a combination of extensive and intensive coverage can provide the most effective supervision. While most of the area is guarded intensively, one or two positions are desig-

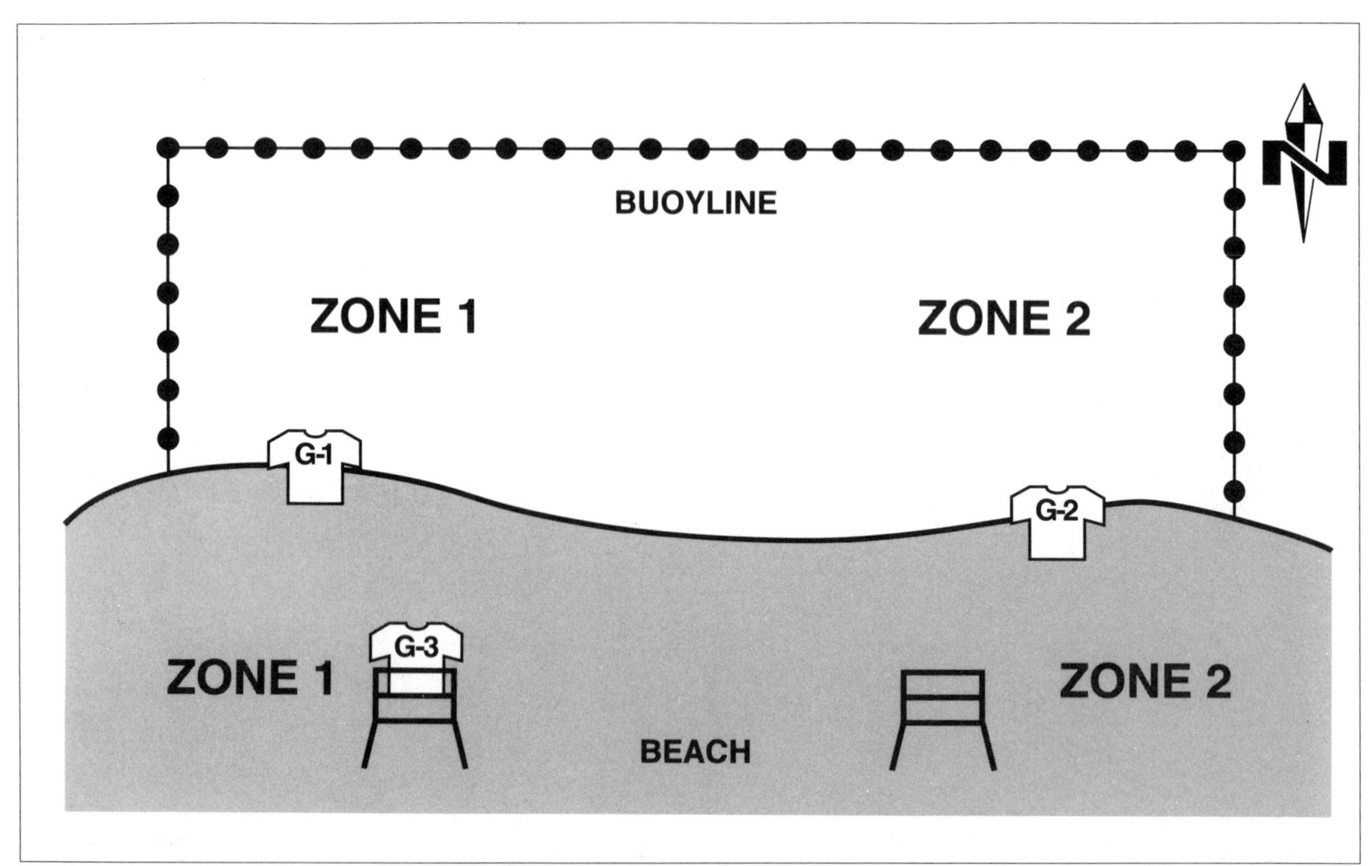

Combined Zone and Global Coverage

Lifeguard G1, walking, is responsible for Zone 1 (west half of water and beach area). Lifeguard G2, walking, is responsible for Zone 2 (east half of water and beach area). Lifeguard G3, positioned on west tower, is responsible for Zones 1 and 2 (all water and beach areas).

Lifeguard Supervision – 3 Basic Approaches

Intensive (Zone) Coverage

Advantages

- Lifeguards rotate to the adjacent zone at regular intervals to help stay alert.
- Some zones may be more demanding than others in terms of patron activity, physical characteristics, angle of the sun, and comfort. Zone rotation allows lifeguards to share the less demanding and most demanding positions.
- Some lifeguards may be more experienced at some skills than others. It is possible to assign lifeguards to a zone where their experience matches the zone requirements (e.g., use of special equipment).
- Where the facility is large or has multiple activity areas, the intensive approach is the only practical solution to the requirement for adequate observation of the entire area.

Limitations

- Where zone margins are not well defined, lifeguards may not cover their entire zone.

Extensive (Global) Coverage

Advantages

- Each lifeguard observes the entire area. Where two lifeguards are on duty each swimmer is scanned by two pairs of eyes.
- Lifeguards can adjust position more freely to suit the activities and locations of bathers.

Limitations

- Lifeguards do not rotate positions and therefore have little change of pace throughout the hours on duty.
- The size of the zone supervised is often large, there observation of swimmers is usually made from a greater distance.

Combined Approach

Advantages

- Overlapping of zone coverage and global coverage provides double supervision of swimmers.
- The lifeguard(s) in the extensive supervision role have an overview of all activity and are best positioned to relay communication to the entire lifeguard team.
- From their overview position, lifeguards can identify trends and patterns in the usage of the facility.
- The lifeguard in the extensive supervision role can provide quick contact with other services such as police, ambulance and fire, and delivery of emergency rescue equipment, without jeopardizing supervision of any area.

Limitations

- Because of the nature of the extensive role, this position usually requires height (as in towers) or mobility (as in boats).

nated as extensive supervision stations from which lifeguards can see the entire area, or at least every lifeguard on duty. At a beach, this may be a position on a raft or boat at the buoyline looking into the area, or at the top of the beach, looking over the land to the waterline. In a pool or waterpark an elevated position overseeing the entire area such as a chair or tower, or the platform at the top of a water slide, will be designated as the extensive coverage station.

Some zones in a facility (or spots within a zone) are known to be "hot" because of the number of patrons, the nature of patron activity, or because some physical characteristic (a hole, drop-off, slope) or leisure accessory (slide, inflatable, rope), demands frequent lifeguard attention. The experienced lifeguard staff takes these "hot" spots into account when designing the size and shape of zones, and planning lifeguard rotation cycles.

b) Sight lines.

The lifeguard's line of sight and field of vision are important factors in choosing positions for effective observation of a designated zone. Human vision is best focused when the observed object is directly in front of the eyes. Objects in the lifeguard's peripheral vision cannot be seen clearly or in detail. This is why lifeguards must be careful to keep turning their heads to clearly monitor the whole area.

Ideally, lifeguards should be positioned to minimize the distance the head must turn in order to effectively scan the zone. Whenever possible, the lifeguard's sight lines

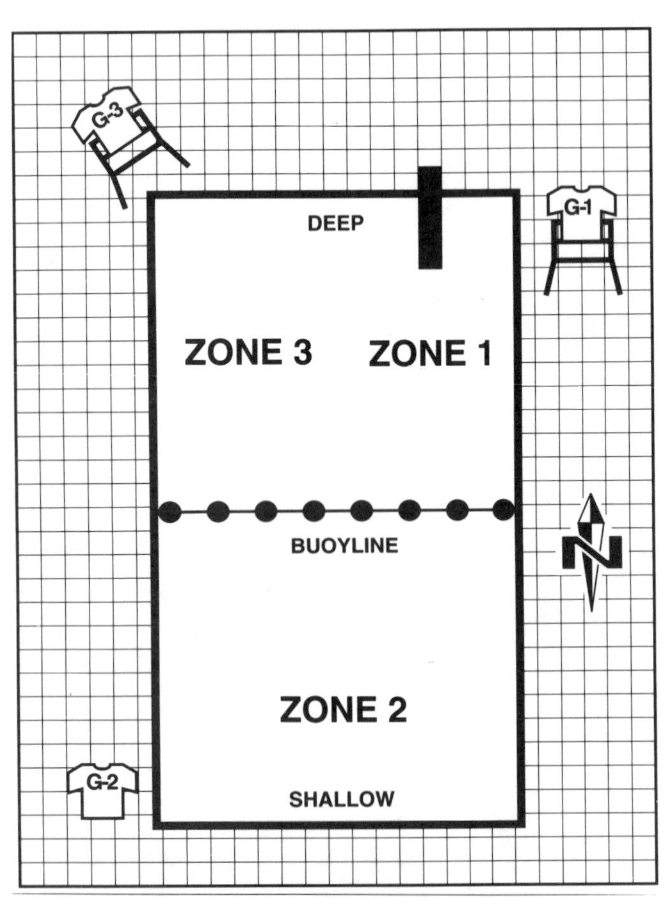

Zone Coverage

Lifeguard G1, positioned on east chair, is responsible for Zone 1 (east half of deck and deep water area to buoyline). Lifeguard G2, walking on deck, is responsible for Zone 2 (deck and shallow water area to buoyline). Lifeguard G3, positioned on west chair, is responsible for Zone 3 (west half of deck and deep water area to buoyline).

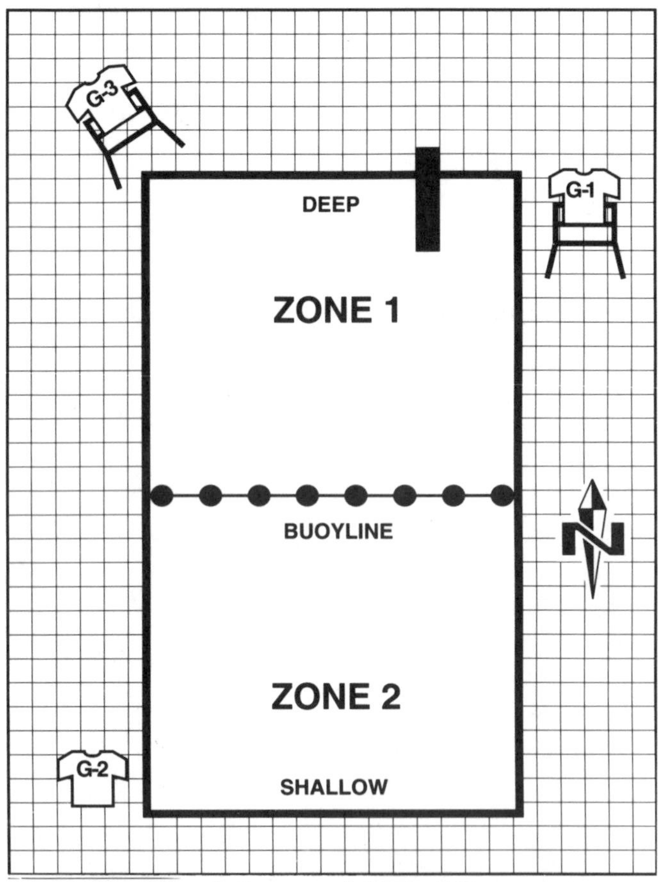

Combined Zone and Global Coverage

Lifeguard G1, positioned on east chair, is responsible for Zone 1, (deck and deep water area to buoyline). Lifeguard G2, walking on deck, is responsible for Zone 2, (deck and shallow water area to buoyline). Lifeguard G3, positioned on west chair, is responsible for Zones 1 and 2 (all water and deck areas).

should take advantage of the design of the aquatic facility. For example, a corner position offers good sight lines in a regular 25 metre pool, because the V-shape made by the corner approximates a normal visual field. If appropriate for the facility, create triangular-shaped zones to create the desired perspectives. Triangle shapes are often used in determining intensive coverage for several lifeguards supervising one facility.

c) Elevated stations.

While lifeguards need not always supervise from a chair or tower, an elevated station does give lifeguards a broader perspective than supervision from ground level. Scanning from a raised chair, platform, or tower also reduces the effects of refraction, and minimizes the way in which light or glare from the sun interferes with the ability to see beneath the surface of the water. In addition, patrons can identify lifeguards in a tower or chair more readily than ground-level guards. In a crowded area, it is useful to combine lifeguarding from a height with roving ground patrols.

d) Ground-level patrols.

A lifeguard assigned to a walking patrol or ground-level station can provide effective public relations and education and efficient enforcement of safety rules. Roving lifeguards can stay in closer verbal contact with patrons than tower guards. Mobile or roving supervision is effective for getting close to a number of different problem locations, and mobile lifeguards can monitor several locations closely within the designated area. Roving patrols can also assist by covering "blind spots" created by physical structures. Roving patrols are sometimes used to look out for small children who are either lost or straying from their parents.

Roving is especially effective when one of the lifeguard team is free to roam without responsibility for a particular zone. These

Pool Chair

Waterfront Tower

rovers can include in their circuit a wade through the shallow water or a walk through a picnic area. Free roaming rovers can monitor the "big picture" and keep other lifeguards informed of activities outside their assigned areas.

Roving lifeguards are careful to avoid turning their backs on any part of their area. The mobile lifeguard will, on occasion, have to walk sideways or backwards, to maintain eye contact with the designated area.

Note that ground-level lifeguards have a limited view of the swimming area and many patrons tend to be shielded from view. Because of their closeness to the patrons, ground-level lifeguards are more prone to distractions.

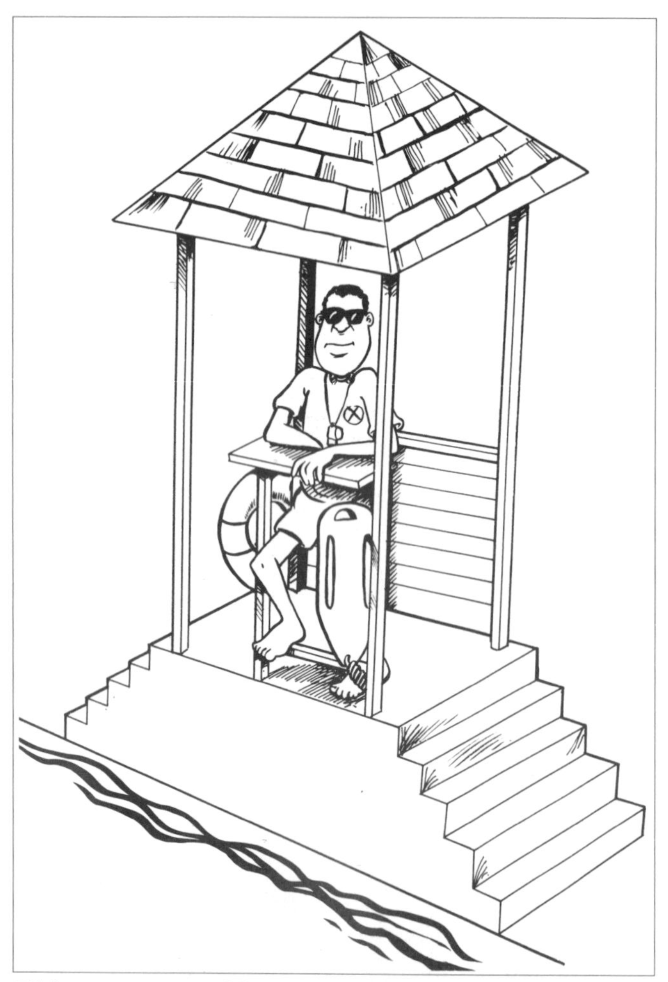

This tower provides easy side access, sun protection, and footrail for standing.

e) Rotations and breaks.

Rotations help keep lifeguards alert by providing variety and relief from the demands of any single post. Lifeguards should rotate positions on a regular interval (e.g., every 15 to 30 minutes depending on the circumstances).

Rotations should occur at a specific time and on a pre-arranged signal. One lifeguard moves at a time. The lifeguard at the least demanding post rotates to the most demanding post.

If a break is included in the rotation, the lifeguard coming from a break usually relieves the lifeguard with the most demanding post. In turn, that lifeguard relieves the next most demanding post and so on until all lifeguards have changed positions.

Each rotation allows lifeguards to share information about potential hazards or noteworthy activities in that zone. Be prompt and remain alert – information sharing should be brief and must not distract from effective lifeguard supervision. If an elevated chair or tower is used, one guard assures constant supervision while the other climbs up or down.

In addition to rotation of supervision stations, lifeguards need periodic relief from the intensity of supervision duty because a lifeguard's vigilance and physical endurance are reduced by fatigue. These breaks or relief periods should be incorporated into the rotation schedule so that at least one lifeguard is "on break" during each rotation. Lifeguards on a break from supervision duties are considered on-duty and on-call for any emergency.

f) Shifting to cover.

From time to time, lifeguards need to leave their post to respond to an emergency, communicate with a patron, or change positions for better coverage. In each case, the lifeguard signals to others on duty. When one lifeguard changes position, other lifeguards must also shift their positions to cover the gaps left by the first lifeguard's shift. Never leave an area of the swimming facility unsupervised – accidents take just seconds to happen.

SCANNING

Scanning is the systematic visual observation of the facility, its patrons, and their activities. Effective scanning must be considered the foundation of the lifeguard surveillance system. Scanning requirements and techniques are affected by different factors including:

- the number of patrons and their activities
- the number of lifeguards and their location
- the facility design and layout
- the supervision zone shape and size
- lighting conditions

Scanning a beach is significantly different from scanning a swimming pool but the basic principles are the same. Effective scanning assumes that lifeguards can see the entire area, that they know what they are looking for, and that they will recognize it when they see it.

- Lifeguards must be positioned with clear, unobstructed sight lines.
- Lifeguards must move to counteract patron interference (especially in ground-level supervision).
- Lifeguards must take steps to minimize the effect of reflection or glare (e.g., change position, use polarized sunglasses).
- Lifeguards' scanning strategy must compensate for an inability to see below the surface (e.g., waterfront environments), and for distance from patron activity (e.g., use of binoculars).
- Lifeguards must practice to develop and improve perception skills.
- Lifeguards must understand the signs of potential trouble, and the characteristic behaviours of those in need of help. (See *Recognizing Trouble* in Chapter 3.)

a) The senses and what they tell us.

Lifeguards use their senses to monitor what is happening around them so they can anticipate and spot trouble.

❑ **Vision**

Track the general ebb and flow of patrons (e.g., the number of people swimming, which areas are most tightly congested). Follow the progress of patrons who are at high risk of injury or accident. Watch for changing weather conditions. Monitor the positions and activities of other lifeguards.

❑ **Hearing**

Listen for unusual sounds such as people arguing, many people talking at once, equipment breakage. Listen for signals from other lifeguards or patrons (e.g., whistles, shouts for help). Listen for sounds that come from beyond your visual field – you can hear people behind you although you cannot see them. Listen for sounds of potential environmental hazards such as thunder.

❑ **Smell**

Smells can betray the use of liquor or some drugs, some chemicals which might indicate a leak or spill, or smoke from a fire or cigarettes.

❑ **Touch**

Feel the sun's heat, the roughness or slipperiness of the surfaces underfoot, drops of rain, or a breeze developing into stronger winds.

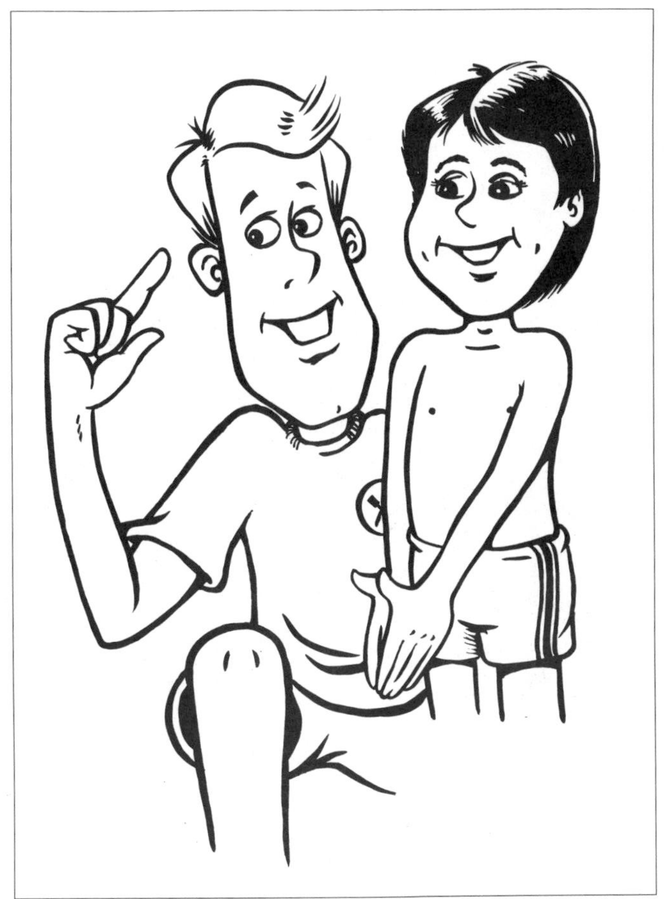

Walking patrols offer an excellent opportunity to educate patrons.

b) How to scan.

Studies indicate drownings can occur in seconds. Some victims may struggle, some slip quietly below the surface, and despite the lifeguard's best efforts, he or she may not see the event. The less time it takes to effectively scan a zone, the better.

Lifeguards who have worked in a facility for a time come to know the characteristic sights and sounds, and patterns and rhythms of activity which are normal for that facility during any given period.

- Focus on people and what they are doing. Make eye contact whenever possible. Watch the face.
- Look and listen for the unusual.
- Avoid staring fixedly at the same thing. Give your eyes a break by focusing momentarily on some distant object or the horizon.
- Use your peripheral vision to detect movement.
- Never stop scanning when speaking with a patron.
- In outdoor facilities, monitor changes in environmental conditions (weather and water) for impact on patron behaviour and safety.

c) Where to scan.

Sweep your eyes over your zone, moving your head to see things to the right and left, and looking behind you regularly. Take note of patrons and activity right in front of you. Chair or tower lifeguards should look below them. Include adjacent lifeguards on each sweep to receive any visual communications they might be sending and to check the area behind them.

Scan below the surface and, in swimming pools, scan the bottom regularly. Attend to the "hot spots" more often (e.g., diving boards, rafts, drop-offs, buoylines, ladders, toys). Ensure that each person who enters the water from a dive, slide, or diving board, resurfaces. Note that an activity "hot spot" can move with the people who create it.

d) Scanning strategies.

Lifeguards use a variety of strategies to organize and sort through sensory input, which can be overwhelming on crowded days. Commonly used techniques include:

- ❑ **Head counting**
  Try to count the number of people in your area on each scan. When the number changes, find out why.

Constant scanning is the foundation of the lifeguard surveillance system.

- ❑ **Grouping**

  Sort patrons into groups by age, sex, risk potential, activity, and combinations of the above. Monitor changes in the groups.
- ❑ **Mental filing**

  On successive sweeps, build patron profiles which take note of swimming ability, skill, activity, or other relevant factors. Track changes in patron behaviour or activity on each scan.
- ❑ **Profile matching**

  On each scan, measure what you see against the characteristic profiles of potential trouble or victim types.
- ❑ **Tracking**

  Track the progress of individuals who submerge (from the diving board or the surface), and those who fit the high-risk profile (e.g., the lone child at the water's edge).

SAFETY CHECK SYSTEMS

In addition to scanning and rotation of lifeguard positions, lifeguards might use other procedures which can increase safety:

- ❑ **Water checks**

  During very busy periods, lifeguards signal all swimmers to leave the water. These checks (sometimes called "safety checks" or "water clears") allow lifeguard rotation to occur when swimmers are out of the water. Also, lifeguards may seek cooperation, make announcements, or use the opportunity to educate patrons. When the crowd is light or when water checks are signalled too often, patrons become justifiably upset at having their activities unnecessarily interrupted. At the start and end of operations each day, lifeguards should tour the facility to ensure that no one is in the swimming area and that equipment is in proper condition.
- ❑ **Safety stops**

  An alternative to clearing the water is a safety stop: patrons are asked to tread water or stand in shallow water. If the crowd is particularly excited (especially when the noise in indoor pools becomes very loud), a safety stop tends to restore normal behaviour. In a wave pool, the regular pauses in the wave action serve the same purpose as a safety stop. Many bathers leave the water when the waves stop. Lifeguards can initiate this natural bather turnover by stopping the waves to relieve overcrowding.
- ❑ **Buddy and check-in systems**

  A buddy system might be used when organized groups are involved (e.g., camps). Swimmers are paired, and when a pre-arranged signal is given, buddies link hands and remain in place. The lifeguards note that each pair of buddies is safe and that each individual is looking out for his or her partner.

  The buddy system can be combined with a check-in by name. Each pair is given a number. When the buddy signal is given, pairs call out their numbers in numerical sequence.

  The check-in and check-out system can be used without buddies. As patrons enter the swimming area, they move their peg or tag to the "in" board. As individuals leave, they shift the peg to the "out" board. A staff member usually supervises the check point to avoid an unnecessary alarm if a patron forgets to check out.

SPECIAL POPULATIONS

Special attention should be paid to patrons with disabilities or conditions that put them at greater risk than others. Some of these conditions are visible, but other are not. Individuals with seizure disorders are particularly vulnerable in the water and should never be in or near the water alone. These individuals require close supervision.

Lifeguards may discern disabilities in patrons as a result of physical appearance, coordination, comprehension, behaviour, or combinations of these. While these individuals need to be monitored, lifeguards are cautioned to avoid focusing on a patron with a visible disability to the extent that other patrons are inadequately supervised. When groups of disabled participants come to the facility together, extra lifeguard staff may be required to provide adequate supervision.

LEISURE AND FLOTATION ACCESSORIES

Floating apparatus, toys, and other leisure accessories are popular at many aquatic facilities and lifeguards need to cultivate a positive attitude and exercise some judgment in supervising and regulating them. Such accessories have implications for patron activity and behaviours and require lifeguard awareness of the hazards and risks each poses.

Lifeguards should have input to decisions about the type, use, number, and optimal location for leisure accessories such as slides, floating toys, tarzan ropes, or cargo nets. The number, location, and type of leisure toys in use affects lifeguarding in the following ways:

- Leisure accessories often increase the number of lifeguards required for safe supervision. Each major apparatus produces certain patron behaviours and activities which require direct lifeguard supervision. Lifeguards should be positioned appropriately with an unobstructed view of patron activity on or around the apparatus. Lifeguards might be positioned on some apparatus.
- Lifeguards should experience each piece of equipment or apparatus to become comfortable with its specific characteristics and familiar with its potential for patron trouble. Rules about the use of each apparatus should be developed with lifeguard input.
- Patrons of all ages and swimming ability are attracted to leisure accessories. Lifeguards will need to educate patrons about the safe use of toys and floating apparatus, and remain alert for enthusiastic patrons with inadequate strength or swimming ability.

Toys and floating accessories are fun and increase patron enjoyment of the aquatic environment. In some circumstances, these toys and accessories may pose a hazard to the user or other patrons. The following factors should be considered in planning policies concerning buoyant aids and toys brought to the facility by patrons:

Large inflatables require direct supervision.

- Items made of glass, those with sharp points, or those with sharp or hard edges pose a hazard to the user or other patrons.
- In outdoor environments, winds, waves, and currents can pose a risk to weak swimmers or non-swimmers who rely on buoyant aids and toys such as air mattresses, dinghies, water wings, and lifejackets for support.
- Patrons should be educated to take personal responsibility for the safe use and direct supervision of their personal water toys and accessories.

DIVING BOARDS

Diving board activity needs specific lifeguard supervision because of the varying skill level of patrons and because some behaviours on diving boards increase the risk of injury.

Lifeguards help prevent accidents on and around diving boards by establishing and enforcing safety rules. These rules should control access to the board(s) and prevent collisions between divers and swimmers. Common diving board safety rules include the following:

- One person on the board at a time.
- One bounce before the take-off.
- Take-off from the end of the board only.
- Exit immediately from the water at the closest point after entry.
- No swimming underneath the board.

In addition, lifeguards should:

- Assess what other rules might be needed to ensure patron safety (e.g., restrictions on the type of dives or entries permitted).
- Monitor patrons – especially children – who decide to retreat from the board down the ladder. These people risk falling on the way down. In such cases, the lifeguard should climb the ladder and assist the patron to return safely to the ground.
- Clearly indicate at the access point whenever a diving board is closed.

HOT TUBS AND WHIRLPOOLS

The shut-off switch for a hot tub or whirlpool should be located on deck. A clock should be located in a conspicuous place for viewing by users of hot tubs and whirlpools.

Safety rules for patrons using hot tubs and whirlpools commonly include the following:

- Check for safe temperature – a maximum of 40 degrees Celsius.
- Enter and exit slowly. Headache or dizziness are signs to leave the water immediately.
- Do not use the hot tub or whirlpool alone.
- Limit length of use to 10-15 minutes at one time.
- Children under 12 years of age should be supervised by an adult at all times. Children under five years of age are not allowed in these facilities.
- Pregnant women should use a hot tub or whirlpool only with approval of their doctor.
- Persons suffering from heart disease, diabetes, and high or low blood pressure should consult their physicians prior to use.
- Do not use hot tub or whirlpool while under the influence of alcohol, antihistamines, anticoagulants, vasoconstrictors, vasodilators, tranquilizers, stimulants or narcotics.

WADING, TEACHING, AND OTHER SHALLOW WATER POOLS

Shallow water pools are found both in standalone situations in playgrounds or parks for example, and as part of a larger aquatic facility. In either case, these pools require qualified supervision.

The supervision of shallow water pools within larger aquatic facilities is relatively straight forward. Staffing and emergency procedures are designed for the entire facility and will include requirements for a shallow water pool. However, stand-alone wading pools are often not regulated in terms of lifeguarding requirements. They are isolated and too often attending staff have no back-up support. It is essential that these pools are supervised by lifeguards or individuals trained in supervision techniques and procedures, victim recognition, shallow water rescue, and first aid. Emergency procedures should be designed which provide for efficient communication with the emergency medical system.

Riders may attain speeds of 30 to 60 km/h on some slides. ***(See* Water Slides *in Chapter 13.)***

SCREENING PATRONS

Cooperation from patrons can greatly assist a lifeguard's job. Ask parents to stay close to their small children. Encourage swimming with a friend. Promote the attitude that everyone should be concerned with safety at the facility. Educating patrons about safe practices helps the lifeguard supervise efficiently by increasing the number of eyes and ears on the lookout for trouble. (See Chapter 7, *Public Relations and Public Education.*)

When sufficient staff are on duty, a staff member stationed at the entrance to the swimming facility can assess the potential risk of each patron. The person at this station greets patrons and makes them feel welcome, while learning useful information which can be communicated to the supervising lifeguards. Rotating this job gives every lifeguard an opportunity to get to know regular patrons.

The lifeguard might diplomatically ask individuals with medical alert insignia to check their medication or identify their medical problem before entering the water. If the staff member suspects patrons to be under the influence of drugs or alcohol, he or she could ask them not to swim on that occasion. The lifeguard could also remind parents of their responsibility in supervising their children.

COMMUNICATION WITH PATRONS

To prevent accidents, lifeguards must communicate successfully with patrons to stop dangerous activities and to warn and educate them about potential hazards. During emergencies, lifeguards must maintain communication with patrons both to direct and to reassure them.

Adapt communication signals and techniques to suit the specific characteristics of your facility and its clientele. Factors such as acoustics, noise levels, distances, the type of patrons, and the desire for positive public relations all influence the appropriate communication.

Communication is two-way. Learn to convey information calmly, clearly, and accurately. Practice effective listening skills to ensure that you accurately receive information important to a rescue.

a) Whistle signals.

A whistle is a useful tool in an indoor swimming facility as well as for outdoor facilities where background noise is minimal. Lifeguards' whistles have a loud, piercing shrill that sound even when wet. Constant whistle signals annoy patrons. Because swimmers can become accustomed to continuous whistles, they may ultimately ignore the signals. Use whistles only when essential. An example of a whistle signal is:

- **1 short blast means "attention"** (followed by instructions).
- **1 long blast means "emergency: leave the water."**

Educate patrons to respond quickly to lifeguards' signals and insist upon speedy reaction to "clear the water" signals.

b) Voice communication.

The most effective means of preventing accidents or correcting inappropriate behaviour is direct communication between the lifeguard and the patron. Move as close to the patron as possible. Lower yourself to the patron's physical level and use polite, firm tones and language.

Ensure that your zone is supervised during communications with patrons. Keep conversations brief and keep your eyes on the area. If you must communicate for any longer than a few seconds, signal another guard to cover your area.

Where close communication is not possible, use devices such as megaphones to project your vo ice. In large cosmopolitan areas, lifeguards have to account for a variety of languages spoken by patrons.

c) Public address systems.

Once an emergency response has been initiated, a public address (P.A.) system may aid in crowd control.

Announcements should be brief. Speak slowly, enunciate each word clearly and pause between sentences. Avoid indicating panic or annoyance in your voice. Repeat announcements can be useful; however, avoid over-use of the P.A. system.

P.A. systems are also used for important announcements during public swims, but announcements should not be so frequent that they annoy patrons or that they are eventually ignored. Limit the staff authorized to use the P.A. system. Use a tape recorder to practice public address skills.

P.A. systems are available in a variety of forms. Various models have effective ranges under different conditions. Test units before purchasing. Ensure the unit will do the job required for your specific situation.

d) Flags.

See *Flags on Shore* in Chapter 12.

FACTORS IN DROWNINGS IN SUPERVISED AREAS

Drownings in supervised aquatic facilities are rare. However, the chances that a drowning will occur in a supervised area are greatly increased by a combination of:

- a failure to **R**ecognize the signs of distress or drowning
- **I**ntrusion of non-lifeguard duties on a lifeguard's primary task – preventive lifeguarding
- **D**istraction from surveillance duties.

Based on his research study into drownings in the United States from 1919-1980, Frank Pia found that swimming-related fatalities in supervised areas can be caused by any one or a combination of the R.I.D. factors listed above.

a) Failure to recognize.

Fatalities in supervised aquatic facilities are often unwitnessed drownings in which neither the lifeguard nor nearby swimmers notice the drowning victim struggle and slip below the surface. Training in victim recognition and effective scanning techniques, combined with vigilant, attentive, and alert lifeguarding minimizes (but does not eliminate) the chances of an unwitnessed drowning. (See *Recognizing Trouble* in Chapter 3.)

b) Intrusion of non-lifeguard duties.

The intrusion of maintenance or other recreational tasks on the supervision responsibilities of the lifeguard is another factor in drownings in supervised areas.

The primary task of the lifeguard assigned to supervision duty is accident prevention and, secondarily, rescue response in an emergency. Since near-drownings and emergencies can occur at facilities with only a few patrons in attendance, lifeguards should never be assigned recreational or maintenance duties while they are a member of the surveillance team.

Attempting to reduce aquatic-related fatalities means realizing that the majority of a lifeguard's time is spent preventing people from placing themselves in dangerous situations or in engaging in hazardous behaviour. When the preventive work of a lifeguard is effective, potential life-threatening conditions are corrected before accidents occur. To the uninformed observer, however, a lifeguard engaged in surveillance work might appear less than fully occupied and therefore available for additional duties.

Administrators should be aware that any requirement that lifeguards perform non-supervision functions when they are, or should be, part of the surveillance team, sharply increases the chances of drownings and accidents. Asking a lifeguard on supervision duty to clean pool facilities, to rent umbrellas or chairs, take admission tickets, or give swimming lessons, is simply asking for trouble.

Lifeguards never perform maintenance and administration tasks while supervising swimmers.

c) Distraction.

Any distraction that takes the lifeguard away from active surveillance of bathers for more than a brief period must be viewed as a serious disruption in safety supervision. The lifeguard must detect the surface struggle of the drowning non-swimmer within seconds to keep a routine rescue from becoming serious or fatal. The consequence of inattention can be catastrophic. Educate patrons and friends to understand that you cannot talk at length with them and why you can not give them your undivided attention during brief exchanges.

WEATHER CONCERNS

Lifeguards need to be alert to weather conditions and have up-to-date weather forecasts to prepare for the hazards associated with certain types of weather. (See *Facility Evacuation* in Chapter 4. See *Weather* in Chapter 12.)

THE SUN

Lifeguards (and patrons) in outdoor facilities are at risk from the dangers of exposure to the sun. Ultraviolet radiation reflects off sand, water, and concrete and is present even on cloudy days.

Exposure to solar radiation can be extremely damaging to the skin causing sunburn, premature wrinkling, and skin cancer. The body defends itself by producing melanin which darkens the skin pigments (suntanning) adding protection from the sun. People with light or fair skin, which produces less melanin, are at greater risk from ultraviolet radiation.

Both suntans and sunburns are signs of skin damage. Even after the burn fades the damage remains and builds with each burn. The sun is the main cause of skin cancer (the most common cancer in Canada). It is significant that the Canadian Cancer Society advocates avoiding the sun as much as possible.

There are three types of skin cancer: basal cell, squamous cell, and the more deadly malignant melanoma. The first two, usually grow slowly and rarely spread, although the squamous cell can occasionally spread rapidly. Melanoma, on the other hand, can spread in the blood or lymphatic system.

Prevention and early detection are essential. Be alert for any unusual skin condition such as a sore that does not heal or a mole that darkens, changes shape, or becomes itchy. It is particularly important to prevent overexposure in children and teens. There is evidence that a single severe burn during childhood or adolescence may lead to melanoma later in life.

Protect yourself from the sun by using:

- covered towers or chairs
- umbrellas, parasols
- wide brimmed hats
- protective clothing
- sunglasses which are polarized and which block ultraviolet light
- sunscreens
- zinc oxide

Sunscreens are rated with a number according to a sun protection factor (SPF). The higher the SPF, the greater the protection. The Canadian Cancer Society recommends using a sunscreen with an SPF of 15 or higher.

Lifeguards should use a sunscreen with as high an SPF number as possible. The effectiveness of the sunscreen varies with the skin type.

CLOUDS AND SKY

The direction and speed at which clouds move indicate the movement (or absence of movement) of an air mass. Clouds which build up over many hours take a long time to break up; therefore, overcast conditions can persist for a long period. If clouds approach slowly, the storm will not likely materialize for several hours, but fast-approaching clouds indicate an imminent storm.

High, light cirrus clouds which thicken into heavier cirrostratus or cirrocumulus clouds, forecast a storm.

Lower altocumulus clouds forming into layers mean thunderstorms as do cumulonimbus (heavy black bottomed) clouds. Stratus, stratocumulus, and nimbostratus clouds are lower cloud layers that produce rain showers when they build up.

Light fluffy cumulus clouds signal fair weather.

The adage:

"Red sky at night; sailors delight.

Red sky at morning; sailors take warning."

is unreliable in areas where air pollution is a problem. (A red sky at night is supposed to indicate fair weather the next day, while a red sky at sunrise suggests rain later in the day.)

A morning rainbow is a bad sign whereas an evening rainbow forecasts good weather.

BAROMETRIC PRESSURE

Changes in the barometric readings are the earliest signs of a weather change. Decreasing (falling) pressure precedes unsettled weather. Increasing pressure during a storm or unsettled weather accompanied by changes in wind direction signals clearing. A steady barometer during good or bad weather indicates that those conditions will persist.

Be sun smart. Protect yourself from the sun with glasses, shirt, and sun screen.

TEST YOURSELF

1. *Tour a local swimming facility. Make a list of recommendations based on your assessment of potential hazards. Speak with another lifeguard or manager at that facility about your findings to learn how the staff deal with these hazards.*
2. *Evaluate the supervision procedures at a local facility. Assess the positioning of lifeguards. Discuss your evaluations with an experienced lifeguard or NLS instructor.*
3. *Observe a swimming facility in your neighbourhood. Plan how you might best supervise activities there. Where would you position yourself? Where are the potential accidents most likely to happen?*
4. *Make a list of the rules at your local swimming facility. Beside each rule, note why the rule is necessary. Interview a supervisor at the facility to ensure your answers are correct and to learn the rationale for rules you cannot justify. Can you explain to a patron the reason for each rule?*
5. *Interview a local weather reporter to learn about practical methods of predicting weather. Have a contest with a partner or among the staff to see who has the best record of forecasting each day's weather at the end of a specified period of time.*

Chapter 3

Aquatic Emergencies: Recognition and Intervention

Chapter Focus

Timely and successful intervention in an emergency springs from the confidence that lifeguards know what to look for and can recognize it when they see it.

Lifeguards are always part of a team – whether it consists of fellow lifeguards or other staff members trained in the emergency procedures of the facility. Effective and efficient teamwork results from clear and concise communication and, in an emergency, planned and practiced response procedures.

Think About the Unexpected

"I whistled twice to get the attention of the new guard across the pool. The noise level was so bad I didn't bother to yell. I gestured that I wanted her to cover my area. We had three guards on."

"I climbed down from my chair and approached the anxious eight-year-old whom I knew shouldn't be in deep water. As I directed him back down to the shallow end, I glanced back across the pool to see where the new guard was."

"She was definitely not covering my area and she wasn't in her's. Out of the corner of my eye, I spotted the shallow-end guard running toward the deep end. Following his line of sight, I spotted a guard shirt in the water."

"The new guard was in the water holding someone and screaming something to the guard approaching from the shallow end. The patrons closest to the problem stopped moving and watched. I became suddenly aware of the rest of the 112 patrons in the pool who fell under the sole surveillance of my gaze."

RECOGNIZING TROUBLE

Effective safety supervision reduces, but cannot prevent, all accidents. Lifeguards need to cultivate a heightened awareness of what is going on in their facility, and become skilled in recognizing and interpreting individual and group activities, behaviours, and patterns.

For lifesavers, who may never actually have to rescue anyone, it is hard to gain expertise in victim recognition. This is not true for lifeguards who will be afforded daily opportunities to learn what people in difficulty look like.

CHARACTERISTICS OF DIFFERENT TYPES OF VICTIMS

While working as a lifeguard at Orchard Beach, Bronx, New York, Frank Pia studied the characteristics of tens of thousands of bathers who were drowning and being rescued. He classified their behaviour into two types: distress victims and drowning victims.

Descriptions of characteristics of different victim types serve as a guide to enhance victim recognition by lifeguards. All victims may not display all the characteristics described.

a) Distress victims.

The victim in distress is unable to return to safety without assistance usually because of fatigue, cramps or currents. But because of the distress victim's swimming or floating skills, he or she may attract the attention of the lifeguard, or of other nearby swimmers by calling for help or attempting to wave one or both arms.

Signs of distress include:

- Victim attempts to communicate distress by calling for help or waving an arm.
- Victim attempts to swim to safety, but with a weak or ineffective stroke. When a patron is observed making little or no progress, he or she is in distress.

Distress victims may signal for help.

- Victim seems in pain and holds his or her arm, leg, head, or stomach. Such victims might be suffering injury, shock, or both.
- Victim is visibly holding his or her breath, cheeks puffed out and not looking comfortable.
- Victim's face shows wide-eyed fearful look.

Lifeguards must remain alert for the initial signs of patrons in distress. Speedy recognition and response is vital. As victims of water accidents experience increased stress, they become more internally focused. Rapidly, they become oblivious to things going on around them. They become less accessible to visual, verbal, or supportive aids. Their actions become more and more sporadic and purposeless.

Without timely rescue, distress victims will progressively deteriorate and begin to demonstrate characteristics of the drowning victim.

b) Drowning victims.

The characteristics of a distress victim in trouble are different from those of the drowning non-swimmer. Drowning victims are unable to support themselves in water over their depth. They have no supportive swimming skills. Drowning victims can be either at the surface or submerged. Drowning victims are more difficult to recognize especially when located a considerable distance from the lifeguard.

Drowning victims can be passive or active. The passive victim, because of a sudden loss of consciousness, slips below the surface without calling out for help or struggling. Passive drowning may be caused by a blow to the head, heart attack, stroke, hyperventilation, cold water immersion or intoxication.

Frank Pia calls the classic behaviour exhibited by active drowning victims an "Instinctive Drowning Response". This active victim, a conscious drowning non-swimmer, exhibits the following behaviour:

- no call for help or wave
- upright body position
- non-supportive leg action
- vigorous arm movements either to the sides or extended in front in an effort to raise the head above the surface

- head tilted back; face turned toward shore or help
- face and eyes show panic

All data and reports of drowning and rescue incidents indicate that few drowning victims call for help. The drowning victim is reluctant to open his or her mouth to make a verbal cry for aid.

As the drowning progresses the victim's head sinks lower and lower in the water. The arm movements become less visible and more feeble, until only the top of the head and grasping hands can be seen. Indeed, the entire drowning behaviour can be almost invisible below the surface of the water. The process can last as long as 60 seconds or take as little as 10 seconds.

LOOKING FOR TROUBLE

Some patrons indicate by appearance or behaviour that they require close attention. Learn to recognize the indicators which help lifeguards anticipate and prevent problems or accidents.

At waterfront facilities, because lifeguards know that specific bottom or water conditions can be sources of trouble, they can prevent or minimize accidents because of their ability to recognize potential danger.

Lifeguards, ordinarily located at some distance from the victim, must acquire the ability to recognize the need for assistance from afar. Despite uncertainty, always apply the principal rule of lifeguarding: whenever you suspect trouble, respond immediately. A response may be necessary when you see:

- Unusual gestures or facial expressions which suggest calls for assistance, for example, breath holding or a child with WIDE open eyes and a fearful expression.
- Poor swimmers with weak or ineffective strokes who stand up or look up frequently. Watch anyone moving from a horizontal to a vertical body position.
- Shallow water waders who do not like to get water in their face.
- Unsupervised children. Attend to any children who are carelessly supervised or who are playing in the water alone or near drop-offs. Whenever possible link these children with their parent or guardian. Reinforce with the parents their responsibility to supervise their children. Even with conscientious parents, it is often a lapse in supervision, not merely a lack of supervision which causes problems.
- Older adults who lack confidence in the water or who look frail.

Look for wide open eyes and a fearful look on drowning victims.

Rough play on wet decks can spoil the fun.

- Patrons wearing medical alert insignia.
- Patrons whose behaviour suggests alcohol or drug use.
- Crowds gathering may indicate an out-of-the-ordinary activity or an accident.
- Persons knocked over by a wave or by other swimmers. (Competent swimmers, because they recover quickly, usually do not find waves difficult.)
- Patrons with poor vision due to hair over their eyes or having removed their glasses.
- Individuals with heavy bones or above average muscle bulk tend to be sinkers.
- Distance swimmers who hyperventilate before entering the water.
- Individuals playing roughly can result in injuries, choking, or unexpected submersion.
- Shallow water divers (include those diving from a partner's shoulders or cupped hands).
- Parents or friends who instruct their children or friends to do things beyond their skill levels.
- Dare devils who attempt dangerous tricks.
- Teasers who unexpectedly grab or dunk friends or other swimmers.
- Occasional swimmers whose inappropriate or outmoded bathing attire might identify them as patrons who do not swim regularly. These patrons might be unsure of their abilities, and are likely unfamiliar with bottom and water conditions.
- Swimmers turning 360 degree circles in the water often are seeking the nearest safety point or are looking for a lost friend.

WHAT TO LOOK FOR AT THE POOL

- Corner jumpers who attempt to leap across the corner of the pool.
- Side jumpers who leap from the side of the diving board toward the sides of the pool, or those who jump from the sides of the pool and try to turn around to face the side again in mid-air.
- Gutter grabbers and rope holders who move into deep water.
- Swimmers under diving boards or slides, and at the ladders.
- Disoriented patrons who have been doing somersaults, flip turns, dives, or who have just come down a water slide, twisting and turning at high speed.

WHAT TO LOOK FOR AT THE BEACH

Waterfront patrons, many of whom swim infrequently, or who frequent swimming pools, are often unaware of the hazards associated with beaches. Swimmers typically underestimate the strength of the force created by large masses of moving water, and overestimate their

Gutter grabbers can move along the pool edge into deep water.

Swimmers under the slide do not recognize the danger.

swimming ability. Parents must be especially watchful for their children who may be quickly swept away by the strength of the waves.

Conditions continually change the bottom and shore situations making these hazardous particularly for the young or weak swimmer. Lifeguards are advised to pay particular attention to the following:

- Swimmers at the outer fringes of the supervised area who have over-extended themselves or who have drifted unknowingly into boating lanes.
- Swimmers near rips, inshore holes, and drop-offs. Lifeguards commonly rescue children close to shore, but also weak and non-swimmers who quickly find themselves over their heads in currents or drop-offs.
- Swimmers near wharfs, rocks, jetties, and piers who get too close and risk being swept against these (sometimes barnacle-covered) structures.
- Swimmers who attempt to dive over a wave, striking the bottom and injuring themselves.
- Swimmers unaware of changing depths as a result of tidal variation.
- Floating toys in offshore winds. Offshore winds quickly carry toys away from shore luring children and weak swimmers into deeper water.
- Attractive offshore hazards (islands, sandbars, floats, rafts, buoys, moored boats, and towers) can entice weak swimmers beyond their depth or cause swimmers to over extend their abilities.
- Swimmers who do not account for decreased ability and fitness levels early in the season. In addition, cold and unpredictable spring water conditions rapidly sap swimmers' strength.
- Large waves, although fun for surfing or body surfing, are troublesome for the elderly, the very young, and weak swimmers of all ages. Rolling surf can knock swimmers off their feet, batter people against the shore or rocks, and create rip currents and undertows. Swimmers can panic in breaking waves because these waves will not support them.
- When waves are submerging a swimmer heading for shore, he or she gasps for breath. Swimmers in control of themselves usually look behind at the warning sound of approaching wave. Distress swimmers intent on reaching shore disregard all else.
- A victim signals alarm as he or she turns toward safety and faces the beach. Watch for this action in combination with poor progress, weak strokes, or unnatural behaviour.

Children require direct supervision by an adult.

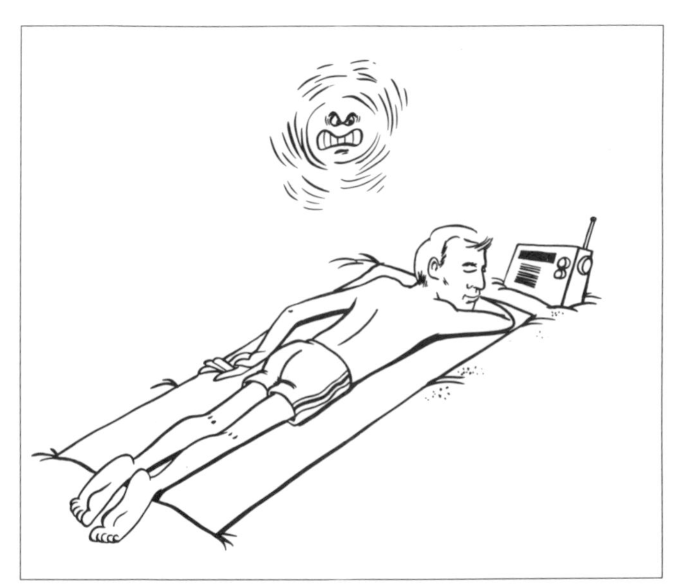

Over exposure to the sun may result in sunstroke and skin damage

PREPARING FOR EMERGENCIES

The expectation that accidents will happen motivates lifeguards to invest in preventative measures. The realization that accidents will happen in spite of their best efforts to prevent them motivates lifeguards to design and practice emergency procedures.

ESTABLISHING EMERGENCY PROCEDURES

Emergency procedures provide a framework within which lifeguards can respond quickly and appropriately to each emergency, no matter how unique. Emergency procedures answer the questions "Who will do what? When? Where? How?"

A *major emergency* involves an urgent and life-threatening accident. A *minor emergency* needs a quick response but if handled promptly, the results are not as potentially serious. However, what appears to be a minor emergency initially can, on closer inspection, turn out to be a major incident. In addition, a minor emergency can quickly deteriorate into a major one.

While no one can predict the exact circumstances of an accident, preparation is possible for the types of emergencies which occur more frequently in supervised aquatic facilities (a lost child is one typical example). Preparation for alternative actions is also necessary in case rescuers are required to alter their approach during the emergency.

Answers to the following questions are needed to prepare a written emergency plan:

- Where are lifeguards located and how many are on duty?
- What communication system is being used among lifeguards?
- Where is the emergency equipment? How will it get to the incident site?
- Who responds first? Second? Third?
- Who takes the major responsibility for handling the incident? For giving directions? For crowd control?
- Where are the preferred locations to remove victims from the water?
- Which auxiliary services – police, fire, ambulance services – should be called and under what circumstances? What is the response time for these services?
- Who summons auxiliary help ? Where is the nearest telephone or radio to make the call?
- Where are the access points for emergency services?
- What signals do lifeguards use to communicate with the public?
- Who talks with police, press, relatives?
- What reports are needed? Who completes them and initiates the follow-up action resulting from the emergency?

AUXILIARY SERVICES

Public swimming areas are often close to centres which provide additional help. Because these auxiliary services are normally under municipal authority, details of their specific roles vary from place to place. The lifeguard staff should know the location and services provided by these agencies in the community. Contact them at the beginning of the season if you are working in a summer program.

a) Telephone company.

The 911 emergency number provides access to fire, police, and ambulance services in one call. Where 911 service is not available, post telephone numbers of emergency services at the emergency telephone and dial directly. (Community emergency numbers are listed in the front of the telephone book.) Alternatively, telephone operators, who are trained to contact emergency services, can provide the appropriate telephone number or connect you directly.

b) Police.

Police can be called for assistance in case of theft, crowd control, or persons who are disturbing the peace. In the event of a serious accident or death, police will conduct an investigation. In remote areas, police will radio for other assistance when required.

c) Local hospitals.

Emergency departments are equipped to deal with accident cases. If other emergency services personnel have not done so, notify the hospital that a victim is coming and explain the nature of the accident.

d) Ambulance services.

The training of the personnel, and the equipment carried in ambulances vary. In most large centres, the ambulance carries resuscitation and oxygen equipment and the attendants are well trained in pre-hospital emergency care and basic life support; many are paramedics who can provide advanced life support.

e) Fire department.

Many fire departments have special rescue squads trained to deal with all types of community emergencies. Most fire department employees are skilled in first aid and cardiopulmonary resuscitation (CPR).

f) Poison control.

In large cities, a Poison Control Centre is usually located in one of the central hospitals. Check your local telephone directory for this number.

g) Hyperbaric centres.

In a small number of locations across Canada, a scuba diver recompression chamber provides treatment for pressure-related problems.

PRACTICING EMERGENCY PROCEDURES

Real emergencies happen suddenly and require split-second decision making under stress. Well rehearsed emergency procedures result in a confident, controlled, and orderly lifeguard response.

Established procedures mean that as many decisions as possible about how and when to respond have been made long before an emergency arises, leaving the lifeguard free to focus on the victim's problem and how to solve it.

a) Written procedures.

Decisions regarding the type of communication system, specific rescue procedures, type of equipment, and the delegation of tasks during an emergency should all be well thought out and written down.

b) Teamwork.

Practice sessions for real emergencies help develop teamwork. The ultimate goal in emergency response is the efficient functioning of the lifeguard team. All staff – office personnel, cashiers, locker room attendants, supervisory staff, as well as lifeguards – should understand, practice, and evaluate the emergency drills.

Ideally, local rescue and auxiliary services should be familiar with all procedures. Professional emergency response personnel may participate in practice sessions for their own benefit and to acquaint aquatic staff with the methods and equipment they use.

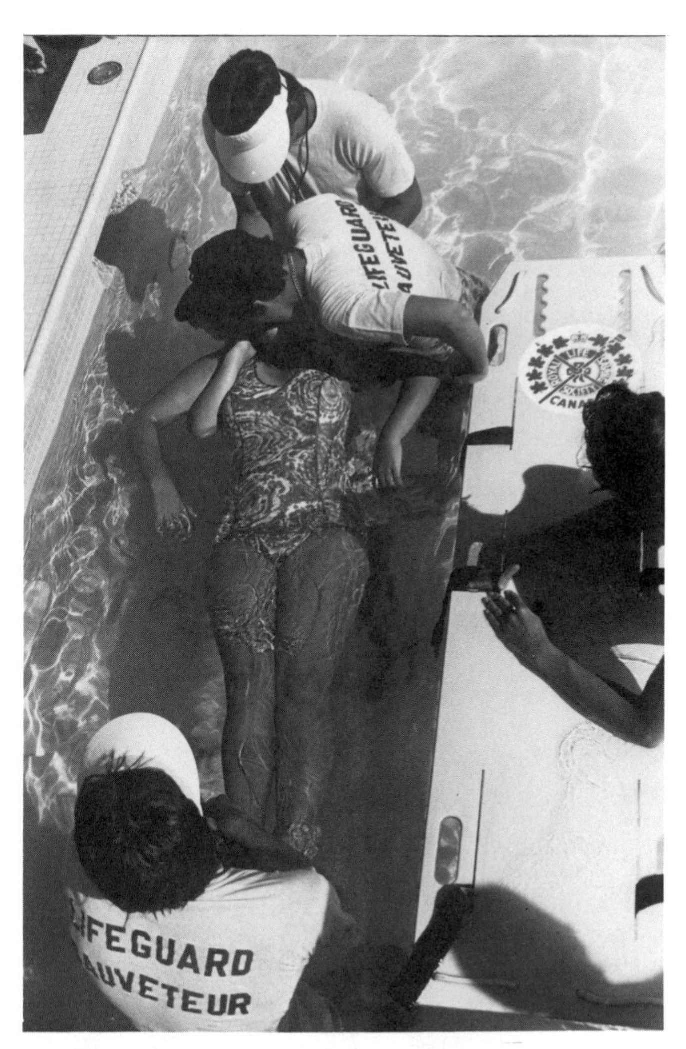

Well rehearsed procedures improve performance. Photo: Peter Cooper.

c) Simulated emergency situations.

In addition to developing confidence in dealing with emergencies, simulated emergency situations provide opportunities to keep the senses and response skills sharp. Simulated emergencies can approximate the stresses of a real situation. Low stress situations are used while lifeguards practice the basic rescue procedures. Gradually, additional stressors are added by:

- Increasing the number of victims or rescuers (or both) in the simulation.
- Raising the level of acceptable performance.
- Increasing bystander complications.
- Increasing the spontaneity and unexpectedness of the simulated emergencies by randomly organizing them over longer intervals.
- Varying the way instructions are given.
- Limiting the time allotted to perform the rescue.

d) Apprenticeship.

It is not possible to simulate the stress of being directly responsible in an actual supervision situation. A useful bridge from simulated situations to real supervision contexts is apprenticeship. This is the opportunity to work side-by-side with an experienced lifeguard on duty. Should a genuine emergency arise, the inexperienced lifeguard has the chance to apply his or her skills in a real setting with the experienced lifeguard nearby to assist. The distressed patron is not jeopardized while the apprentice gains experience and confidence.

Should no accidents occur during the apprenticeship period, the apprentice can learn from talking with and observing the actions of the experienced lifeguard.

Lifeguard competitions provide superb opportunities to perform in simulated emergencies.

e) Mental rehearsal.

Mental rehearsal is an effective way to practice while on duty. Imagine what you might do if certain accidents were to happen involving the patrons in your area. As your eyes pass over danger spots and potential accident victims, visualize your reaction and rescue procedures.

f) Evaluation and revision.

Emergency response procedures, as well as the individual lifeguard and team performance, should be critically analysed and evaluated following each practice. The same type of evaluation also follows any actual emergency. Established procedures and their effectiveness can then be reaffirmed or the procedures revised.

INTERVENTION IN AN EMERGENCY

MINOR EMERGENCIES

Minor situations can quickly become major ones. The sooner the victim is assisted, the less likely the possibility of a major problem.

A minor emergency is one to which the nearest lifeguard responds. The general procedure is:

- Recognize the emergency quickly.
- Signal to adjacent guards that there is an emergency, and respond. Adjacent lifeguards cover the zone left unsupervised and await further communication regarding the nature of the emergency. At least one lifeguard moves close enough to the emergency site to provide speedy back-up should the first responder have difficulty or should the minor emergency develop into a major one.
- Communicate with fellow lifeguards regarding the nature of the emergency.

- Administer minor first aid or otherwise assist the victim according to the nature of the problem.
- Refer the victim to the appropriate location (first aid station, parents, home, back to the water).
- Write the report, documenting the details of the emergency and its outcome.
- Signal fellow lifeguards of your return to duty.

During a minor emergency, a solitary lifeguard cannot effectively supervise the swimming area and other patrons. When a lifeguard must leave his or her station or roving patrol, the other lifeguards cover the abandoned area of supervision. They may need to shift positions to cover the area left unsupervised. (Lifeguards on break might be recalled for additional coverage until the emergency is over.) The remaining lifeguards maintain a heightened vigilance and monitor the minor emergency. Inter-lifeguard communication is essential in monitoring the status of the emergency.

MAJOR EMERGENCIES

A major emergency usually requires the involvement of more than one lifeguard. In a major emergency, the following checklist must be completed to ensure a complete and professional response:

- Recognize the emergency quickly.
- Signal to fellow lifeguards.
- Support the victim quickly.
- Assess the emergency as major or minor.
- Clear the area of patrons (entire pool area if necessary).
- Activate the emergency medical system (telephone calls).
- Complete the initial assessment of the victim.
- Move the victim (and first aid supplies or equipment) to the focal point (See Chapter 4, *Lifeguarding Skills and Procedures*.) Treat the victim for injury or illness as appropriate including treatment for shock and psychological stress.
- Maintain control of patrons.
- Communicate with the lifeguard supervisor.
- Complete the appropriate reports.

This checklist describes what must be accomplished during and immediately following most major emergencies. The procedure must be adapted to the circumstances of each emergency as priorities may vary with the situation. Maximizing speed, efficient victim care, and the safety of all are the ultimate objectives of the checklist. The lifeguard team must complete the checklist items using all the lifeguards effectively.

Many lifeguard teams employ the following breakdown of duties to complete their checklist:

a) Initial lifeguard.

After signalling to other lifeguards, the first responder goes immediately to the accident scene. The first responder is responsible for the initial support of the victim (if in the water), and for primary assessment of airway, breathing, circulation, and life-threatening bleeding, and for communicating with fellow guards.

b) Second lifeguard.

The second lifeguard immediately goes to the assistance of the first responder. Where lifeguards employ body contact to support the victim, immediate back-up by a second lifeguard is critical to the first responder's safety.

The back-up lifeguard provides assistance with victim support and removal from the

The first responder is reponsible for primary assessment.

water, and if necessary, assists with airway management or life-threatening bleeding, then initiates secondary assessment and first aid treatment, and relays information to other lifeguards. If only two lifeguards are on duty, the back-up guard ensures the water is cleared and that contact is made with emergency medical services.

c) Third lifeguard.

The third lifeguard completes the evacuation of the local area or the whole water area if necessary, obtains current information on the victim, telephones for assistance, brings first aid supplies to the emergency scene (focal point), obtains information from witnesses or friends of the victim, and ensures ongoing control of the patrons.

d) All lifeguards.

Once the emergency is under control, the lifeguards (usually the third responder) begin to collect information necessary for completing reports and recording the victim's status. For example, they interview witnesses and record vital signs.

The entire lifeguard team participates in transferring the victim(s) to the care of the ambulance crew. The team acts together to return the facility to normal use, and subsequently team members evaluate their response to the emergency. (See *Critical Incident Stress* in Chapter 6.)

COMMUNICATION AMONG LIFEGUARDS

An effective and reliable communication system results in the prevention of emergencies and an efficient response to them. When responding to emergencies, lifeguards must communicate effectively with other lifeguards to alert them to a situation and to permit everyone to operate as an efficient team.

a) Whistle signals.

Whistle signals are useful in facilities where the sound carries clearly. An example of a typical whistle signal among lifeguards is:

- **2 short blasts signal attention or alert to other guards.** This signal asks all lifeguards to look to the source of the whistle. Lifeguards often use two short blasts (or hand signals) to indicate they must leave their stations to respond to a

Signal adjacent lifeguard, then point to location to indicate "look".

Signal adjacent lifeguard, then rotate arm to indicate "rotate zones".

minor emergency or to speak with patrons, or to point out a potential or actual incident close to the other guard.

- **1 long blast signals a major emergency.** Train patrons to clear the water on this signal.

b) Voice communication.

Whistle signals convey limited information. When more information is needed, talking is a superior method.

Voice communication can occur when lifeguards rotate stations. Rotations provide a chance to convey information concerning particular problem areas, identify individuals who may get into difficulty, and relay other important messages. Ensure that the area remains supervised and that you remain alert.

Voice communication is essential in emergency situations. Lifeguards need to communicate instructions, information, suggestions, and encouragement to fellow guards. Practice vo ice communication during simulated emergencies to develop verbal exchanges which are calm and succinct.

Some lifeguard teams use verbal codes when communicating with one another. These signals convey messages without revealing information to patrons. For example, a certain number may indicate the need to telephone the police or ambulance, or indicate an assessment of a victim's condition without further alarming the victim. Weigh the value of verbal codes against the need to reassure victims. Hearing lifeguards speaking a code may increase patrons' stress since they will not understand what is happening. Calm and reassuring vo ice communication with the victim during a rescue is essential. (See *Communication with the Victim*, below.)

c) Hand signals.

Lifeguards often find that a pre-arranged system of hand signals is a useful means of communication, especially in large facilities where sound carries poorly.

Hand signals vary widely. The most important consideration is that all lifeguards at the facility use and interpret these signals consistently and instantly. If hand signals

One arm, rescue can or flag raised vertically over head means "help needed".

A horizontal signal over head means "OK" or no help needed. But no signal is interpreted as "assistance needed".

slow communication in any way, use an alternate form of communication.

(Several dialects of signing enjoy widespread acceptance among the hearing-impaired. These include American Sign Language and Exact English Signing.)

d) Telephone or two-way radio.

See *Communication Systems* in Chapter 12.

COMMUNICATION WITH THE VICTIM

Although a victim in a water rescue might fail to respond to instructions, the manner in which you communicate may have a calming effect. Gentle tones and calm soothing rhythms are the sort of para-language that might penetrate the victim's limited awareness of the surroundings. How you say something may be as important as what you say. Calm, relaxed, and decisive movements and gestures help reassure a victim.

A confident tone of voice and a reassuring manner are part of victim care.

a) Reassurance.

Although each victim will react uniquely, there are some characteristics common to accident victims in general. Expect the victim's concentration to be focused on his or her problem – pain or breathing for example. Considerations of death, family, or embarrassment may add to the victim's anxiety. What you communicate and how you communicate it, verbally or non-verbally, is an important part of victim care.

Initial reassurance may start with supportive physical contact from the lifeguard while moving the victim to safety. Subsequent reassurance will address the emotional as well as the physical needs of the victim.

b) What to say.

As soon as practical, get the victim's name and use it. Introduce yourself by name to the victim and let him or her know you are a lifeguard. Tell the victim what you are going to do before you do it. Ask permission. The following are the types of questions (both open-ended and specific) which may provide useful information:

- "Are you okay?"
- "What's the problem?"
- "What's your name?"
- "Has this happened before?"
- "Do you hurt anywhere else?"
- "Do you have any medical problems we should know about?"
- "Will you let me help you?"
- "Are you here with anybody else?"
- "Whom should we call for you?"

Listen carefully to the response to your questions. When more than one lifeguard is in attendance, avoid overloading the victim with questions from more than one person.

c) How to say it.

Tone of vo ice, facial expressions, and body language all convey information. Make and sustain eye contact whenever possible. Maintain a calm and confident tone of vo ice. Your manner and especially your facial expressions should communicate confidence in the successful outcome and your ability to manage it.

COMMUNICATION WITH EMERGENCY SERVICES

When a major emergency occurs, contact emergency medical services. Effective lifeguard performance must be supplemented immediately with medical care. Many communities use the 911 emergency telephone number which connects the caller to a trained dispatcher who directs the call to one or more of the emergency response systems – ambulance, police, or fire department. Once connected the operator leads the conversation, seeking the information crucial for obtaining the required assistance. In areas not yet equipped with the 911 system, know the individual telephone numbers for each service. Many facilities have direct-line telephone communication to the appropriate emergency services. (See *Sample Emergency Telephone Procedure* in Chapter 3.)

Assign a responsible person to meet the emergency response team and direct them to the accident scene. Once the ambulance team arrives, they assume responsibility for the care of the victim(s). Be ready to offer help if needed, information about the cause of injury, and the method of care and any change in the status of the victim (records of changes in vital signs and results of secondary assessment). Emergency response teams follow their own protocols or action plans – they will ask for this information as needed. Assist, as required, with crowd control and first aid.

In many instances, emergency response teams will not assume responsibility for an aquatic accident victim until the victim is removed from the water. Ambulance and paramedic services are happy to discuss their role and responsibilities with lifeguards and are often willing to visit the facility to clarify their duties and emergency response procedures.

Sample Emergency Telephone Procedure

- Dial 911 or individual emergency service number.
- Confirm the service you want (ambulance, police, fire).
- There is a medical (or other) emergency.
- I need an ambulance (or other service)
- My name is . . . .
- I am a lifeguard at . . . .
- The address is . . . .
- The best cross street to use is . . . .
- The telephone number is . . . .
- We have a (victim description: status of ABCs) . . . .
- We are treating by . . . .
- When do you think you will arrive?
- Do you have any instructions for us?
- Someone will meet you at the entrance.
- The directions for emergency access are: . . . .
- Would you please confirm the address?

DO NOT HANG UP UNTIL THEY DO

Things To Do Until Help Arrives

- Rescue scene assessment
- Primary survey
  - ABCs
- Secondary survey
- Provide oxygen if needed/available
- Position the victim appropriately for his or her condition.
- Treat for shock; place a blanket over and under victim.
- Comfort and reassure the victim. Tell the victim what is happening and what you are doing.
- Keep bystanders away.
- Call family or friends for the victim. Take care of personal belongings.
- Stay calm yourself. Work with the ambulance team when they arrive.
- Complete the accident report form. Do not discuss the incident; details should be confidential.

TEST YOURSELF

1. *Make arrangements to "shadow" guard with an experienced lifeguard. Follow this lifeguard and test your powers of observation against his or hers. Ask questions like, "What are you watching for?" or "What are the particular hazards in this area?" Discuss your experience with your National Lifeguard Service instructor in order to learn more.*
2. *Take up a position in a swimming area while you are blindfolded. Have others make a variety of sounds around the area. Can you identify patron activity and behaviour? Report your observations to a partner to check your accuracy.*
3. *Watch a film or video tape of real or simulated accidents in a crowded area. Can you spot the accidents? Can you suggest ways they might be prevented by a change in supervision procedure?*
4. *Improve the speed of your recognition and reaction through drills. Here are three examples:*
   - *A patron (or other lifeguard) releases a coloured ball in a zone. The lifeguard must see it within ten seconds and be holding it within 20 seconds. Holes can be made in the ball so that it will sink within 30 seconds.*
   - *Someone tosses balls of two different colours in the water. One colour represents a minor emergency situation, the other colour a major emergency. Your job is to notice the ball, signal appropriately, then get to the ball as fast as you can. A timer stops when you hold the ball above the water. The same drill can be used with more than one guard.*
   - *Assign swimmers a number and have them plan a major or minor situation they can simulate individually. Space the swimmers around the facility. When a number is called, that swimmer simulates an accident. The lifeguard's job is to recognize, signal, and quickly support the victim. The timer stops when the victim's head is supported above the surface. Compare response times over a period of practices to check on speed improvement.*
5. *To understand the notion of a panic-stricken non-swimmer, try this exercise. Cross your legs and your arms across your body in deep water to simulate a non-swimmer's lack of supportive ability. Note your reactions to being unable to support yourself. As you run shorter and shorter of air, you may experience rising tension and anxiety. Are your actions becoming more and more violent as you try to stay at the surface? Remember this experience to help you understand what it is like to be a victim in distress.*
6. *Meet with representatives of various emergency services such as police, fire department, ambulance, or paramedic. Ask them to describe their role when responding to emergencies in your facility or community.*

7. *With another lifeguard or lifeguard candidate, determine which of the following accidents you would treat as major emergencies and which you would treat as minor ones. (Assume several lifeguards are on duty with 50 swimmers in the water.)*
   - *A non-swimming patron slips into water over his head.*
   - *A patron suffers from a leg cramp.*
   - *A patron slips on the deck breaking her wrist.*
   - *An elderly patron complains of severe chest pains.*
   - *A young child slips off the slide and falls two metres onto the deck.*
   - *Several patrons near the filter room complain of headaches and nausea.*
   - *An adolescent suffers a seizure in shallow water.*
   - *A small child is reported missing.*
   - *A woman in her twenties who belly-flops from the one meter board has the wind knocked out of her.*
8. *Perform as a team in applying first aid to a victim of a simulated accident. Discuss the results of these exercises and offer suggestions to improve your ability to verbally communicate.*
9. *Design ten "case cards" which outline patrons' typical unsafe behaviours, e.g., child running on a slippery deck, adult diving into shallow water, parent encouraging a child to perform beyond his skill level. Role play these cases to practice communicating with patrons.*
   Discuss the results of the role playing including each player's description of his or her feelings about the case. Make suggestions to one another for improving your communication skills.
10. *Practice making an emergency telephone call using the sample emergency telephone procedure form in Chapter 3.*

Chapter 4

Lifeguarding Skills and Procedures

Chapter Focus

The essential task in a rescue emergency is to intervene quickly, remove the victim from danger, and manage any life-threatening problems.

Unlike lifesavers, lifeguards perform rescues in an environment where hazards are known, minimized, or controlled, with more sophisticated equipment and with other lifeguards to assist. Specific emergency procedures are planned and practiced. Well trained lifeguards possess the maturity, judgment, skill, knowledge, and fitness to assess risk and to make decisions about alternative techniques and procedures.

Because lifeguards use many of the water rescue skills they learned as lifesavers, the techniques detailed in The Canadian Lifesaving Manual are not repeated here. This chapter focuses on rescue procedures from the lifeguarding rather than the lifesaving point of view.

Think About the Victim's Problem

"I'm a pretty fair swimmer – or so I thought until the day I had to be rescued. That was the scariest, and most embarrassing day of my life!"

"One minute I was fine and the next thing I knew I was in over my head. It was like stepping into a hole. I was taking a breath just as the bottom disappeared. I guess I panicked a little because I couldn't get my breath and my feet couldn't find the bottom."

"I remember thinking that I was going to die, that nobody saw me. There were lots of people swimming right near me, but they didn't seem to notice anything was wrong. I strained trying to get my mouth out of the water to call out, but I just got more water. The waves kept washing over my face. I couldn't see anything, and all I could hear was a kind of dull roar. I felt myself losing strength. It was all I could do to stay near the surface."

"When that lifeguard lifted my head out of the water, I took the biggest breath of my life and started to cry."

WATER RESCUE SKILLS

THE RESCUE RESPONSE

The most critical decision a lifeguard must make is whether or not to go into action, and the stress of sudden exposure to an aquatic emergency can cause uncertainty. The response is always – when in doubt, intervene immediately.

Some lifeguards find it helpful to develop a "response habit." When they think they see a victim in distress, they make a physical move such as raising their hand, or standing up, or moving toward the potential problem location. This physical action primes them for intervention and helps overcome potential psychological blocks to initiating a rescue.

The longer a distressed victim faces a life-threatening problem without a solution, the more panic-stricken and dangerously unmanageable he or she may become. The sooner the victim's immediate problems of lack of support and inability to breathe are solved, the more cooperation the victim may be able to provide in reaching solid ground.

The rescue checklist provides the lifeguard with a framework within which to make decisions about the appropriate rescue response. The checklist links what the lifeguard knows about victim recognition and victim behaviour to lifeguard reaction and selection of procedures. Lifeguards must have a set of skills within each item on the checklist.

❑ **Recognize**
- Recognize that there is a need to act.
- Determine the problem.

❑ **React**
- Signal fellow lifeguards.
- Obtain appropriate equipment.

❑ **Rescue**
- Enter the water.
- Approach and assess the victim.
- Provide support to the victim.
- Get the victim to safety; initiate treatment.
- Complete the follow-up procedure.

❑ **Report**
- Complete the report.

Entries must combine safety with speed of rescue.

ENTRIES

Speed of support for the victim is important. Quick support of the victim's head and shoulders above the surface reduces the risk of drowning, and eases the victim's fear providing reassurance which may allow the victim to cooperate. Therefore lifeguards need the skills to move safely and quickly from their station to the victim. Note that in trying to provide a speedy response, lifeguards must take care to avoid personal injury caused by an inappropriate or poorly executed entry. Practice methodically, then pick up speed with practice.

From ground level, lifeguards select one of the following entries appropriate for the circumstances:

- slip in, wade in, or run in
- stride entry, running stride entry
- shallow dive, running shallow dive
- head-up dive, running head-up dive

Whether to enter the water directly from an elevated chair, tower, or platform is a matter for the lifeguard's judgment. In many situations it is unsafe or unwise to enter the water from a height. Factors to consider include:

- location and condition of the victim(s)
- height of the chair, tower, or platform
- depth of the water
- use or choice of rescue aids
- appropriateness of entry (jump, dive, stride)
- patron safety (number of bathers in the area)
- lifeguard skill and safety

CONTACT AND NON-CONTACT RESCUES

Lifesavers are trained to avoid contact rescues and to use a rescue aid at all times. Lifeguards, on the other hand, make both contact and non-contact rescues. In contact rescues, they may or may not use a rescue aid. In making decisions about the use of contact or non-contact rescue techniques, and rescue aids, lifeguards should consider the following principles:

- The victim's head and shoulders should be supported above the surface at the earliest possible moment.
- The safety of the rescuer must be assured. Whenever a lifeguard undertakes a contact rescue, a second lifeguard should enter the water to provide immediate back-up if required.

Other factors to consider include:

- the type and proximity of rescue equipment
- the availability of back-up support
- the condition and location of the victim
- the number and location of other patrons
- the rescue environment (depth, waves, currents, etc.)

Obviously, a solo lifeguard would make different decisions from those made by a lifeguard working as part of a team of lifeguards. For details on reaching and throwing assists, see *The Canadian Lifesaving Manual.*

a) Rescue aids.

To protect the victim and other patrons from injury, select a soft rescue aid whenever possible. The following rescue aids are widely used:

❑ **Reaching poles**

Exercise caution to avoid striking or tripping patrons with a reaching pole during a rescue.

❑ **Rescue cans and rescue tubes**

Rescue cans and tubes are two of the most versatile pieces of rescue equipment used in pools, waterfronts, and surf situations. The rescue can (or torpedo buoy) is made of formed polyethylene and filled with air. The rescue tube is made of soft foam with a vinyl cover. The rescue can is firm, while the rescue tube is flexible. The tube may be placed around the victim under the arms and fastened in that position with a spring clip. Both pieces of equipment feature a shoulder loop and line and good buoyancy. The rescue can will support three or four people.

For rescue, place the shoulder strap over one shoulder and under the opposite arm and tow the can or tube behind you. Extend the aid to the victim for support with instructions to hold onto it. If the victim is more distressed, approach from behind. Force the aid around the victim's middle, doubling him or her over the can or tube.

When the rescue tube is used, clip the tube around the victim, ensuring that the victim is calm enough for you to approach safely to clip the buckle. Should the victim attempt to grasp you, slip out of the shoulder loop and back away into ready position and encourage the victim to grasp the buoyant aid to stay afloat. Slip back into the shoulder loop or use it as a towing line and swim to shore while maintaining visual and verbal contact with the victim.

Rescue poles with body-hooks support the victim above water and do not rely on a victim's ability to grasp the pole.

❑ **Throw bags**

The throw bag consists of a nylon bag stuffed with braided polyethylene line attached to a styrofoam disc at the base of the bag. Ties can be knotted on the outside of the bag to form a grab loop for ease of carrying. As the name implies, this is a rescue aid thrown in much the same manner as other throwing assists. Throw bags have limited buoyancy and are unlikely to provide adequate support to a victim.

❑ **Ring buoys**

While typically very buoyant, ring buoys can be difficult to throw with accuracy. Caution must be exercised to avoid injury to either the victim or to patrons when throwing a ring buoy in a crowded swimming area.

❑ **Flutterboards, lifejackets and PFDs**

Although not designed for use as rescue aids, flutterboards (also called kickboards) lifejackets and PFDs (personal flotation devices) can also be used by lifeguards. They are light, easy to carry, and provide enough buoyancy to support a swimmer's head at the surface and are easily clutched by the victim in difficulty. Flutterboards should be taken, not thrown to the victim. The waist straps of lifejackets can be tied together to form a modified shoulder loop.

b) Reach.

Assist a victim close to the side of the pool or dock by lying or kneeling down and extending a hand. If the victim is too far from the edge to be reached, slip into the water and, while retaining a grip on the edge or gutter, extend the other arm.

c) Underwater push.

An underwater push to the side or to shallower water can be used. Jump or dive into the water and swim close to the victim. While still underwater, push the victim towards the side or shallow water.

This technique must be used with caution. Avoid lifting and forcing the victim against the pool wall. Contact may be made from in front or from behind depending on the victim's position. You can push against the victim's legs or hips or grasp and push under the victim's arms.

d) Walking assist.

The lifeguard can walk the victim to safety. This is used primarily for younger swimmers. If the water is slightly over your head, grasp the victim around the waist to support the victim's head above the surface.

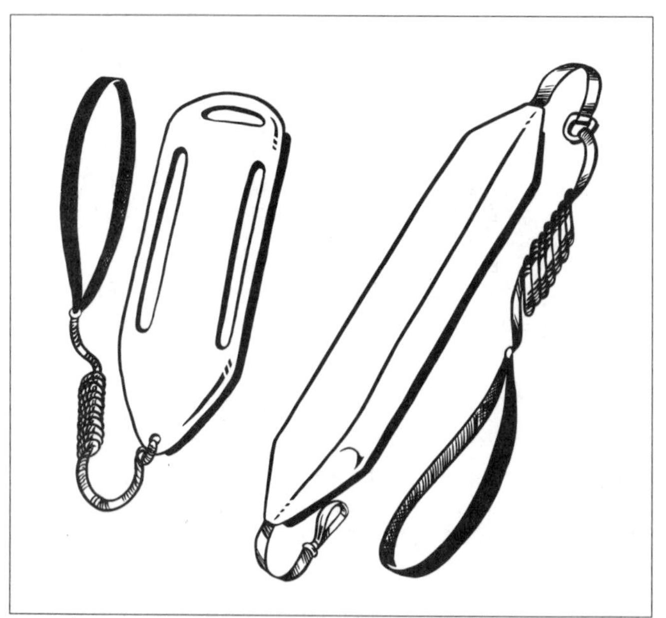

Rigid plastic rescue can (left). Flexible foam rescue tube (right).

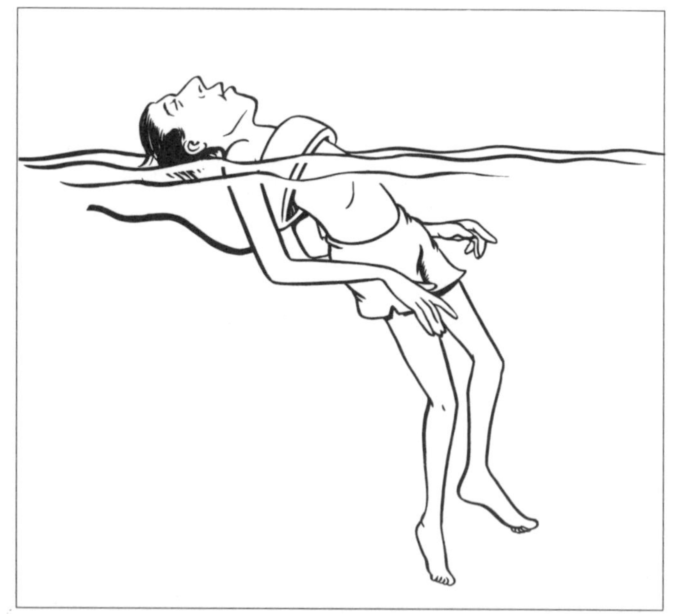

The rescue tube can be fastened around unconscious victims to support them face-up providing a good position for rescue breathing if required.

Submerge to push off the bottom and move towards shallower water.

e) Carries.

The goal in every rescue is the speedy support of the victim's face above the water and a quick transfer of lifeguard and victim(s) to the nearest point of safety. Safety means solid ground, such as the beach, shallow water, or edge of pool deck or dock. With any of these carries, the lifeguard can also use a rescue aid.

Various assistive carries may be used for weak or non-swimmers: underarm carry, chin carry, arm carry, tired swimmer carry. Assistive carries are suitable for pools and in calm waters. A swimmer tired or exhausted from over-exertion or cramp may be gently assisted to safety in this way.

The lifeguard can use a variety of control carries: double chin carry, head carry, cross chest carry, modified body carry, arm grasp carry, elbow carry. See *The Canadian Lifesaving Manual* for detailed descriptions of each of these carries.

❑ **Hip or "Pia" carry**

A control carry designed specifically for use by lifeguards is the hip or "Pia" carry. Approach the victim from behind and below, encircle the victim's waist with one arm and support the victim's buttocks or thigh on your hip. This keeps the victim's head clear of the water while you swim to safety with a one-arm pull and a whip or eggbeater kick. The priority is to keep the victim's head (and shoulders) out of the water while staying low and behind the victim. The lifeguard should attempt to keep his or her head clear of the surface and reassure the victim while moving to safety.

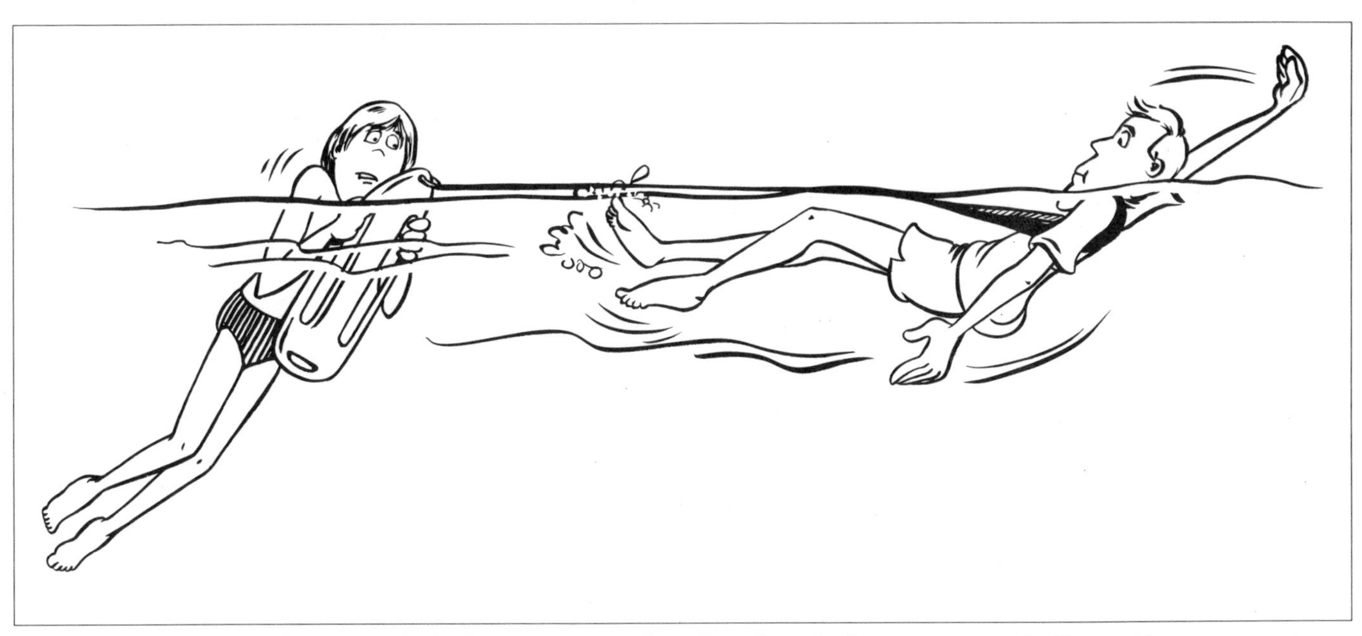

The rescue can provides good victim support, visual and verbal contact, and allows the rescuer to use both arms for swimming.

Push the submerged victim to the surface.

This carry is used only over short distances where safety can be reached within 10 - 15 m and when there is at least one other lifeguard available as back-up.

f) Non-breathing victims.

The priority in rescue of the unconscious non-breathing victim is to get the victim's head out of the water, the airway open and clear, ventilations assessed and maintained, and circulation assessed and maintained. Since these priorities are very difficult to execute in deep water or at the pool or dock edge, immediate movement to shallow water and/or removal from the water is essential.

The use of aids is dependent on their immediate availability and their potential to help or hinder in the approach and victim recovery.

The rescue breathing turnover and carry (with or without an aid) is an effective method for recovering an unconscious victim quickly to shallow water. Cover the victim's mouth and nose with one hand and ascend (if necessary), pushing off the bottom if possible.

Reach over the face-down victim's back with one arm (while still covering the victim's mouth with your other hand), and pull the victim towards you onto his or her back while sliding your arm over the victim's arm and under the victim's shoulder to support the victim's upper back

The hip or "Pia" carry provides good victim support over a short distance.

The rescue breathing carry provides control of victim's head and airway, while moving quickly to shallow water.

by grasping the back of the victim's neck or opposite arm.

If a buoyant aid is used, grasp the aid on the far side of the victim with the hand reaching under the victim's back.

REMOVAL OF A VICTIM FROM THE WATER

For detailed descriptions of removal techniques refer to *The Canadian Lifesaving Manual.*

Removal of a victim from the water may be difficult depending upon the victim's condition and the location where removal takes place. Avoid further injury to the victim. If the victim is already injured, twisting, pulling, or jolting movements can complicate these injuries. Rough handling of the non-breathing victim promotes regurgitation.

In most emergencies, lifeguards remove the victim from the water to land. However some accidents may occur on the deck, beach, or dock area. In all cases, prepare seriously injured victims for transport by ambulance to the hospital.

If the victim is not breathing, begin rescue breathing; removal from the water is secondary. If the victim requires cardiopulmonary resuscitation (CPR), it must be performed on a suitably hard, flat surface. In this case immediate removal from the water is necessary. Minimize interruptions in rescue breathing during removal from the water.

A patron who is capable of climbing the ladder should be assisted with the lifeguard firmly holding both rails while following behind the victim.

When additional lifeguards are present to assist, the removal is easier for all concerned. Teamwork is important in the transfer. Lifeguards should practice these procedures in the role of both director and assistant.

In any removal, get the victim clear of the water in a short period of time. Shock is an important consideration in victim care; a victim whose feet are left dangling in the water loses heat more rapidly than the victim who is completely dry and covered with a blanket.

Avoid unnecessary single rescuer manual lifts. If possible, wait for assistance and ensure that you have full control of the victim throughout. Whichever removal technique you select, be sure that it is the least complicated choice and that you:

- Work with your legs, not your back.
- Maintain the victim's head above the surface.
- Minimize the risk and discomfort to the victim.
- Minimize movement of the victim.

Master one or two removal techniques initially, for example, one single-rescuer technique and one multiple-rescuer technique and practice them to the point of proficiency. Expand your capabilities in inservice training.

FOCAL POINTS

Focal points are pre-determined locations where lifeguards take all victims (except minor pullouts) for follow-up. In a rectangular pool for example, the focal point is often some-

Before lifting the victim, the lifeguard on deck reaches under the victim's arms and grasps both wrists securely; the lifeguard in the water holds the edge with one hand and wraps the other arm firmly around the victim's hips.

where along the edge of the shallow area. Select focal points with consideration for:

- available space
- proximity to equipment
- location of emergency exits
- inter-lifeguard and external communications, including location of the emergency telephone
- visibility
- ease of removal

It might be necessary to designate several focal points depending on the size and design of your facility. Pre-selecting the focal point permits fellow lifeguards to anticipate your destination during a rescue. Rescue and first aid equipment can be stored discreetly near the focal point making access to this equipment faster and easier in an emergency. If the focal point is in shallow water, lifeguards find it easier to support and manage a distressed victim.

SPECIFIC LIFEGUARD PROCEDURES

Many large aquatic facilities, especially those which are part of recreational complexes or systems, will have specific procedures for non-aquatic emergencies such as fire, theft, or vandalism. How the lifeguard staff participates in these procedures should be determined by those responsible for the aquatic facility. Where no such procedures exist, it will be up to the aquatic facility management to prepare suitable procedures. (See *Coordination of Staff in a Recreation Complex* in Chapter 9.)

TEAMWORK AND BACK-UP

A second lifeguard should never be far behind a lifeguard making a rescue. Fellow lifeguards can help support either the victim or each other should either get into difficulty. They can assist with equipment, help both rescuer and victim to safety, and participate in decision making.

In a minor emergency in which a lifeguard enters the water, a second lifeguard shifts to take a position as close to the incident as possible while still covering his or her assigned area. From this position, the second lifeguard can assess and monitor the situation as it unfolds and provide immediate assistance if needed. Where lifeguards use body contact to support the victim, immediate back-up by a second lifeguard is critical to the first responder's safety.

See also, *Teamwork and Back-up* in Chapter 5.

SINGLE LIFEGUARD SITUATIONS

While situations in which only one lifeguard is on duty are not encouraged, it is recognized that this may be the case in many small or private pools (e.g., hotel, motel, apartment, condominium, or private club pools). In such cases:

- Emergency procedures for the facility must be designed for the single lifeguard who must have an effective, rapid method of contacting the emergency medical system. Other facility employees should be part of and trained in the procedures for an aquatic emergency. (Government regulations in some areas require another person trained in the emergency procedures of the facility to be within easy call.) In the event of an emergency, this person notifies police/ambulance services of the emergency before directly assisting the lifeguard. The person may be signalled by a call for help, by sounding a siren, or by ringing an alarm. If absolutely necessary assign a mature, capable patron to telephone and activate the EMS.
- In a rescue situation, the lifeguard working without the support of other trained lifeguards should consider himself or herself a lifesaver and act accordingly (only as a last resort, would you use a body contact rescue on a conscious victim, for example).
- If a single lifeguard must leave his or her post for any reason, swimmers must be asked to clear the water.

BYSTANDERS

Bystanders at an accident scene can assist with crowd control, assist with simple first aid, bring first aid supplies, open doors or gates, and perform other helpful tasks as needed.

Choose bystanders who volunteer to help. They likely have the appropriate attitude and willingness to follow your instructions. Be direct and specific in giving bystanders instructions.

There is always the possibility that bystanders may themselves be direct (or indirect) victims of the accident. The sight of blood or injuries psychologically traumatizes some people. People may panic if the cause of the accident is not known or if lifeguards do not take time to reassure them. Some people have actually sustained injuries as a result of being near the accident scene.

Calm bystanders by explaining the situation and by issuing confident, positive instructions concerning expectations from bystanders. Ensure that no one else is injured before placing the facility back into operation.

CROWD CONTROL

During and after an emergency, lifeguards may have to deal with a large number of patrons who are attracted and/or inconvenienced by the incident. Lifeguards should have a pre-determined plan to both protect and control a crowd in an emergency. Crowd control aims to protect the members of the crowd from injury, protect the victim of the emergency and lifeguards dealing with it from interference, and ensure safe and speedy access for emergency response personnel.

The behaviour of people in a crowd will vary with these circumstances:

- the number (and type) of people in the crowd
- the space available to accommodate the crowd
- the ability of the crowd to see the incident
- the ability of the lifeguards to communicate with the crowd
- the authoritative manner of the lifeguards

At least one member of the lifeguard team should be assigned the responsibility for crowd control. He or she might recruit additional suitable mature individuals from the crowd to assist.

Clear, specific, and authoritative communication is essential. Use the communication device appropriate for the size of the crowd and the nature of the incident. For minor incidents or small crowds, vo ice communication may be adequate. In other circumstances, the public address system or megaphones may have to be used. Inform the crowd of the emergency and ask for their assistance. Establish an appropriate perimeter and maintain it with the assistance of fellow lifeguards or responsible bystanders if necessary. Whenever possible, identify or create a physical barrier ("against the wall," or "behind the flags," etc.).

The head and neck are immobilized using the victim's extended arms. Photo: Peter Cooper.

In a swimming pool, patrons could be instructed to sit against the perimeters of the facility until the ambulance arrives. The yellow tape used by emergency services and construction crews might be used to create a physical barrier.

MANAGEMENT OF SPINAL INJURIES

Spinal injuries can result from impact with the bottom after diving into shallow water or, less frequently, from a jack-knifing of the spine upon impact. With proper management, the spinal cord which has not been severed or damaged on the initial impact, can be protected against catastrophic injury.

a) Principles and tasks.

Proper management of a spinal-injured victim requires the coordination of many skills into a sequence which immobilizes the spine, maintains airway, breathing and circulation, and allows for victim removal and transport. Lifeguards must use judgment in making decisions about how and when to stabilize the victim on a spineboard and remove the victim from the water. Factors which will have to be considered include:

- the number of lifeguards available
- whether and how bystanders might be used
- the characteristics of the removal site (e.g., depth of water, distance from deck/dock to the surface, surf conditions)
- the victim's condition
- the victim's size
- the lifeguards' size and strength

The above factors may alter the techniques selected but will not alter the principles of care nor the essential tasks which are:

❑ **Recognize**
- Quick, accurate recognition of the accident and clearing of the area.
- Entry which minimizes movement of the victim (i.e., creates no waves).

❑ **Immobilize**
- Face-up recovery of the victim at the surface with immobilization of the head and neck.

❑ **Maintain airway**
- Assessment and ongoing maintenance of ABCs (airway, breathing, circulation).
- Effective resuscitation if necessary.
- Reassurance and continuing communication with the victim.

Immobilization and airway management are the essential tasks when handling a spinal-injured victim. Photo: Peter Cooper.

- Contact emergency medical services.

❑ **Stabilize**

- Minimal movement of the victim.
- Recruit help if required.
- Effective lifeguard teamwork (and supervision of bystanders, if used) – stabilization of the victim on a spineboard and removal from the water.

b) Number of rescuers.

The first responder immobilizes the victim in a face-up position at the surface using one of the techniques described in *The Canadian Lifesaving Manual.* Thereafter, which rescuer does what depends on the number of lifeguards available and the condition of the victim.

Always, the first step is to assess and maintain ABCs. An ABC problem takes priority – immobilization is maintained insofar as it is possible under the circumstances. (With only one lifeguard, immobilization may not be possible.)

Normally, a back-up lifeguard assesses ABCs. If the victim is responsive and breathing, the second lifeguard may support the victim's hips at the surface. If the victim is unresponsive and non-breathing, the victim requires immediate CPR. The second lifeguard should administer 2 rescue breaths and the victim should be removed quickly on a spineboard with just a chest strap and head support to minimize neck movement. Begin chest compressions as soon as the victim is removed from the water.

If there is no ABC problem, the second rescuer brings the spineboard to the shallow water removal point, while a third lifeguard takes over head support from the first lifeguard, ensuring constant immobilization of the head and neck throughout. However, in the slant-board procedure (see below), the transfer of head support happens after the victim is placed on the board.

The first lifeguard, freed from head support, is responsible for the placement of the spineboard under the victim. Additional assistance for this task is desirable. With fewer than three lifeguards, it is advised that suitable bystander assistance be recruited, especially for the removal.

❑ **Flat-board procedure**

Position the spineboard alongside and parallel to the victim. Knife the board on an angle below the surface under the victim. Control the board as it floats upward to support the victim.

The slant board spinal procedure can be performed by two lifeguards. The first lifeguard positions the victim over the slanted spineboard.

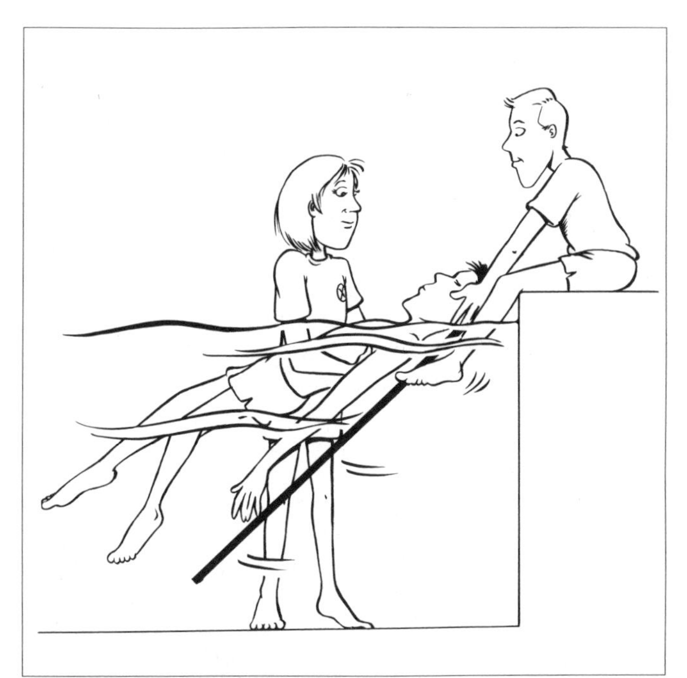

Control of the head is transferred to the second lifeguard who is on the pool edge. The first lifeguard then secures the victim to the spineboard.

- **Slant-board procedure**

  Knife the foot of the spineboard vertically into the water at the shallow water removal point, and stabilize it on a slant with your feet (if sitting) or arms (if kneeling). Alternatively, having entered shallow water, support the head of the slanted board on your lap or knees.

  The lifeguard carrying the victim positions the victim over the submerged slanted spineboard, while a second lifeguard helps guide the victim into position. Both lifeguards control the raising of the submerged portion of the spineboard and ensure the victim is centred on it.

  Bystander assistants may not even have to get wet if they work from the deck or dock. In waterfront, surf, or waterpark situations, assistants will have to wade into shallow water with the board and then follow the lifeguard's instructions.

  The slant-board procedure can be performed in deep water if the transport of the victim to shallower water is impossible or impractical.

- **Strapping the victim on the spineboard**

  Strap the victim in place beginning with the chest and hips. (If the head were strapped first, an unexpected movement of the body might cause neck injury.) Use an appropriate cervical immobilization device to stabilize the head and neck. Strap the feet last.

  ABC complications can be managed quickly by applying just a chest strap and quick head support for immediate removal to permit care on land.

- **Removal of the victim from the water**

  Wherever possible, remove a spinal-injured victim from shallow water. The spineboard removal requires a minimum of two people, but three or four are desirable. Usually two rescuers are in the water with one lifeguard on the deck or dock. Once the victim is secure, position the board perpendicular to the pool or dock edge. As the two lifeguards in the water sink the foot of the spineboard, the lifeguard on land carefully guides the board onto the deck or dock. If the board/edge does not permit sliding, rescuers will have to lift the board.

  Take care to ensure that the straps are firmly fastened and that no jolting or jarring occurs during the removal.

  Lifeguards should have a solid footing while maintaining a firm grasp of the board.

  In deep water with no access to a low edge (e.g., far off shore, beyond the surfline, in a high walled deep tank), lifejackets or other flotation devices might be used to support the rescuers. Removal can be made vertically if necessary with immobilization maintained.

  Dry the victim and treat for shock while completing a victim assessment.

c) Victim on land.

If the victim is found on land, advise the victim not to move and immobilize the victim in the position found. Do not attempt to place the victim on a spineboard unless danger requires immediate removal. If the victim is standing, help immobilize the head and neck and assist the victim to a sitting or laying position on the ground.

Leave a prone or side-lying victim in this position unless presented with an ABC problem that cannot be managed in the position found. Careful repositioning is required with immobilization provided if possible.

MISSING PERSON AND SEARCH PROCEDURES

Lifeguard response to a missing persons report will vary with the aquatic facility and the nature of the report. The immediate concern is whether or not the missing person is in the water.

a) Guidelines for swimming pools.

In a swimming pool, check the water first and immediately. The need for a full underwater search is extremely unlikely, since lifeguards will close the pool if they cannot see the bottom clearly. One of the following options should be used:

- Signal to initiate a safety stop and scan the pool bottom from lifeguard chairs or the deck.

  OR

- Signal other guards you are leaving your post. Don mask or goggles and enter the water to check the swimming pool bottom.

  If the missing person is not in the water, initiate the land search procedures outlined below.

b) Guidelines for waterfronts and beaches.

An immediate water search is initiated when the missing person is known or believed to have been in the water, or when the whereabouts of the person is unknown. However, water searches are often impractical in surf beaches. A visual search with binoculars should be undertaken.

Lifeguards must not endanger their own safety in attempting to search in dangerous water conditions. *Search Procedures* in Chapter 5 outlines specific water search techniques.

In general, emergency procedures for missing persons follow these steps:

- Determine where the missing person was last seen, how long ago, and probable whereabouts.
- Obtain an accurate description including name, sex, age, height, weight, bathing suit or clothing worn, colour of eyes, hair and skin, and swimming ability.
- Quickly pass this information to other guards. All guards immediately scan their zones, both land and water.
- At the same time, use the public address system to describe the missing person and request that individuals with relevant information report to the nearest lifeguard.
- Continue to question the patron who reported the missing person to determine where he or she has already looked. (Often people delay reporting a missing person until they have made a search themselves.)
- Conduct a land search. Direct the patron, available facility staff (and bystanders if necessary) to check:
  - » the missing person's home
  - » dressing rooms, showers, washrooms, saunas, whirlpool
  - » concession stands or snack bars
  - » playground and picnic areas
  - » parking lots and family car
  - » boats, docks
  - » other likely locations
- Continue to reassure the patron who has made the report.
- When land searches fail to find the missing person, notify police and other backup services.

EMERGENCY OUTSIDE THE SUPERVISED AREA

From time to time, an emergency outside the supervised area (e.g., an injury or medical emergency in the facility parking lot, playground, adjacent park, or a boating or scuba diving accident beyond the buoy lines) will be reported to the lifeguard staff.

Mindful that the lifeguard's responsibility is to the patrons in the supervised area, decisions must be made whether, to what extent, and how the lifeguard staff might respond to the outside emergency. The following questions must be answered:

- What is the nature of the emergency? Is it life-threatening?
- Will the situation resolve itself without lifeguard intervention?
- Can the situation be resolved by others without lifeguard intervention?
- Can patron safety be ensured if the lifeguard staff responds to the emergency?
- How?

As a general principle, if the emergency is life-threatening and cannot be resolved by others, the lifeguard staff should take the appropriate steps to safeguard patrons in the supervised area and intervene in the outside emergency to save a life.

THEFT

An individual reporting a theft should be referred to the facility manager, police, or other appropriate authorities. (Lifeguards should be supportive and helpful, but they should not leave their supervisory duties for such an incident.) If a suspect is identified and in the facility, no direct accusations should be made. Facility management, not the lifeguard, should assume responsibility for following up with police. File the appropriate reports.

VANDALISM

Preventing vandalism is a continuing challenge. From time to time, lifeguards will discover broken glass on pool decks, picnic tables in the middle of a supervised water area, or equipment damaged or missing. Steps should be taken to report and correct the situation before the facility is opened to the public.

Individuals or groups who are observed in the act of damaging facility property or equipment should be approached and warned. Names, addresses, and identification of the vandals should be obtained, and if cooperation is received, they should be advised that damage repair costs will be charged to them. If cooperation is not received, lifeguards should call police and attempt to identify the suspected vandals. File the appropriate reports.

FACILITY EVACUATION

a) Fire.

Each facility should have an emergency procedure for a report of fire. The lifeguards' priority is to protect patrons and remove them from threat to their safety while quickly contacting the fire department. Lifeguards should be trained to operate facility fire extinguishers to douse or contain small fires.

b) Lightning.

While lightning is a serious threat to swimmers in outdoor facilities, there is little to fear and seldom a need to close the facility if appropriate precautions are taken. Clear the water, and instruct patrons to move inside, dry off, and avoid wet areas. Ask them to stay clear of sinks, shower rooms, telephones, and electric appliances.

Staff comfort children overcome by chlorine gas fumes at outdoor swimming pool. Photo: Canada Wide/Mark O'Neil.

Lightning most commonly strikes trees or objects on open water. Do not permit people to take shelter under trees. Avoid doors and windows which face large trees. (The insides of cars are particularly safe because of the insulation rubber tires provide.)

c) Chlorine gas leak.

Protection of the facility staff and patrons is the overriding lifeguard priority. Follow these steps:

- Clear the pool.
- Open all exit doors.
- Direct patrons to safety outside the building or to a sealed-off area within the building. In an outdoor facility, direct patrons to higher ground up-wind of the source of the leak.
- Contact the police and fire departments and chlorine gas supplier.
- Ensure no one enters the chlorine storage room without emergency breathing apparatus.
- Provide appropriate emergency care to anyone suffering from exposure to chlorine.

d) Power failure (indoor pool).

The emergency lighting system should come on automatically.

- Clear the pool and ask patrons to sit on the deck until the extent of the problem is understood. Ensure that all swimmers are out of the water.
- Check whether all lights in the facility are affected or just those in the pool. If only the pool is affected, check the circuit breakers. (If lights are out throughout the facility, contact the utility company to learn when power may be restored.)
- Secure emergency flashlights, and communicate with patrons in the change rooms.
- Explain the situation to all patrons. If power is not to be immediately restored, guide them to the change rooms and use flashlights to help gather their clothes and exit the building. If necessary, allow a specific number to leave at intervals, for example, patrons closest to dressing rooms move first.
- At least one lifeguard remains on deck until all patrons have departed and the pool doors are locked.

UNSUCCESSFUL RESCUE AND DEATH OF A VICTIM

Clinical death is defined as the cessation of breathing and heart action. Irreversible, or biological death occurs when the brain cells die. Brain death occurs about four to six minutes following clinical death, but instances are documented of survival 40-60 minutes following cessation of breathing. (Most of these cases are young children suffering from cold water immersion.)

The lifeguard must never assume death and thus fail to perform resuscitation.

The common perception that an unsuccessful rescue effort resulting in the victim's death must be due to the rescuer's error or negligence is totally inaccurate. CPR recovery research indicates that only a small percentage of the rescue efforts involving cardiac arrest are successful. Spinal injuries can result in total or partial paralysis despite the best efforts of skilled rescuers. Victims of near-drowning may suffer complications beyond the control of lifeguards.

Lifeguards must realize that their best efforts, no matter how well practiced or how well executed, may prove unsuccessful. Accept this.

The following steps are recommended to deal with the body of a dead victim in an emergency situation:

- ❑ **Immediately**
  - Contact the police and ambulance services.
  - Cover the victim (head to toe) with a blanket.
  - Keep bystanders well clear of the scene.
  - Report the incident to your employer or supervisor, and complete an accident report.
  - Be sympathetic to the emotions and concerns of family or friends of the deceased, bystanders, yourself, and fellow lifeguards.
- ❑ **Soon after**
  - Avoid discussion with the news media or bystanders.
  - Meet with fellow lifeguards and employers to review the steps followed in the emergency.
  - Seek support for your emotional needs.

Lifeguards involved in traumatic emergencies should be aware that they will likely suffer from varying degrees of stress during and after the incident. Following a fatality, lifeguards can contend with their own personal trauma by openly discussing the event with fellow lifeguards, employers, and professional counsellors. Further information, including the need to seek help, is found in *Critical Incident Stress* in Chapter 6.

TEST YOURSELF

1. *In a small group, work at a variety of stations designed to test your team's ability to recognize, approach, support, and remove a victim in a variety of circumstances:*
   - *victim in a diving well*
   - *victim in shallow water*
   - *non-breathing victim*
   - *injured victim*
   - *victim wearing winter clothing or a PFD*
2. *Play "follow the leader." The leader performs various skills, such as:*
   - *climbing the tower and jumping to the ground*
   - *removing a partner from deep water*
   - *eggbeater kick over a distance*
   - *towing or carrying a partner through the water*

   Keep the activities safe and ensure that a qualified person remains out of the game to supervise.
3. *Imagine you are responsible for setting up emergency procedures for your local facility. Draw up a "chlorine gas leak emergency procedure" specific to your facility. Ensure your plan includes:*
   - *necessary staff training*
   - *evacuation routes depending on wind direction*
   - *which local emergency services to contact and why*
   - *Review your plan with the manager of the local facility or with your NLS instructor for comments.*

Chapter 5

Waterfront and Surf Rescue

Chapter Focus

Effective safety supervision at waterfronts and beaches depends in part upon the lifeguard's knowledge of the characteristics of the facility including currents, depths, and tidal effects. This chapter introduces the skills and knowledge a lifeguard working in these environments must master to prevent accidents and to make effective rescues. Although the focus is on beaches at large lakes and oceans, much of the information can be applied to conditions found on rivers, smaller lakes, quarries, and ponds.

Think About Lifeguarding a Beach

The beach lifeguard faces very different challenges from those of the pool lifeguard. Is lifeguarding a beach more difficult than lifeguarding a pool?

Think about a rescue in waterfront conditions. How will big waves affect each aspect of a rescue: rescue aid, entry, approach, securing the victim, tow or carry, and removal?

An inflatable rescue craft is one of the items on your list of equipment. What do you need to know about inflatables? How stable is your boat in rough water? What are the chances of a swimmer receiving one of the worst aquatic injuries, a propeller injury? How do you negotiate the surf to reach a person in trouble? How do you get a victim into the rescue boat?

When you need to pick up a boardsailor, do you leave the sailboard and bring in the sailor? Can you stow a sailboard in the rescue boat for return to shore?

Very small children will be playing at the beach. How will you deal with parents who allow their children to wander?

PRINCIPLES OF WATERFRONT RESCUES

SPEED

Lifeguards must initiate rescue procedures immediately upon the first suspicion of a victim in distress. Practice rescue techniques that maximize the speed with which you can reach and support the victim.

If a victim submerges in a waterfront facility, rescue attempts become complex. You will have more difficulty locating a victim once he or she is under water. Water conditions at most Canadian beaches and ocean fronts make submerged objects very hard to spot. In addition, undertows, currents, and rips quickly transport the victim from the point of submersion.

ENTRY POINT

These four facts are vital for determining the point of entry which is crucial to the speed of your rescue:

- Running on the beach is faster than swimming.
- On a sandy bottom, running in water less than waist deep is faster than swimming.
- A current will carry a victim away from where you first sighted him or her.
- Swimming with a current is faster than swimming against it.

WATER ENTRY AND APPROACH

Because running is faster than swimming in water shallower than your waist, make a running entry into the water. Take progressively higher strides as the water deepens. To prevent the waves from pushing you backwards, jump over or dive through them. Once you regain your footing, continue running. Use your hands as paddles to help your forward momentum, keeping yourself bent forward. When you reach waist deep water, dive forward in a series of "dolphin dives" until you are deep enough to begin to swim.

Keep your eyes on the victim as much as possible to track his or her movement; visual contact may only be possible from the crest of a wave. In salt water, practice ducking through waves and blinking the stinging salt water from your eyes. When ducking waves, submerge deeply enough to avoid being pushed backward but shallow enough to maintain your forward momentum. Anticipate the drag the waves produce on any aids you are towing.

TEAMWORK AND BACK-UP

Practicing teamwork is essential in waterfront and surf beach rescues. Except for very simple rescues, you must have more than one lifeguard at the scene – often in the water. Some lifeguard teams designate a head guard who carries a distinctively marked rescue can or buoy. He or she is the last lifeguard to enter the water as the head guard's primary job is to direct and coordinate the rescue operation.

Landmarking the victim's location is useful if the victim submerges during the rescue operation. Before entering the water, the first

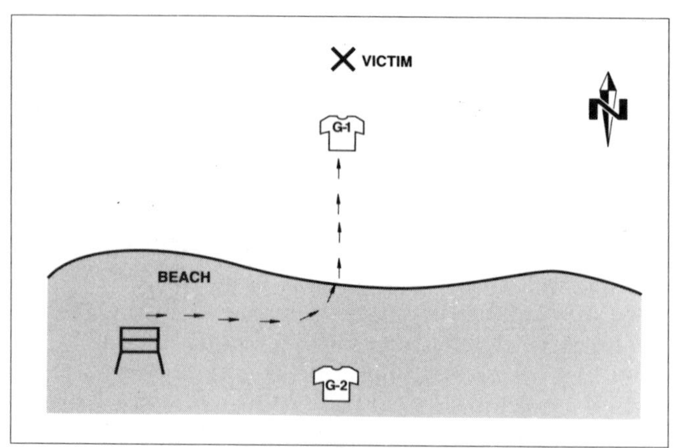

Lifeguard runs to appropriate entry point, and continues running through shallow water.

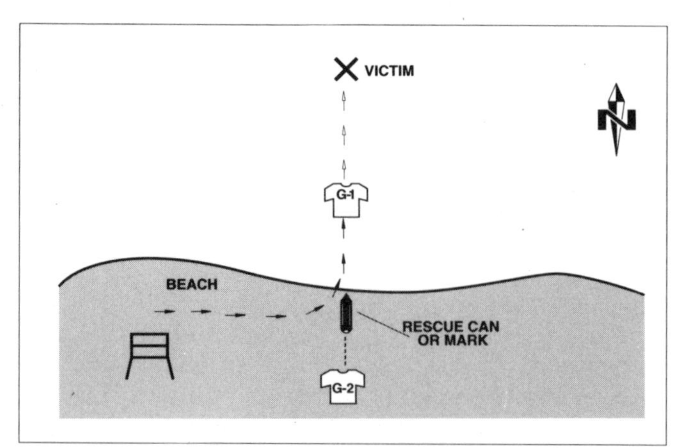

Landmarking by the back-up guard is useful where the victim might submerge far from shore.

lifeguard draws a line in the sand pointing toward the victim's location. A back-up guard then plants a rescue can at one end of the line and stands at the other end. This line of direction serves as a reference point for the lifeguard making the rescue in the water. Other landmarks can be used to mark the victim's location.

SWIMMING RESCUES

Refer to *The Canadian Lifesaving Manual* for detailed information on assistive and contact rescues. (See also Chapter 4, *Lifeguarding Skills and Procedures*.)

Provide the victim with buoyant aid support at the earliest possible moment. Victims need to have their heads up and out of the water before they will become calmer and more manageable.

Instruct the victim how to grasp the buoyant aid using calm language with an authoritative tone. Watch the victim's eyes for warning signs of increasing panic and be prepared for defensive action if the victim attempts to grasp you for support.

You can rescue many victims by towing the victim and rescue device at the end of its line while maintaining visual contact with the victim. Encourage the victim to assist rescue efforts by kicking. Direct the victim not to let go of the buoyant aid (rescue cans become dangerous missiles if propelled by powerful waves).

In rough surf or with a very weak swimmer, you may need to be very close to hold the victim onto a rescue can or tube. Instruct the victim to hold the aid to the chest. Approach from behind locking the victim between you and the aid. (Physical contact, although reassuring to a victim, places you at greater risk if he or she panics suddenly.)

In surf conditions where on-coming waves are common, keep one hand free to place over a victim's mouth and nose when you duck under waves. This protects the victim from ingesting water. (Explain to the victim what you will be doing and why!) Ducking under waves is necessary to avoid being pushed by the waves onto a rocky shoreline or one unsuitable for exit. You may need to tow or carry the victim farther out to sea beyond the breakers depending on the nature of the shoreline and the severity of the surf. Rip currents are useful by assisting you in the transportation. Calmer water conditions allow rescue boats or paddleboards to approach more safely.

If you are closer to the beach than the surfline, you can swim laterally out of the rip currents and allow the waves to carry you both to shore.

DROP-OFF RESCUES

Non-swimmers caught beyond their depth are frequently the cause of emergencies at waterfronts. A short step past a drop-off or a buoyant object drifting beyond shallow water can result in the quick drowning of a weak or non-swimmer. A non-swimmer wading from a moored boat toward shore may suddenly be in trouble when a sandbar gives way to a bottom trough.

With the underwater push technique, the lifeguard approaches from behind, submerges below the victim, and either lifts or pushes the victim toward safety. Use the bottom for leverage to push the victim(s) to safety. Repeat the action until you reach shallow water.

The hip or "Pia" carry, described under *Contact and Non Contact Rescues* in Chapter 4, is also an effective technique for this rescue.

Hip Carry

EXITS FROM THE WATER

When you reach the shore with the rescued swimmer, exit quickly to protect the victim from the pounding surf and to minimize further injury. (See Chapter 4 and *The Canadian Lifesaving Manual* for information about appropriate removal techniques.) With more than one rescuer, the following techniques can be effective:

a) Two-rescuer carries.

One rescuer, standing between the victim's legs facing the feet, grasps under each of the victim's knees. From behind the victim, the other rescuer reaches under the victim's arm pits and hooks the fingers across the victim's chest or abdomen. (Alternatively, the rescuer hooks his or her arms under the victim's shoulders.) Both rescuers lift and carry the victim to the beach beyond the breaking waves.

Always remove the victim feet-first, watching ahead of you to avoid tripping over debris.

b) Three or more rescuers.

The victim can be carried in a face-up or face-down position by three or more lifeguards, who line up on both sides of the victim. One lifeguard supports the head, a second supports the upper back, the third supports the victim's hips and upper legs. A fourth rescuer supports the knees and lower legs.

Alternatively, rescuers can create a kind of human stretcher supporting the victim by linking hands under the victim's head, shoulders, hips, and knees.

If heavy surf prevents you from exiting at your entry point, you have two choices: swim out to sea beyond the surfline to await rescue by boat or other rescue craft; or swim parallel to the beach to reach a safer exit point.

RESCUES IN UNUSUAL CONDITIONS

RESCUES OF MULTIPLE VICTIMS

When several people get into trouble at the same time, the cause of the problem can have a significant bearing on your preferred course of action. Consider these three examples and the implications for the lifeguard's response:

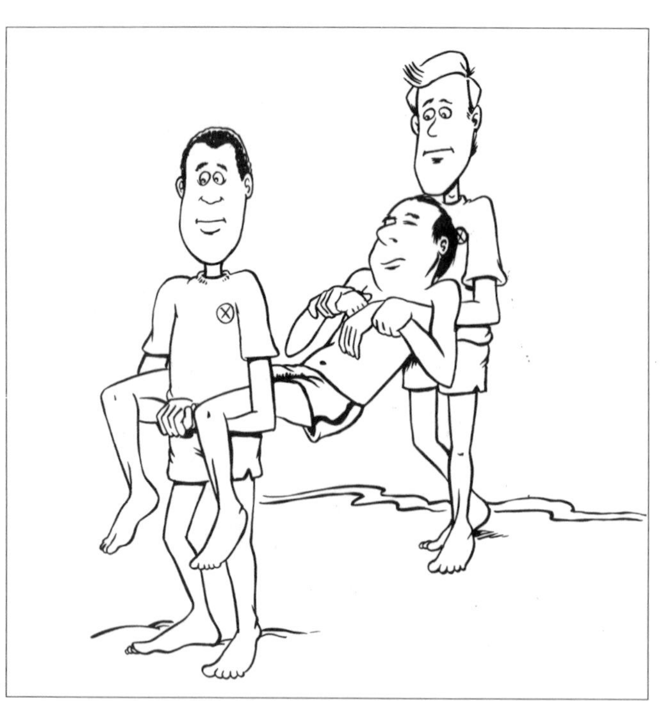

The lifeguard at the victim's head reaches under the arms to grasp both wrists securely.

The two lifeguards at the victim's head grasp each other's wrist securely under the victim's back; their other hands support the victim's head.

- people caught in a rip or undertow
- would-be rescuers becoming victims in an attempt to help someone in distress
- capsize of a boat

In rescues of multiple victims, first signal for back-up from other lifeguards. Attempt to determine which victim is most in need (one might be unconscious, while others can support themselves). The first rescuer provides assistance to the victim in most immediate need. Back-up lifeguards attend to the others in priority of their distress.

Push nearby floating objects to some victims while you concentrate on the critical victim. Part with your own aid only as a last resort because you become more vulnerable to the possible grasps of desperate people. Consider taking several rescue aids to the site even though they may slow your progress considerably.

If back-up guards are slow to arrive, consider assistance from the strongest swimmers nearby. Do this only when enough buoyant aids are available to protect these helpers from contact with a distressed swimmer. With this additional help you can simultaneously rescue a group of distressed swimmers. Verbally instruct the victims to cling to the buoyant aids.

Waste no time escorting rescued swimmers in shallow water. Leave them in the care of back-up lifeguards or other patrons.

The potential for a lifeguard to be grasped by a victim is far greater in a multiple-victim rescue. Exercise extreme caution and be prepared to use defense and release methods (see *The Canadian Lifesaving Manual*).

RESCUES IN ROCKY AREAS

Speed must be tempered with caution in rescues in rocky areas. A rescuer injured during the approach is of little assistance to the victim.

Heavy surf, pounding rescuers against sharp rocks or boulders, is lethal. Begin swimming as soon as possible, even in water that is only knee deep, since footing is treacherous on a rocky bottom. Propel yourself by using your hands to grip rocks on the bottom. Fins are a valuable aid to move you quickly into deeper water. If you are unable to scramble down a ledge, make a shallow jump or dive if the water is sufficiently deep. Time your entry carefully to coincide with the arrival of a high swell to maximize the amount of water under you.

Ducking under waves maintains forward momentum, but you risk hitting submerged boulders or the rocky bottom. Surfers duck feet first to protect their heads.

If you hit rocks during your exit, use your rescue can as a shield. Although the temptation to protect the victim with your own body is strong, remember that an injury to you can doom both of you.

Study your beach well. Rocky conditions do remain fairly stable. Your familiarity with the bottom and its hazards can make the difference between successful rescues and personal injury.

RESCUES OF SCUBA DIVERS

When possible, engage the assistance of another equipped scuba diver for rescuing a submerged diver. If performing the rescue yourself, follow these steps:

- Release and disengage the diver's weight belt. If the diver does not become buoyant, use the inflator to slowly inflate the buoyancy compensator. Avoid using the CO_2 inflator as this is an all-or-nothing inflation device that can surface the diver too quickly. Use CO_2 inflators only as a last resort.
- Slowly ascend keeping the diver's head level and not tilted downward. This allows expanding air in the diver's chest to be released preventing lung damage.
- On reaching the surface, continue as for surface rescues.

Air embolism is always a possibility in a scuba accident. Transport victims of scuba accidents in a feet-raised head-lowered position. See *The Canadian Lifesaving Manual* on pressure-related disorders.

RESCUES INVOLVING SPECIAL EQUIPMENT

PADDLEBOARD RESCUES

Paddleboards provide lifeguards with a method of reaching a victim quickly and returning to shore safely. In addition, a paddleboard has enough buoyancy to allow effective rescue breathing in deep water or to support several conscious victims.

Situations in which a paddleboard is unsuitable are:

- Very crowded swimming areas where a clear path to the victim is impossible.
- Heavy surf where waves are over 1.0 m high (unless the rescuer is highly skilled).

For clarity, the descriptions of paddleboard techniques refer only to one rescuer. However, all techniques can be adapted for two paddleboard rescuers. In addition, other lifeguards can go to the aid of the original rescuer(s) on paddleboards, or swim out with rescue cans, rescue tubes, or other suitable buoyant assists.

It should be emphasized that paddleboard skills need to be practiced.

a) Launching the board.

For a fast and effective launch in calm water with a sandy bottom, grasp the board by its two deck edges and run with it into the water. When you reach knee deep water or the drop-off, launch the board forward on the surface while simultaneously diving onto the deck of the board and firmly grasping both edges with your hands.

The rescuer either kneels or lays down on the paddleboard. Propelling the board from a kneeling position is usually faster and

To launch, dive onto board and firmly grasp both edges.

easier, but is generally used only in calmer water.

Use the same aggressive launch in surf. Run until running is slower than paddling, then launch when lulls in the breakers occur. Take advantage of backwashes and launch in locations where drop-offs or deep holes reduce the effect of waves.

b) Steering the board.

The rescuer propels the paddleboard using a simultaneous overarm stroke (as in the butterfly) or an alternating arm stroke (as in the front crawl). Position yourself so that the board rides flat on the water. Overweighting forward causes the bow to plow under the surface; too much weight in the stern reduces the speed. Both situations make steering more difficult. Steer the board toward port or starboard by:

- Dragging the foot in the water on the side to which you wish to turn.
- Propelling with greater strength with the opposite arm to the direction in which you wish to steer.
- Leaning to place more weight on the side to which you wish to turn – this causes greater drag on the turning side.

All three manoeuvres can be performed simultaneously or in combination.

Any of the following techniques will stop forward motion of the paddleboard:

- Quickly assume a sitting position and drag your lower legs in the water.
- Slide off the board into the water while holding onto it, or flip it over as you roll off.
- Drag your arms in the water in a vertical "hold" position.
- Contact a victim who is stationary in the water.

The various methods of making a 180 degree turn on a paddleboard, while spectacular to watch, are not necessarily useful in rescue. Usually, the board is easiest to turn around while the rescuer is in the water and the victim is on the board or in the water holding onto it.

c) Navigating waves.

Experienced lifeguards avoid surf while using a paddleboard. They enter the water during lulls and take advantage of rips to ride through the waves. If you must break through waves to effect a rescue, use the following techniques.

Position your board low in the wave and maintain a strong forward momentum to prevent the board from being lifted and thrown back by the surf. When meeting waves, paddle strongly aiming the board at right angles to the wave. To push through, grab both rails and keep the nose of the board down by lunging forward toward the front of the board just before impact. In smaller waves, thrust your weight forward as described. Then, at the moment of impact, raise yourself off the board in a push-up action which allows the main force of the wave to pass between you and the board.

Great skill is required to use a paddleboard in medium and large waves. "Rolling" is a difficult technique designed for use in large waves. Just before a large breaker hits you, take a deep breath and flip the board upside down while holding the rails close to the board's nose. In this position, the nose of the upside-down board is buried as deeply as possible under the wave with you

To steer left, use the left foot as a rudder.

Secure the victim to the paddleboard.

under the board. Once through the wave, right the board and continue paddling.

"Rolling" is dangerous and should be used only as a last resort and after proper training. The curl of the wave will suck upwards on the board. If any portion of the wave's force strikes underneath the nose of the board, it (and possibly you) will be thrown up and backwards over the front-breaking face of the wave. Stay bonded to the board, force the nose down and jerk it underneath the breaker. Wrapping your legs around the board can assist you in bonding to the board.

d) Rescue of a conscious victim.

The victim is likely panicky and showing signs of escalating distress. As you approach, grasp the victim's arm and slide off the board on the side opposite the victim. Instruct the victim to reach across and grasp the opposite side of the board. Place your hand over the victim's hand to secure the victim to the board. Reassure the victim. Victims usually calm down when supported by the paddleboard, with their head out of the water. Instruct the victim to kick into a horizontal position. Tilt the board slightly towards the victim and get the victim to slide onto the board, with their head towards the bow. Assist by grasping the victim's leg at the knee and pulling the legs onto the board. Once the victim is secure, turn the paddleboard towards shore and tow it to safety.

Flip the board quickly and smoothly.

The following technique may also be used to get a victim onto a paddleboard.

Turn the board upside-down as you reach the victim. Grasp and draw both of the victim's arms across the overturned board. Secure the victim by placing your hand on top of the victim's hands. Reassure and calm the victim down. Flip the board toward you by pushing down with your knee on the near side of the board while pulling up with one hand on the far side of the board. The victim will now be lying face down across the board. Turn the victim to face the bow and get the victim to grasp both sides of the deck.

Caution: Flip the board quickly to avoid excessive pressure on the victim's chest and arms. Bruises can result when the victim is rolled over the board.

When the victim is secure and balanced, tow the board to shore. If the water is calm and the victim agreeable, the lifeguard may get on the board behind the victim and paddle to shore.

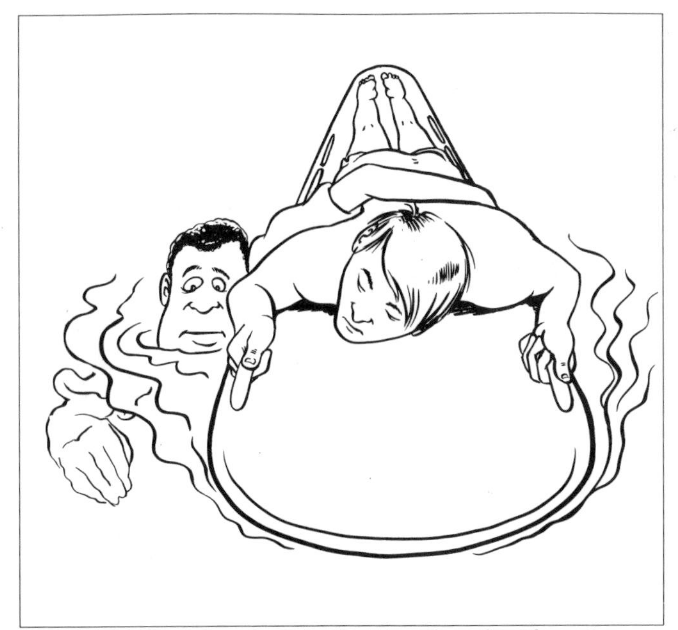

Position and secure victim; maintain visual and verbal contact during return to shore.

e) Rescue of a non-breathing victim.

Steer the paddleboard alongside the victim. Hook your arm over the victim's arm and between the victim's shoulder blades. Use your other hand to hyperextend the neck and check for breathing. Begin rescue breathing, stabilizing your position by letting your legs hang down on the opposite side of the board.

If the victim is submerged, flip the paddleboard upside down to slow its motion in the wind and waves while you bring the victim to the surface.

Continue rescue breathing until the victim begins breathing or assistants arrive to take over or push both you and the victim to shore as rescue breathing continues.

To open airway, reach over the victim's near arm and support the neck from beneath. Use the other hand to control the head and check breathing.

f) Rescue of multiple victims.

A paddleboard should provide ample buoyancy to support several people hanging on to it. Victims can lock arms across the board for a better grip. Multiple victims in cold water may do this as their ability to hold onto the board itself is minimal.

If you know you are going to the aid of more than one victim, take a rescue can in addition to the paddleboard. With the shoulder loop in place, tow the rescue can out to the victims without causing drag on yourself.

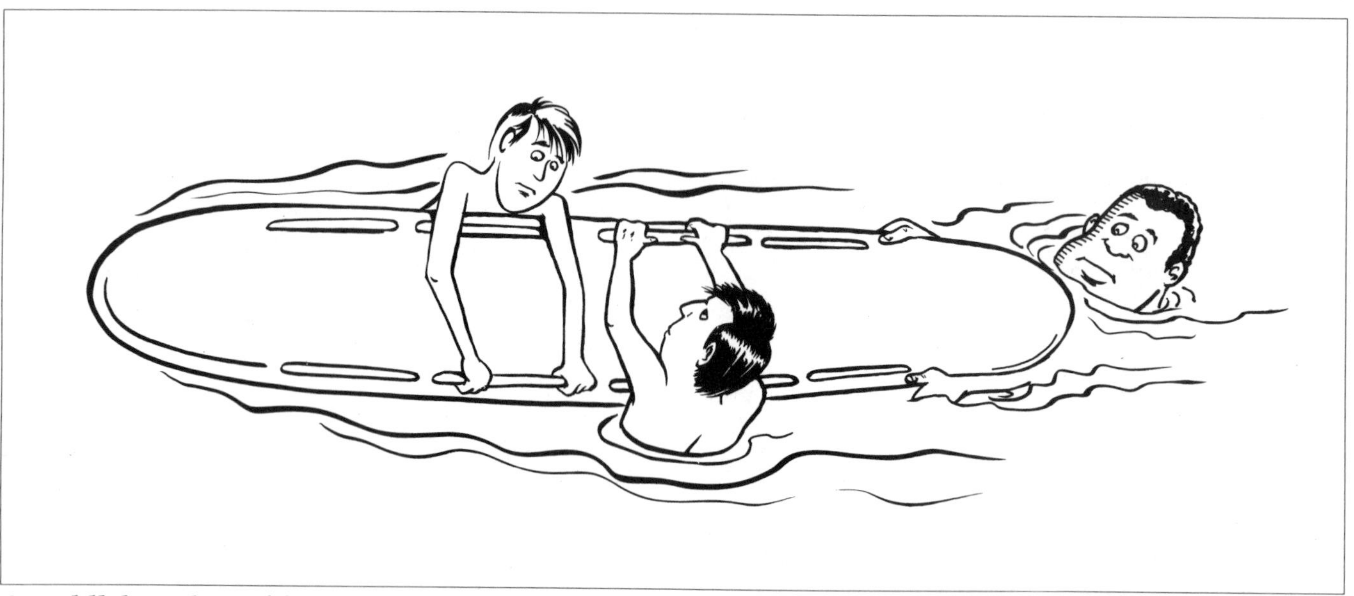

A paddleboard provides ample support for several people.

BOAT RESCUES

Lifeguards must be trained in and practice the safe operation of rescue craft. Follow boat safety rules concerning the use of small craft, and take special care when responding to emergencies in large waves or near currents (including dangerous hydraulic currents at dams or weirs).

a) Rescue of victims far out from shore.

Strong offshore winds can sweep an individual out to sea on an air mattress, innertube, sailboard, or other object. The victim who is too far out lacks the strength to paddle back to safety. Sometimes the victim abandons the buoyant object and attempts to swim to shore. If the distance is too great, the swimmer becomes exhausted and requires assistance. Under these circumstances, use the boat to effect the rescue or signal the rescue boat to pick up the victim.

Two lifeguards are recommended for a boat rescue. If the boat is equipped with oars, one lifeguard rows while the second lifeguard directs the rower and keeps an eye on the victim. In heavy swells, both lifeguards may be required to row. When a power vessel is used, one lifeguard watches the victim and gets ready to enter the water, while the boat operator manoeuvres the craft into position.

Head directly into the waves while launching; if necessary wait for a lull between sets of waves. Where possible, approach the victim from the leeward side (opposite the wind).

From a rowboat, throw a line or use a reaching assist and gently pull the victim to the stern. One lifeguard assists the victim into the boat while the second balances the craft. If conditions are too rough to bring the boat close enough to the victim, one lifeguard enters the water with a rescue can or tube and tows the victim back to the boat. The second lifeguard assists both victim and rescuer into the boat. Administer first aid immediately including treatment for shock. On the return to shore in rough water, proceed stern first to avoid being swamped.

From a power vessel, one lifeguard enters the water with a rescue can or tube and approaches the victim while the second lifeguard operates the boat. If you are inside the surfline, take the victim to shore using your can or tube. When outside the surfline, assist the victim on board and begin first aid.

With a non-breathing victim, work your way back to the boat as quickly as possible. In calm water, begin rescue breathing from the side or stern of the vessel. The second lifeguard lifts the victim on board while you are providing rescue breathing, or the lifeguard takes over rescue breathing while you get the victim on board.

b) Rescue of multiple victims.

Rescuing a number of victims with a boat is similar to the single victim procedure. Assist the victims in most critical need into the rescue boat first. Support with buoyant aids those who are able to wait a little longer in the water.

Question the victims in the water to discover if there are any injured victims or missing persons. Bring injured victims on board first and treat their injuries as soon as possible.

If the time required to pick up all victims will be lengthy, or if you must turn off a power vessel to avoid injury, anchor it in position while completing the pick-up. Once anchored, both lifeguards assist the victims on board. In surf or extremely rough water, anchoring is impractical; keep the engines idling.

c) Assistance to another vessel.

On supervised beaches equipped with powered rescue boats, the lifeguard can give assistance to other vessels. Boaters can get into difficulty from running out of fuel, malfunction of engines, running aground, striking underwater obstacles (which damage propellers or the hull), and fire on board. A disabled vessel drifting into the lifeguarded area may be signalling for assistance.

Lifeguards at beaches and waterfronts should be familiar with recognized marine distress signals. The radio vo ice call "Mayday" is repeated three times followed by the name of the distressed vessel, its position, and the assistance needed. It is broadcast on ch 16, VHF Marine Band. The morse code S-O-S (3 short-3 long-3 short) can be broadcast on the 500 kilocycle band.

The Canadian Coast Guard recommends that visual signals for any vessel in distress be a round-shaped signal suspended above a square-shaped signal. A distress cloth is a 1.8 m x 1.2 m fluorescent orange flag with a black square and black circle imprinted side by side on the cloth. Visual signals also include people repeatedly moving their arms away from their sides to shoulder height and down again, a red flare, an orange smoke flare, and a flashlight or spotlight signalling S-O-S. Vessels in trouble can also signal by continuously sounding a bell, horn, or whistle.

The rescue boat approaches the disabled vessel to determine the problem. If possible, tow the vessel away from shore and anchor it. Before receiving the tow line of the disabled vessel, explain the procedure and the fact that the rescue boat does not accept responsibility if damage occurs. Fasten the tow line to the bow cleat. If this cleat is too small, use the eye on the bow of the vessel. Slowly and gently increase the tension on the line. Keep speed very low while under way.

Do not accept responsibility for towing vessels to shore or to marinas. Where it is impractical to get the disabled vessel in tow, anchor the vessel and assist the victims into the rescue boat. If necessary, swim the victims from the disabled vessel to the rescue boat. If the disabled vessel is in danger of sinking, fasten a marker float to it for ease of location later.

Rescue boats can be called upon to assist small capsized centreboard- or daggerboard-type sailboats. Approach and determine the condition of the sailors. With directions, they may manage to right their own sailboat. The standard procedure for most small sailboats is to unfasten the halyard (the line used to raise the sail). The halyard

One lifeguard ensures the boat is launched directly into the waves.

is usually fastened to a cleat located on the hull at the base of the mast or on the mast itself. Gather the sail around the boom. Stand on the centreboard and grasp the side or gunwale of the boat. Most small boats can be righted by this method. Once upright again, the sailors can head for shore on their own. If their condition prevents them from making it on their own, tow the sailboat after taking the sailors on board the rescue boat.

WATER SEARCH PROCEDURES

For general principles and how to conduct a land search, refer to *Missing Person and Search Procedures* in Chapter 4.

Begin an immediate water search procedure (written and practiced for your facility) when a lifeguard or patron witnesses a victim submerging, or has reason to believe that a victim has submerged, or the location of the missing person is unknown.

LOCATION KNOWN

- Establish and mark the general location. (E.g., draw an arrow on the beach, mark the direction with a rescue can)
- Signal fellow lifeguards for back-up and assistance in the search. At less populated, controlled beaches, clear the water of other patrons. Occasionally, patrons exiting the water find the submerged victim on their way to shore.
- One lifeguard remains on land or in a tower to direct the rescuers and the crowd. This guard also scans the water for the victim or for bubbles on the surface of calm water. The other guards go to the location where the victim submerged.
- The search lifeguards use a circular or single line of surface dives depending on their numbers. Remember that currents or undertows can move the victim away from the point of submersion. Shift your search area if indicated. If you are unable to locate the victim after several minutes, initiate the more methodical search described in *Missing Person and Search Procedures* in Chapter 4.

FACTORS IN TYPE OF SEARCH

The swifter the rescue, the better the chance of recovering the victim alive. The following factors are important in considering the type of search procedure by lifeguards established for a specific beach or waterfront:

a) Water depth.

Water depth affects decisions about the techniques used (are surface dives required?), communication among the search team, and whether or not and how bystanders might be used.

Scuba gear greatly assists searches in water depths greater than four metres. Searches that must be conducted at water depths greater than nine metres or in situations requiring prolonged underwater searching should be undertaken by certified scuba divers. Usually the search is for a body rather than for a victim with a chance of being resuscitated. When the victim at this depth is a scuba diver, the specific circumstances determine the possibility of reviving the diver. The deeper the area to be searched, the greater the number of personnel required to conduct an efficient search.

b) Size of the area.

The larger the area, the longer the duration of an effective search. Where speed is called for, as is the case of a missing swimmer, the number of capable personnel is a limiting factor.

c) Visibility.

The lives of the rescuers must be protected. Searchers maintain communication while underwater with visual observation. If visibility is very poor, searchers use their sense of touch to check the bottom and each other.

d) Equipment available.

On all waterfronts and beaches, lifeguards need to be competent skin divers. Lifeguards working at beaches where water depths, visibility, and other factors justify the need for searches using scuba gear, must have scuba diving training. The employer should supply masks, fins, snorkels, and weight belts. A suitable rescue boat, anchors, and lines are also required. If scuba gear is needed for searches, the necessary equipment must be available. A source of air for refilling tanks should be near the waterfront or search operation. If this is not possible, spare tanks should be available.

e) Qualifications and number of lifeguards or assistants.

The staff must be qualified to use the equipment (regular use and ongoing training is vital). The larger the staff, the greater the areas which can be searched at one time. A large team of lifeguards provides greater flexibility in the number who need to be certified.

f) Other factors.

Tides, currents, water temperatures, and underwater hazards all influence the type of search procedure which is appropriate for a specific waterfront or beach.

SEARCH METHODS

a) Straight line search.

A straight line search of the shallow water area is common because you can safely and beneficially use patrons to assist.

Line up the recruited swimmers along the beach with arms linked. Explain the procedure then take up a position at the end or in the centre of the line. (Alternatively, the lifeguard might direct the search and supervise the searchers without participating in the search.) Ask swimmers to walk into the water and search with their eyes and with their feet. Instruct anyone who thinks he or she has located the victim to wave their arms and call to you. The line continues to move seaward until approximately chest deep water is reached. At this point, turn the line around to return the searchers to shore repeating the procedure.

This procedure has some limitations. Searchers create turbidity if the bottom is clay or mud. Pot holes or varying depths of water present a real hazard to the searchers. If any step beyond their depth, they can cause another emergency. One never knows the capability of swimmers in a public area. Some patrons who fear the situation can fail to indicate the victim to the lifeguard. Others can faint or falter in

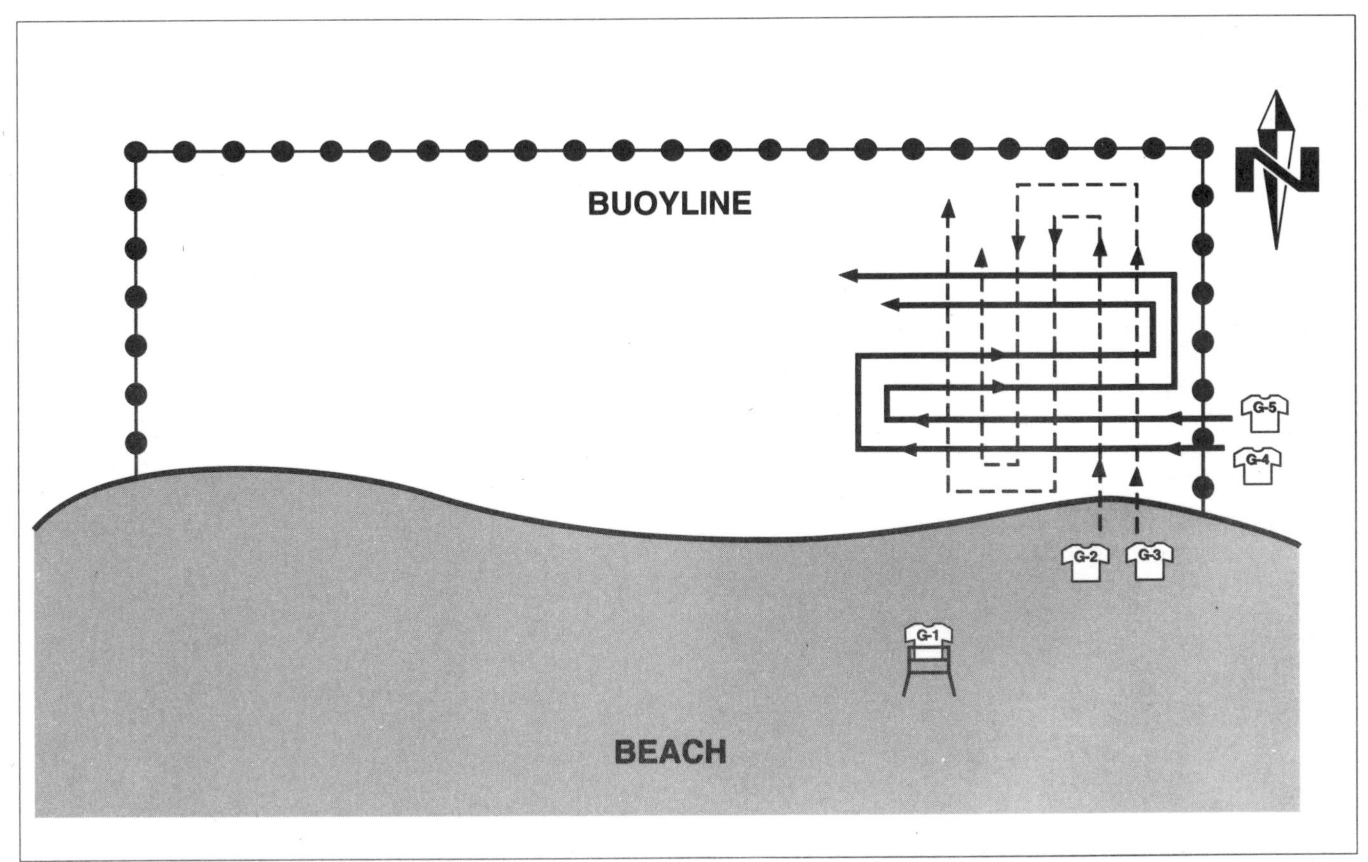

In pairs, lifeguards perform a grid pattern search of the area, starting with the victim's most likely location.

the moment of urgency. The lifeguard directing the line must be alert to problems among the searchers.

b) Straight line grid search.

A straight line grid search of deep water is performed only by trained personnel. Lifeguards not equipped with special gear, or with skin and scuba equipment search using surface dives. Depending upon the equipment available, this method can be used at a variety of depths. In all cases, a lifeguard directs the search from the surface.

If water is murky, a facemask is the minimum equipment required even in depths of 2.4 m to 3.0 m.

Set out markers to ensure adequate coverage in an undefined area (an open expanse of water not defined by floatlines and docks). Divers swim side by side maintaining an awareness of the person on either side of them. If visibility is inadequate to see the person on either side, then searchers must grasp hands or a line anchored for the purpose. Thus, the line moves at the pace of the slowest diver. Where the search is performed by skin divers, the line surfaces frequently. The person at the extreme end of the line adjacent to the marker is the leader. The line surfaces at this diver's pace.

Skin divers surface approximately every 6.0 metres. As the search progresses, distances that searchers can cover in one breath decrease.

Once a full sweep of the area is completed, divers return sweep, overlapping the area covered (hence the term grid). Divers can be guided by a surface swimmer or by a slow moving boat towing a weighted line for scuba divers.

A variation of this straight line search is a line set in an inverted "V" shape. The leader is the diver at the head of the "V" and searchers keep pace with him or her.

c) Circular patterns.

Circular patterns vary. The pattern can be only a portion of a circle, for example, a semi-circle. The search can start from a specific point in the water. A marking line to which the searchers hang on with one or both hands is their control.

If the control point for the semi-circle (or greater) is on land, an individual holds onto one end of the line on shore. As the semi-circle (or greater) is completed, the shore lifeguard pays out more line. The width between sweeps depends upon visibility.

Knots or markers in the marker rope prevent searchers losing their position on the line. Searchers must take care to keep the line taut throughout the procedure.

This method is suitable for use from a shore position, where the searchers move in semi-circles. It can also be used to search the area around a narrow dock. The searchers are then describing almost full circles from one side of the dock, around the end and back toward the other side.

If the search is initiated from a point in deep water, full circles are described by the searchers. Use an anchor and line with a buoy to the surface. In addition, a weighted line on the bottom indicates to the searchers when they have completed each circle. The divers submerge with the anchor line and securely fasten the weighted bottom line. As each circle is completed, searchers move along the marker line to describe circles of increasing circumferences.

Keep the marker line taut at all times. A person in a boat on the surface supervises the search. This type of pattern is suitable when you initiate a search from the last known location of a victim.

d) Random searching.

In random searching, skin or scuba divers search randomly using no specific design or pattern. Anchor a boat in the centre of the activity to supervise the search operation.

Use this type of search when you are reasonably certain that the victim is near the specific spot at which the boat is anchored. Lifeguards who need to check a certain position as quickly as possible use this procedure.

e) Grappling irons or hooks.

Where depth is a risk to safe diving or where water is particularly contaminated or murky, grappling equipment might be used for body recovery. Grappling equipment consists of a weighted line with an attached bar to which triple hooks are fastened. A boat tows the bar back and forth across an area of bottom. The bar is raised for inspection when resistance is noted on the line.

While lifeguards are seldom involved in the actual operation, they assist police or other authorized personnel conducting the grappling procedures.

TEST YOURSELF

1. *List the equipment that should be available for lifeguards at a waterfront or beach. Rank the items on your list from essential "must-have" to "nice-to-have."*
2. *Arrange with the head lifeguard of a nearby waterfront to shadow guard with the lifeguards for a day. Use this opportunity to test and expand your knowledge of waterfronts.*
3. *Arrange with the head lifeguard of a nearby waterfront to participate in one or more in-service training sessions. Work with the rescue equipment and learn from the experienced guards.*
4. *Plan a search procedure specific to a local waterfront. Discuss your plan with the head lifeguard or an NLS instructor.*
5. *Invent a useful rescue aid for a surf beach or inland waterfront.*

Chapter 6

Aquatic Emergency Care

Chapter Focus

The principles, priorities, and techniques of aquatic emergency care are detailed in The Canadian Lifesaving Manual. *This chapter deals with information beyond the scope of the single lifesaver in an aquatic emergency, and focuses on knowledge and skills that affect lifeguard behaviour or performance and victim outcomes.*

Think About Your Response

Ellen reacted quickly as the ladder to the slide crashed onto the deck. She knew the ladder had been checked that morning, but today it had received unusually heavy use. Whatever the reason for the accident, the result was two injured children lying on the deck.

Ellen signalled to her fellow lifeguards and ran to the scene. As she approached, one child sat up and began crying loudly: his left arm and leg were scraped and bloody. Ellen passed him and hurried to the other child who was lying motionless. She feared the worst.

David, the back-up guard, arrived with the first aid kit and stared wide-eyed at the child who was bleeding. This was David's first week on the job – and his first real emergency.

ACCIDENT RESPONSE PLAN

A planned and practiced emergency response procedure improves the performance of the lifeguard team during an actual emergency in two ways:

- Stress on the lifeguard team members is reduced. Many decisions (what to do, when, in what order, by whom), have already been made. The lifeguard can concentrate on solving the victim's problem.
- The accident response is tailored to the specific characteristics of the aquatic facility, and takes into account the emergency services response procedures. Within the framework of practiced emergency procedures, it is relatively easy to adjust to the specific needs of each accident.

In terms of emergency care, a lifeguard needs to perform the following:

❑ **Rescue scene assessment**
- Ensure no further danger to the rescuer(s) and victim.
- Find out what happened and the current status of the victim(s).
- Determine if a spinal injury is suspected.
- Call for assistance.

❑ **Primary survey**
- Check ABCs to determine whether the life of the victim is in immediate danger:

   - » Airway – Ensure airway is open and unobstructed.
   - » Breathing – Look, Listen, Feel
   - » Circulation – Check for life-threatening bleeding or other life-threatening injuries. If victim is unresponsive and non-breathing, start CPR immediately.
- ■ Reduce the risk of imminent death as much as possible. Treat all life-threatening injuries.

❑ **Secondary survey**
- ■ Perform a body check to identify other injuries.
- ■ Monitor vital signs.
- ■ Obtain a detailed accident history from victim, bystanders, friends or relatives.

❑ **Transport**
- ■ Prepare to transfer the victim to the care of an ambulance or emergency response team.

❑ **Record and report**
- ■ Prepare and submit the appropriate reports.

These basic steps should be followed whether the accident is minor or major and whether the lifeguard is alone or working with other lifeguards. Learn the details of each step.

RESCUE SCENE ASSESSMENT

- ■ Sometimes the mechanism or cause of an accident is still present when the lifeguard arrives at the scene. If such environmental hazards as fire, gas leak, the sun, or chemicals pose an immediate threat to the victim or lifeguards, remove or eliminate the threat or move the victim and rescuer(s). Lifeguards must ensure their personal safety at all times.

  Unless absolutely necessary, avoid moving the victim until the extent of all injuries is determined. The first effort is to eliminate the cause of the accident or the threat which still exists. (Observing the scene for dangers might help the first aider to determine the cause of the accident.)
- ■ When an accident occurs, the first aider attempts to find out what happened and to obtain information on the current status of the victim(s). Attempt to determine the cause of the accident. Collect information by observing the scene, asking bystanders what happened, and questioning the victim if possible. Assess and avoid risk to the rescuer or further danger to the victim. Assess the possible injuries or conditions from which the victim(s) may be suffering. This information helps rank multiple victims in priority for first aid treatment.

  Brief questions to bystanders and victim(s) may yield background information not obvious at the scene. For example, does the victim suffer from asthma or angina? Was there some particular cause or preceding event? Did the victim fall and hit his or her head?
- ■ Any victim who has suffered a head injury should be treated for a possible spinal cord injury. Bystander information and/or the mechanism of injury at the accident site may give helpful hints about a possible spinal cord injury.
- ■ Unless the accident is very minor, some assistance is necessary. Alert and inform other lifeguards with signals about the status of the emergency: if further assistance is required, someone is ready to activate the emergency medical system (EMS). (See *Communication with Emergency Services* in Chapter 3.)

PRIMARY SURVEY

- ■ In the case of a conscious, alert, and oriented victim, simple questioning can quickly determine the extent of injuries. In the case of a disoriented or non-responsive victim, you may determine injuries by assessment of the ABCs. Response to touch or sound disclose whether the victim is conscious or not. Open the airway and look, listen, and feel for respiration to determine whether the victim is breathing.
- ■ Identify and deal with any life-threatening emergencies.The following conditions can result in death in a short period of time:
  - » breathing problem
  - » failure of circulation
  - » severe bleeding and shock
  - » acute medical condition
  - » severe trauma

Exposing the chest and performing a rapid body survey reveals any life-threatening, sucking chest wounds and allows the rescuer to discover other life-threatening injuries or serious bleeding. Finer assessments should be left until the threat of death is passed.

SECONDARY SURVEY

- In a primary survey, focus on life-threatening conditions. Speed and accuracy are crucial. The victim, however, may suffer from smaller, relatively less serious injuries which can be identified upon closer and more thorough inspection.

  A body check, the systematic, head-to-toe survey of the victim, identifies injuries not noticed during the primary assessment, and gathers additional information.

  Throughout secondary assessments, check ABCs periodically. (Usually ABCs are checked after assessing each major section of the body.)

  A hands-on head-to-toe body check is completed for all unconscious victims and for conscious victims with a decreased level of consciousness. A victim with a noted decreased level of consciousness can be suffering the effects of alcohol, drugs, head injury, or shock which can mask symptoms of other injuries.

  Perform a body check using the flat of the hands with firm pressure and cover the full surface of all the victim's limbs. Check the victim's entire body for signs of bleeding, scrapes, abnormal marks, medical insignia, and broken bones, etc. Observe the victim's face for signs of reaction during the body check.

- Record the rate and status of vital signs. (See *The Canadian Lifesaving Manual.*) These will indicate changes in the victim's condition over time. This information helps a rescuer to constantly monitor the general condition of the victim. It also serves as a valuable record to transfer with the victim to the ambulance response team.

- The importance of obtaining information (the history of the accident, vital signs, and personal information about the victim and witnesses such as name, address, telephone), is noted previously. Usually, when working in a team, one member takes the responsibility for recording relevant information while other team members collect the information and verbally report it to the recorder. Verbalizing information keeps all team members aware of the changing conditions of the victim(s). Identifying one recorder ensures that this information is retained.

TRANSPORT

- In first aid incidents, either the victim's injuries require further care by a physician or the victim's injuries are attended to sufficiently by the first aider. An ambulance should be summoned whenever injuries are severe or when such transportation is required to keep the victim comfortable. (Review *Communication with Emergency Services* in Chapter 3.)

  When injuries appear minor, notifying the parents or guardian is always good policy. Someone, other than the victim, is informed of the incident and can continue to monitor the victim's condition. Advise the victim and the parent or guardian to see a physician whenever the possibility of complications exists, for example, subsequent infection.

RECORD AND REPORT

- A written record of accidents and incidents is vital to:
  - allow rescuers to monitor changes in the condition of the victim(s)
  - provide emergency personnel with a record of data necessary for prompt action at the receiving medical facility
  - provide data to assess high accident rate zones in the facility or ongoing weaknesses in staff training
  - provide information useful in follow-up investigations, court action, or inquest (See *The Lifeguard and the Law*, Chapter 8)

  Many municipalities and programmers use several documents, depending upon the nature of the incident and the purpose of the record. There may be specific forms for a major accident, a minor accident, a discipline situation, or a first aid assessment.

  Whatever the documents used in specific jurisdictions, the lifeguard who first responded completes a follow-up report immediately following the incident. Other rescuers should also complete a report on their involvement in the incident. (See *Incident Report Guide* in Chapter 6.)

Facility Chart Incident Record

The locations of all incidents are marked on the facility chart for future evaluation.

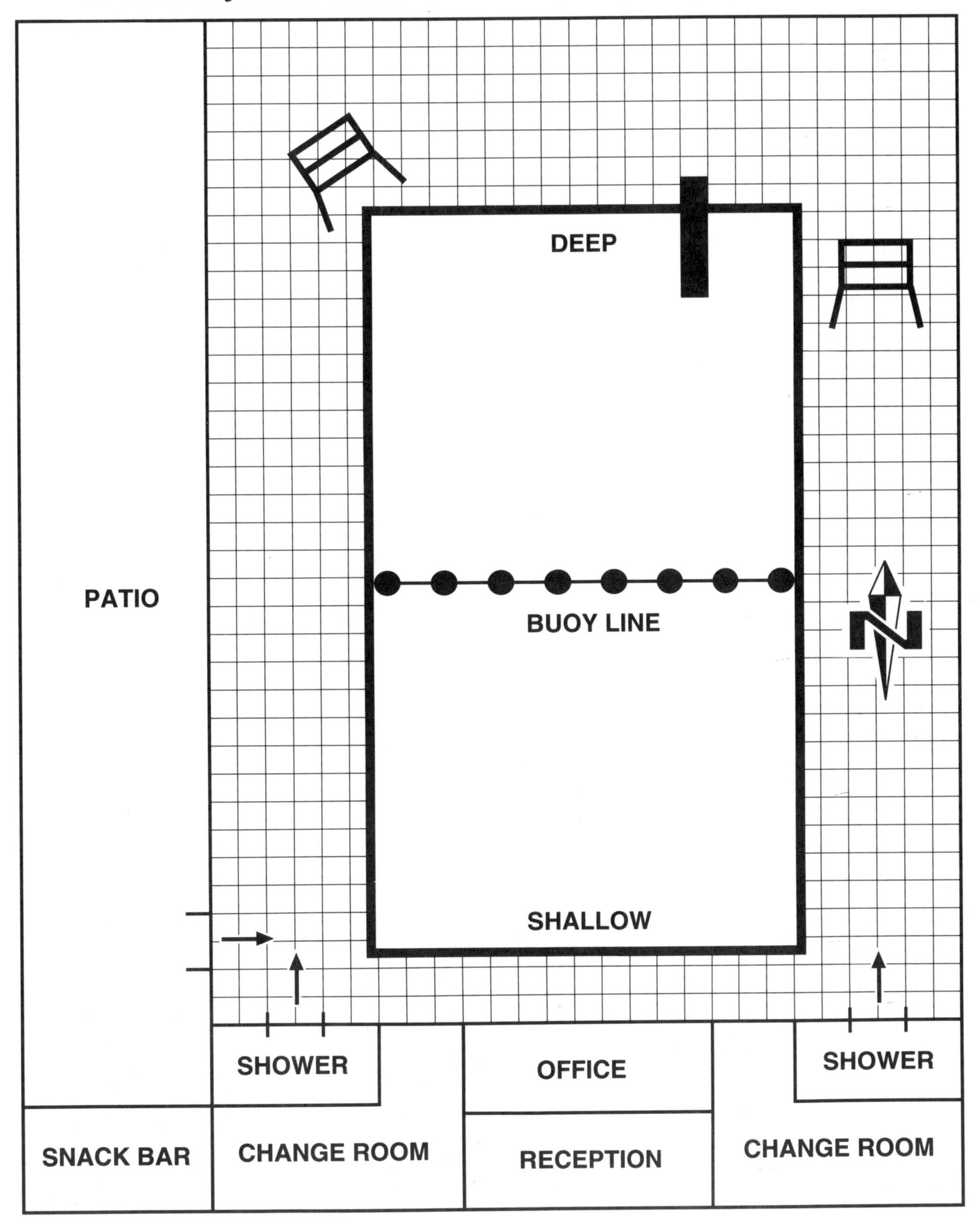

Incident Report Guide

An incident report form guides the documentation of the *when, where, who, what* and *why* of the incident. In the following sample, the data is ordered as follows:

- items 1 & 2 identify *when*
- items 3 & 4 identify *where*
- item 5 identifies *who*
- items 6 to 12 identify *what*
- items 13 to 15 identify *why* (under what circumstances)

The report design and the amount of detail recorded may vary, but at a minimum it must contain this basic information.

1. Date of incident . . . .
   (year) (month) (day)
2. Time of incident . . . .
3. Facility name . . . .
4. Exact location of incident within facility (mark on facility diagram) . . . .
5. Name of person involved . . . .
   (last) (first) (initial)
   Phone . . . .
   (business) (home)
   Address . . . .
   (street)
   . . . .
   (town/city) (province) (postal code)
   Sex ❒ Male ❒ Female
   Age . . . . ❒ known ❒ estimated (over 18 years)
   ❒ estimated (under 18 years)
6. Type of incident: ❒ injury ❒ vandalism ❒ complaint ❒ theft ❒ item lost
   ❒ person missing ❒ other . . . .
7. Description of the incident, including activity at the time of the incident . . . .
8. Description of any injuries, including exact location on body . . . .
9. Specific treatment or action taken by staff . . . .
10. Treatment given by emergency services or others, e.g., ambulance, fire department, police, doctor . . . .
11. Emergency service vehicle #'s: Ambulance . . . . . Fire Dept. . . . . . . Police . . . . .
    Names and phone numbers of non EMS personnel . . . .

12. Treatment refused. ❐ Yes ❐ No

Signature: . . . . Comment: . . . .

Parents contacted (if under 18 years) ❐ Yes ❐ No Comment . . . .

Taken by guardian ❐ Yes ❐ No ❐ n/a Name: . . . .

Resumed activity in facility ❐ Yes ❐ No ❐ n/a

Exited from facility on own ❐ Yes ❐ No ❐ n/a

Transported to hospital by ambulance ❐ Yes ❐ No Hospital name . . . .

13. Environmental conditions

Water (temperature, visibility, waves) . . . .

Air (temperature, wind) . . . .

Deck (wet, dry, condition) . . . .

Beach (clean, condition) . . . .

Bottom condition (hole, drop off) . . . .

Weather (sun, cloud, rain) . . . .

14. Victim followed all rules and safety procedures ❐ Yes ❐ No ❐ n/a

Comment . . . .

15. Related factors (equipment, behaviour) . . . .

16. Witnesses . . . .
(name) (phone)

17. Names of all staff involved . . . .
(name) (phone)

18. Name of person completing report . . . .
(name) (title)

19. Date of report . . . .

SPECIALIZED SUBJECTS

CROSS CONTAMINATION

Lifeguards should understand what risks they assume in the performance of their duties and take precautions to limit or prevent these risks. In first aid training and delivery the risk of acquiring communicable diseases such as AIDS, Hepatitis-B, flu strains, and common colds is only slightly greater than in everyday activities if proper precautions are taken. Clean and maintain training manikins scrupulously in accordance with both manufacturer's instructions and current disease control standards. (Refer to RLSSC policy regarding the practice of rescue breathing in *The Canadian Lifesaving Manual.*)

In performing rescue breathing or CPR, or treating open wounds, lifeguards should exercise caution and follow current medical advice to minimize the risk of acquiring a communicable disease.

a) Gloves.

Wear rubber latex gloves when dealing with any body fluids (e.g., blood, vomitus, urine), especially if the first aider has open lesions on his or her hands.

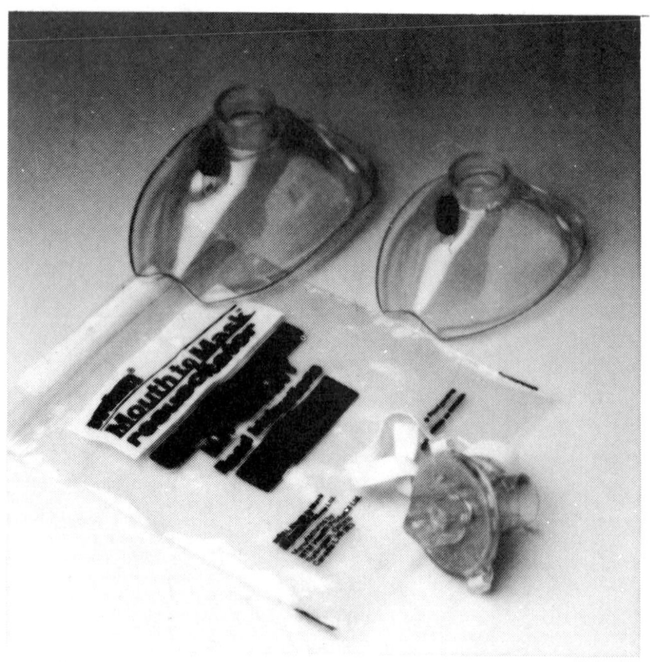

Adult and child pocket masks with oxygen inlets.

b) Pocket mask.

When performing rescue breathing, a pocket mask with a one-way valve (mouth-to-mask) is perhaps the most suitable device for use by lifeguards to prevent cross infection. The pocket mask is sealed over the victim's mouth and nose and rescue breathing is administered through the top of the mask. An oxygen tank can be connected to the mask thereby providing oxygen-rich (maximum 60%) air as rescue breathing is administered.

The pocket mask is also used to provide free-flow oxygen (no pressure from the operator) to a breathing victim who will benefit from supplemental oxygen.

There are many brands of pocket masks available. Those which fit a wide variety of victim sizes (infant to adult) and have a strap to hold it in place are recommended. Other points to consider are oxygen adapter-ports, and the ease of use in lateral position rescue breathing, since near-drowning victims are very likely to vomit repeatedly.

FIRST AID FACILITIES AND SUPPLIES

If a first aid room is being set up for the first time, or if an area is being redesigned to be used as a first aid station, these guidelines are helpful.

- **Convenience**

  The first aid room should be located reasonably near the pool or beach, or in a central location in a waterpark. Doorways and hallways must be wide enough to admit a stretcher or spineboard. The exit door(s) should be equipped with a crash bar rather than a handle and be able to be propped open. Access to the exit by emergency vehicles is essential. The doors should have an appropriate sign and indicate that the facilities are limited to staff only.

- **Size**

  The room should be large enough to allow access from all sides to a victim on a cot, stretcher, or spine board. First aid rooms are generally four metres square (12 by 12 feet) or larger. Where the room is too small or narrow, access to equipment around the perimeter is a problem.

- ❑ **Ventilation and lighting**

  Both should be adequate. Enough light is essential for lifeguards or physician to examine and treat the victim.

- ❑ **Floor and wall surfaces**

  Surfaces which can be washed down with disinfectants are suitable. Where possible, a nonskid floor is best.

- ❑ **Sinks and storage cupboards**

  Two sinks, one at normal level (1 metre) and the other at 0.5 metres from the floor serve most purposes. The low sink is particularly useful at beach areas where minor cuts to the feet can be common.

  Cupboard space should be designated to accommodate items nearest the location where they will be used. Space should permit all items to be stored away rather than left out on counters.

- ❑ **Equipment**

  Place oxygen equipment close to the door for fast removal to the pool deck or beach. Post a sign indicating "no open flame and no smoking" where oxygen is stored or used.

  Stretchers and spineboards can be kept in the first aid room and removed to the victim when required. Some lifeguards store these items in the first aid room, but take them to the beach while staff are on duty.

- ❑ **Supplies**

  The following items are useful:

  - blankets, plastic sheets, towels, pillows
  - bandage scissors, forceps, tweezers, safety-pins
  - dressings and bandages of assorted sizes
  - adhesive tape of various widths
  - needles for removing splinters
  - applicators
  - mild antiseptic soap solution
  - disposable drinking cups
  - mineral oil, calamine lotion
  - flashlight or penlight
  - glucose, sugar, or candy
  - table salt for leeches
  - cold packs
  - triangular bandages
  - spineboard and stretcher, and head and neck immobilization device
  - oxygen equipment
  - gloves
  - pocket mask
  - incident report forms, paper, pencil
  - first aid text

  Check equipment regularly and often. Replace missing or consumed material immediately.

MEDICATION

It is beyond the scope of first aid to administer anything classified as a drug or remedy except to a member of your immediate family. Lifeguards may assist (e.g. getting the medication) victims in taking their own medications. Guards may administer a victim's own epinephrine auto-injector (e.g. EpiPen®) in a life-threatening situation if the victim cannot.

OXYGEN

Oxygen is useful in many respiratory emergencies, but personnel who use it must be trained in its delivery. Oxygen can be delivered to a conscious or unconscious victim by a free-flow method in which oxygen is supplied at the mouth and nose for the victim to breathe. Free-flow oxygen is very useful and reasonably easy to administer. Oxygen supplied by free-flow systems is helpful in many first aid situations. Lifeguards working in facilities with free-flow oxygen delivery systems should be trained to use this equipment by their employers.

Oxygen can also be delivered to a non-breathing victim by a positive pressure method in which oxygen is forced through a face mask into the lungs.

The delivery of positive pressure oxygen is considerably more complex, requiring special training and mechanical adjuncts, such as resuscitators and airways. Lifeguards should not be using positive pressure oxygen equipment unless they receive special training. The use of ventilators, aspirators, suction equipment, and airway adjuncts is normally confined to medical and para-medical personnel and those especially trained in resuscitation.

In sick or injured people, there are no dangers in receiving high concentrations of oxygen for a short period.

a) Bag valve mask.

A bag valve mask is a device which forces air into the victim's lungs when the bag is squeezed. The bag and mask can be used alone to deliver room air or it can be connected to a cylinder of oxygen to provide up to almost 100% oxygen. Training and practice with this device is required to provide effective delivery of air.

b) Pocket mask.

See Pocket Mask under *Cross Contamination* in Chapter 6.

c) Face mask.

A face mask covers the mouth and nose to supply oxygen for breathing victims.

d) Nasal cannula.

This device delivers low flow oxygen to the victim through two soft plastic tips inserted slightly into the nostrils.

e) Inhalator.

An inhalator delivers free-flow oxygen to a breathing victim through a face mask which covers the mouth and nose.

f) Ventilator.

A ventilator delivers oxygen under pressure, forcing the oxygen into the lungs of the non-breathing victim.

g) Aspirator.

Also known as oral suction units, aspirators can remove fluid and small debris from the airway (e.g., blood, vomitus).

CRITICAL INCIDENT STRESS

The stress of an aquatic emergency, especially life-threatening emergencies, can cause lifeguards to experience strong emotional reactions and has the potential to interfere with their ability to function, either at the scene or later. Emotional, physical, and cognitive reactions to a critical incident can lead to reduced performance and emotional or physical problems which can manifest themselves in a variety of ways including depression, deterioration in interpersonal relationships, and resignations.

CAUSES

Incidents which can potentially result in what is known as critical incident stress syndrome include:

- Team member injury or death
- Child death
- Knowing the victim or having the victim resemble someone you know
- Incident with unusual sights and sounds or an incident extending over a long period of time
- Bystander death caused by emergency response team
- Incident with profound emotion
- Incident with significant media attention
- Working under a threatening situation such as severe water or weather conditions, multiple victims
- Other incidents that engage the emotions such as needless deaths or unusual saves (how did this person live?)
- Major incidents, and always when rescuers must decide which victims take priority in multiple-victim situations

EFFECTS ON LIFEGUARDS

Acute critical incident stress occurs during the incident, but lifeguards can also suffer from delayed stress responses after the incident. In extreme cases, stress can render the lifeguard incapable of functioning at the scene.

Signs and symptoms of acute critical incident stress include:

- ❑ **Physical**
  - Nausea, upset, sweating and profuse tremors
  - Disorientation and loss of coordination
  - Heart rate and blood pressure increase
  - Hyperventilation and chest pains, headaches
  - Muscle soreness and difficulty sleeping
  - Fatigue

- **Cognitive**
  - Impaired thinking and decision making
  - Poor concentration and confusion, difficulty performing calculations
  - Memory and concentration problems
  - Flashbacks, poor attention spans
- **Emotional**
  - Anxiety, guilt and fear
  - Grief and depression
  - Emotional numbing
  - Feeling lost, abandoned, and helpless
  - Withdraw from others
  - Anger, resentment, and scapegoating
  - Feeling numb, shocked, and overwhelmed

Signs and symptoms of delayed stress response include:

- Increased feelings of depression, anxiety, and irritability
- Sleep disturbances
- Changes in eating habits
- Loss of emotional control
- Feeling of isolation
- Lower sexual drive and menstrual cycle changes
- Lower interest in loved ones
- Marital conflict

In a more acute delayed stress response, intrusive memories, fear of repetition of the event, and other physical and emotional symptoms including the above can be anticipated.

GETTING HELP

Both lifeguards and employers should be aware of and plan to deal with immediate and delayed stress reactions among the lifeguard team members after a major incident. Team debriefings, peer counselling, and the use of outside professional counselling are all useful ways to work through and relieve the stress reaction. A team debriefing meeting might be structured as follows:

- **Introduction**

  Introduce team members, resource personnel, and outline the purpose of the meeting.
- **Fact phase**

  Members share what their role was, and what they saw, heard, smelled during the event.
- **Reaction phase**

  Once the event has been brought back into vivid memory, the facilitator probes thought and feeling reactions: "How did you feel when that happened?" "How are you feeling now?" "Have you ever felt anything like that in your life before?"
- **Symptom phase**

  The facilitator questions individual's reactions to the incident: "What unusual things did you experience at the time of the incident?" "What unusual things are you experiencing now?" "Has your life changed in any way since the incident?" In this way, group members describe their own versions of the stress response syndrome.
- **Teaching phase**

  Input is provided on the stress response syndrome, informing lifeguards of the symptoms they may experience. An effort is made to ensure the participants realize these reactions are a normal response to acute stress.
- **Re-entry phase**

  At the end of the meeting, loose ends are tied up, outstanding questions are answered. Action plans are made allowing participants to begin to make the psychological shift to normal life.

It should be understood that everything said by participants in the debriefing is private and confidential.

Family, friends, and fellow staff members can help individuals suffering from post-incident stress in the following ways:

- Encourage them to talk about how they are feeling about the incident.

Post-Critical Incident Do's and Don'ts

Don't

- Drink alcohol excessively
- Use legal or illegal substances to numb post-trauma consequences
- Withdraw from family, friends, and co-workers
- Automatically stay away from work
- Use off-duty time for training immediately after the incident
- Look for easy answers to explain the reasons for the incident
- Think you are "crazy"
- Have unrealistic expectations for recovery

Do

- Expect the incident to bother you
- Maintain a good diet and exercise
- Take time for leisure activities
- Remind yourself the post-trauma consequences are normal
- Learn as much as possible about critical incident stress
- Spend time with family, friends, and co-workers
- Get extra help if necessary

- Tell them how you feel: that you are sorry that they have been hurt, etc.
- It is okay to remind them that their confusing feelings are normal. Do not attempt to reassure them that everything is okay. It is not.
- Do not attempt to impose your explanation on why this has happened to them.
- Do not tell them you know how they feel. You don't. Often such attempts are really aimed at relieving your own anxiety about how you feel about the incident.
- Be willing to say nothing. Just being there is often the biggest help.
- Do not hesitate to encourage them to get post-trauma counselling from a specially trained professional.
- Do not be afraid to ask how someone is doing. This provides the opportunity for them to tell you as much or as little as needed.
- Remember that as a person who cares for the survivor of a traumatic event, you are a co-survivor. You must also expect that you will experience post-trauma consequences.

TEST YOURSELF

1. *With a partner, research a possible first aid emergency. Set up a simulation of the emergency using simulation materials to indicate common signs and symptoms. Use props to add realism. Prepare a checklist of appropriate first aid steps. Let other pairs of lifeguards perform as rescuers in your simulated emergency. Assess their performance, then switch roles.*
2. *Prepare a portable first aid kit. Review the contents with another lifeguard explaining why you chose each item.*
3. *Invite an emergency physician or paramedic to address your lifeguard team to discuss treatments on which opinions are divided. Make sure your guest understands your level of training, unique factors in an aquatic rescue, and the relatively short time in which lifeguards are likely to care for a victim.*
4. *Research and post the following information at your swimming facility:*
   - *emergency telephone number*
   - *location and telephone number of closest poison control centre*
   - *location and telephone number of nearest hyperbaric chamber*
   - *emergency procedures for chlorine gas leaks*
   - *instructions for use of self-contained air pacs*
5. *With a partner, practice reading and recording vital signs.*
6. *Devise forms for recording accident and victim assessment information which are specific to the needs of your local swimming facility.*
7. *Scrutinize your facility listing all potentially poisonous substances on the premises. Identify the treatment for each poison.*
8. *At a public swim, scan the patrons to identify those wearing medical warning insignia (S.O.S., Talisman, or Medic Alert). Approach the patron to inquire about the nature of the medical condition. If the individual carries medication, educate him or her about the need to inform lifeguards of its location.*
9. *Inquire about participating as an observer on local ambulance calls.*
10. *Develop a quick, easy-to-use checklist that you could tape inside the cover of your first aid kit to help you ensure everything has been done.*

Chapter 7

Public Relations and Public Education

Chapter Focus

Lifeguards must take a leadership role in fostering good public relations and ongoing public education. The benefits of good public relations include trust, understanding, and cooperation from patrons, the community at large and the local media. Public education efforts of lifeguards can be seen as a direct result of, and contribution to, the lifeguard's responsibility for patron safety.

Think About Sunnydale Park

Last year, a small, but highly visible, minority of Sunnydale Park swimming pool patrons made life difficult for patrons and staff alike. They were unruly and sometimes abusive. Many were older teenagers who delighted in causing as much trouble as they could. They ignored the safety rules. A few were suspected of petty theft and after-hours damage to the facility. Their behaviour and language brought constant complaints from parents.

At the beginning of the season, the lifeguards tried to be firm. They shouted themselves hoarse, barred the worst offenders from the pool, and restricted the use of equipment and toys to prevent their abuse. None of these measures worked for long. The culprits found new ways to harass the staff.

The parents continued complaining. The administration insisted that the lifeguards put a stop to the situation. Staff morale was low. And the local newspaper featured a story about vandalism at the pool.

This year the staff members, who were certified together at a National Lifeguard Service course, decided to try to change the situation. They brainstormed ideas during their pre-season meetings, and prepared a plan to restore safety and discipline, attract new swimmers, and improve public opinion of the lifeguards and the pool.

It worked! By the end of the summer, pool attendance had increased, more adults and small children were regular patrons, complaints were no longer directed to the administration, and the lifeguards were dealing with a more cooperative public.

How did this happen? How would you have planned your public relations and public education campaign if you were a staff member? What methods would you have included in your campaign? How would you have interacted with the patrons?

COMMUNICATION OBJECTIVES

Those who come to enjoy the pool or beach may not be as responsible or as aware of safe practices as the lifeguard would like them to be. Knowledgeable patrons make the lifeguard's job more enjoyable.

Public relations is the way that lifeguards communicate (verbally and otherwise) with the public – those presently using their facility as well as the general public. Public education is the process of communicating information to those who need it.

Each staff member has a role to play. Every person employed by or identified with a pool, beach, waterfront, or waterpark influences public opinion of that facility. The basket checker and cashier have as much influence as the lifeguard or pool manager on patrons' attitudes. Basket room checkers and lifeguards tend to know the patrons better than aquatic directors or supervisors who are removed from daily interaction with the patrons.

a) Public relations objectives.

An aquatic facility might have specific public relations objectives which can change with circumstances and go beyond the responsibility of the lifeguard. However, the following objectives are part of the role and responsibility of all members of the aquatic staff including lifeguards:

- To increase public awareness of the facilities and services, both educational and recreational, available at the aquatic facility.
- To enhance and promote the image of the aquatic facility as an attractive, safe, and enjoyable place for aquatic education and recreation.
- To enhance and promote the image of the lifeguard as a caring, knowledgeable, and highly skilled professional.
- To foster mutual respect, understanding, and cooperation between the aquatic staff and the public.

b) Public education objectives.

Public relations efforts and activities often work towards public education objectives which include:

- To increase awareness of the personal responsibility each patron assumes for accident prevention in the facility.
- To communicate information which will help patrons prevent accidents in the aquatic facility, and in other unsupervised aquatic settings.
- To communicate information about emergency procedures.

COMMUNICATIONS EVALUATION AND PLANNING

a) Determine the target groups.

Identify those at whom you wish to aim your public relations and public education efforts. Specify why each identified group is an appropriate target. Is your facility weak in its relations with a particular group of patrons? In what way is it weak? Do you need to publicize your facility more actively to the general public? Why?

b) Identify the reasons for target group behaviour.

You need to know why people are not attending or why they behave the way they do. How does the public perceive the programs, the lifeguards, and the facility? Are they bored? Do they feel they are poorly treated? Do they regard lifeguards as babysitters or as skilled professionals?

c) Determine the communication messages and desirable changes in behaviour.

For each target group, identify what key messages you wish to communicate and what changes in behaviour will tell you that your communication is succeeding.

d) Plan positive strategies.

Decide how to deliver the messages in an appropriate manner for your target group. For example, you might decide to enhance the lifeguard's image as a highly skilled professional by holding public rescue demonstrations or organizing a lifeguard competition.

e) Decide when to implement the strategies.

Begin your communications plan some weeks before the official opening of the facility, and continue until the closing date. A year-round program requires periodic evaluation and adjustment of the communications plan because target groups and objectives may alter from season to season.

Schedule important events such as lifeguard demonstrations for maximum attendance times. Advertise instructional programs well in advance of registration dates. If specific hazards are most prevalent during a particular period, emphasize this.

PUBLIC RELATIONS AT SUNNYDALE PARK

The Sunnydale lifeguard team decided to work towards improved public relations in small achievable steps.

a) Target groups.

First, they determined to target the following groups:

- Older teenagers who were causing discipline problems.
- Parents and adults. Too few adults used the pool and they were the most vocal group of dissatisfied customers.
- The administration who did not recognize the ability of the lifeguards or their working conditions. The administrators controlled the resources for improving the program and facility.
- The pool staff who needed ongoing support because of low morale.

b) Target group behaviour.

For the teenager target group, the Sunnydale staff considered the following questions:

- Why are teenagers breaking the rules?
- Are the rules too strict?
- Is rule enforcement appropriate?
- Are all the rules necessary?
- Do the lifeguards understand why each rule exists?
- Do the patrons understand why the rules exist?
- Do the patrons respect the staff and understand that their safety and welfare are the staff's concern?
- Are the staff breaking the rules as well?

c) Messages and strategies.

When the staff identified why the teenagers refused to follow the rules, they developed strategies they hoped would change the situation. Each strategy addressed the causes of the problem and conveyed to patrons the importance of cooperation for safety. Each lifeguard's attitude was friendly, patient, and constructive which built mutual trust among patrons and staff.

❑ **Review of the pool rules**
Lifeguards eliminated rules which were unfair or unrealistic. The staff became more comfortable enforcing rules which had sound and reasonable explanations. The staff took care to follow the same rules themselves.

❑ **Education with courtesy and patience**
The staff decided to get to know the patrons personally – especially the offenders. They used patrons' names when addressing them and used "please" and "thank you" when dealing with rule infractions. The lifeguards attempted to clearly demonstrate their concern for the enjoyment and safety of each patron, especially the offending teenagers.

❑ **Safe alternative activities**
The staff believed many teenagers broke the rules because of boredom and an inability to organize safe activities that were fun. The staff suggested games to patrons whose behaviour was risky. When teenagers abused the diving board rules, the lifeguards organized alternate activities, such as a diving club, "funny jump" competitions off the board, and

diving instruction. They channelled the teenagers' energies into constructive, safe, and fun activities.

- **Inspire administration confidence**
  The administration did not always accept staff recommendations, and rarely investigated thoroughly the complaints received. To increase the administration's confidence in staff abilities the supervisors were invited to visit the pool frequently. Lifeguards invited members of the council and administration to present awards at special events and competitions. To become better acquainted with each other, they arranged social events, such as barbecues, for administration and staff.
- **Publicize through the media**
  To raise the pool's profile, the lifeguards used the local media (cable TV, radio and TV news, community programs, newspaper). Each week a public service announcement publicized a special event or services offered by the staff.

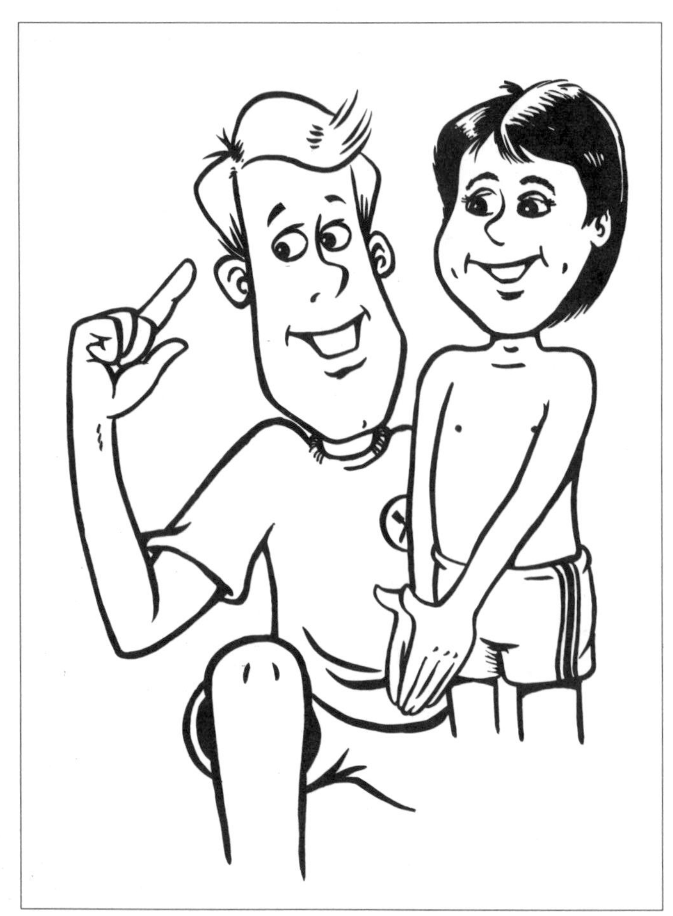

Walking patrols offer an excellent opportunity to educate patrons.

From time to time, all lifeguards experience the difficulties described at Sunnydale to some degree. The challenge is to discover the program, methods, and opportunities which will improve the circumstances. Use the Sunnydale model and decide on additional methods to implement good public relations at a facility familiar to you.

PUBLIC RELATIONS OPPORTUNITIES

Public relations is a full-time concern and on-going process, not something that is done before a special event or after an aquatic accident. Public relations begins with what patrons see and hear and sense the minute they enter the facility, and even before that. The lifeguards' look, uniform, attitude, and moment-to-moment interaction with patrons and other staff members all contribute to the public's perception of what a lifeguard is and what a lifeguard does.

LIFEGUARD BEHAVIOUR AND IMAGE

The general public often does not appreciate that a lifeguard's job is hard work. The perception of the unknowing observer is of someone sitting in the sun somewhat less than fully occupied.

The image of the lifeguard is affected by appearance and behaviour. A lifeguard's stance and "body language" should communicate to the observer that a vigilant and attentive professional is alert to potential trouble and ready to respond.

It should be possible to immediately identify lifeguards by their appearance. Uniforms should be neat, clean, and appropriate for the weather conditions. Distinctive colours aid in identification of staff members.

It is essential that lifeguards model the attitudes and behaviours they hope to persuade the public to adopt. Lifeguards must be seen following the same facility rules designed for the public – whether the facility is open to the public or not.

MAINTAIN A CLEAN, INVITING FACILITY

Lifeguards enhance their public image when they show concern with cleanliness of the facility. A lifeguard who picks up debris and puts it in a waste can creates a powerful impression. You are saying, "Lifeguards are proud of this facility and want to keep it looking neat." Also, you are an excellent role model for the public, encouraging them to dispose of their own garbage. Such actions do speak louder than words.

DEVELOP RAPPORT WITH PATRONS

Being a good host is a matter of attitude – you must want to provide the safest, most pleasant experience you can for your guests – the patrons of the facility. Develop habits that demonstrate to them that their lifeguards do care! Patrons need to observe your concern for their safety, your respect and consideration for them as individuals, and your willingness to use your knowledge and skill in providing them with the best experience you can.

Patrons feel more comfortable when they know your name and your capabilities. You can accomplish such introductions in many ways:

- Wear a name tag, badge, or hat that tells people your name and your role. For example, "Head Lifeguard" or "Kid Patrol."
- Display staff photos with brief descriptions of each individual's training in a prominent location. Patrons connect the names, pictures, and descriptions to the staff.
- Introduce the staff on duty at the beginning of every recreational swim.
- Introduce yourself to new patrons each day. A simple introductory line is "Hi! Are you enjoying your swim today? My name is Tony and I'm one of the lifeguards. If you need anything today please let me know." Patrons appreciate this initial personal contact.

GET TO KNOW THE REGULARS

Make a point of learning your patrons' names, capabilities, and interests. A friendly smile and a pleasant greeting make a warm welcome. Parents, proud of their children's accomplishments, enjoy opportunities to discuss their children. Children delight in showing their skills to an interested lifeguard. Knowing your customers well helps you to supervise their safety and to provide suitable activities that capture their interests.

RESCUE DEMONSTRATIONS

Staging simulated accidents to which your team responds is an effective demonstration of your rescue skills. Such demonstrations publicize your abilities in water rescue and first aid. Seeing efficient, confident lifeguards in action reassures the public about their own safety and raises their respect for you.

Inform patrons beforehand that the accident is a simulation. Keep it brief. As the lifeguards perform the rescue, have a commentator give explanations and field questions.

SPECIAL EVENTS

A variety of activities maintains interest in your programs. Organized special events effectively provide this variety. Organized games, a focus on a theme, competitions, and demonstrations all stimulate patrons to participate. They also show that lifeguards want the public to have fun.

Ten suggestions for special events are:

- Theme days, such as Hawaiian Day, Pirate Day or Superhero Day. Consider prizes for the best costume. Match games, refreshments and music to the theme
- Lifeguard Competitions
- Bake-Your-Lifeguard-A-Cake Day

Hints for Seeking Sponsors

- Approach potential sponsors well in advance. Companies with sponsoring funds need time to budget.
- Plan exactly what you need and the quantities. Know what assistance you are asking from each sponsor to assist them in budgeting.
- Carry identification which assures the sponsor that you are representing a legitimate cause.
- Be courteous. Remember that sponsorship requires effort and generosity on the part of the company. Even if they cannot assist you, express your thanks for their time.
- Send a written thank you letter to all sponsors following the event.
- Avoid frequent returns to the same organizations with additional requests.

- Secret Friend Day
- Teen- (Adult-, Family-, or Senior Citizens-) Only swims
- Swim Meets
- Diving Meets
- Demonstrations (Lifejacket, Small Craft Safety, Diving, Synchronized Swimming)
- Beach Day at the Pool
- Special Holiday Celebrations

Some commercial establishments and local businesses will help sponsor special events by donating refreshments or by contributing money for equipment and supplies. Publicize the names of the sponsors prominently in exchange for their support.

LEND EQUIPMENT

Good public relations may result when the staff lend equipment or toys (e.g., flutterboards, umbrellas, balls, lifejackets, hand paddles) to patrons. Communicate the rules for the safe use of the equipment and establish procedures for collecting (and cleaning) it.

DEVELOP VOLUNTEER PROGRAMS

Encourage members of the community to involve themselves with the facility. Young teens who are volunteer leaders or apprentice lifeguards learn about lifeguarding by helping organize games, shadow guarding, and assisting with maintenance tasks or equipment setup. These duties give the leaders experience for future lifeguarding and provide a structured program to direct their energies positively.

Invite adults to volunteer as organizers, as officials or as chefs for special events. Use volunteers as buddies for disabled patrons who need special assistance. Parents and retired senior citizens enjoy working with children as assistants in lessons or in special play programs.

Include people of all ages in your activities. Involving the public heightens the image of your facility as a community service. The more people taking pride in your program, the more solid your public relations will be.

BULLETIN BOARDS, SLIDES, AND FILMS

Rotate bulletin board posters and pictures to reach those target groups currently participating in your programs. Follow the three F's for bulletin board displays:

Few.................minimum words

Frequent..........change often

Fluorescent......viewer impact

Use films and slides, especially those photographed by lifeguards who accurately evaluate the skills and techniques shown in the films.

Daily Checklist for Evaluating Your Public Relations

- **Equipment**
  - ❑ Was all the rescue equipment inspected and in good order?
  - ❑ Is all equipment painted and clean?
  - ❑ Did lifeguards put equipment back after use?
  - ❑ Did patrons make any comments to guards or to each other about the equipment? If so, are any of these comments valid?
- **Cleanliness**
  - ❑ Was the beach, dock, or pool kept clean and free of litter all day long?
  - ❑ Were change rooms and wash rooms clean throughout the day?
  - ❑ Did the personal cleanliness of each staff member reflect the public image desirable for this pool or beach area?
- **Conversations**
  - ❑ Were conversations with patrons unfriendly or less than polite?
  - ❑ Were rules enforced adequately or am I becoming less concerned about the patrons?
  - ❑ Did I talk to any specific people who are important to this facility, for example, the mayor, councillors, or newspaper reporters?
- **Visual observations**
  - ❑ How many patrons stopped to read the bulletin board?
  - ❑ Is the bulletin board attracting more attention than it used to?
  - ❑ Of all the pictures taken at the pool or beach today, how many would indicate that this is an enjoyable and clean facility?
  - ❑ Did I observe anything today that taught me something about aquatic safety or aquatic recreation?
- **Feelings**
  - ❑ Did any of the rescue emergencies today threaten or scare me?
  - ❑ Am I as competent a lifeguard as I can be?
  - ❑ Did any people really "bug" me today? Why?
  - ❑ Are the lifeguards working together as a group?
  - ❑ Do any of the lifeguards need more direction and instruction?
  - ❑ Do the patrons know "Your lifeguard cares"?
- **Planning**
  - ❑ What needs to be done tomorrow?
  - ❑ Have we tried to foster good relations with the media?
  - ❑ Are there any particular people who should be invited to a special event (training session, demonstration, competition)?
  - ❑ What new efforts can be initiated in the interest of good public relations?

PUBLIC RELATIONS PROBLEMS AND SOLUTIONS

DIFFICULT PATRONS

Sometimes a patron will not respond to your best efforts at education and patience. Immediately report such cases to the head lifeguard or your supervisor. (See *Facility Rules and Patron Behaviour* in Chapter 7.)

SUSPICIOUS CHARACTERS

If you notice an individual exhibiting suspicious behaviour, immediately report to your supervisor. Provide an accurate description of the individual(s).

Report lewd behaviour and cases of exposure or gross indecency to your supervisor and the police.

Note anyone "lurking" about the staff room. Ask if you can help. Determine why the individual is there rather than swimming or sunbathing.

If a patron threatens the safety of a staff member or other patrons, immediately report this to the police. Take no chances – you are a lifeguard, not the police.

COMPLAINTS

In the heat of annoyance, a patron can be unreasonably angry. Suggestions for receiving complaints include:

- Introduce yourself and ask the patron's name. You set a tone for the ensuing conversation.
- Listen. Fully and patiently hear the person out. If listening conflicts with your supervision duties, refer the individual to a supervisor.
- Try to understand the complaint from the patron's point of view.
- Demonstrate that you have heard the complaint by paraphrasing it.
- Remain objective and neutral until you have more information. Report the incident to your supervisor and record it.
- Investigate. If the complaint is legitimate, try to accommodate the patron. If this is not possible, explain the reasons.
- Follow up. Ignoring the complaint escalates the difficulties; patrons feel that the lifeguards do not consider their views. People need to know that they are taken seriously even when you cannot act on their complaint.

ACCIDENTS

Part of your staff manual and emergency procedures should outline the procedure for dealing with the media in the event of a drowning or serious accident. All staff must know the procedure.

Immediately following an incident, limit information given to the media to the facts – never offer an opinion or otherwise comment. Refer reporters to a supervisor who is authorized to speak on behalf of the facility owner or operator (e.g., municipality, summer camp, school, club). Photographs taken are based on the understanding that the exact conditions at the time of the accident cannot be reproduced.

Refer to Chapter 8, *The Lifeguard and the Law.*

PUBLIC EDUCATION OPPORTUNITIES

TARGET GROUPS AND MESSAGES

Educational opportunities for lifeguards extend beyond their own aquatic facility into the community. Talks, slides, and films, to both adult and young audiences, encourage everyone to learn that swimming and water activities are great fun and are most enjoyable when they are done safely. Lifeguards can, therefore, promote aquatics while providing a stimulating educational program in accident prevention.

Certain key target groups should be singled out for particular attention by lifeguards:

- **Parents and grandparents of young children**

  Parents and grandparents should become the target of messages concerning parental responsibility for the supervision of children in an aquatic facility.

- **Male teenagers and active male adults**

  Aquatic accidents and fatalities affect this target group more than any other. This target group is notoriously at risk in terms of

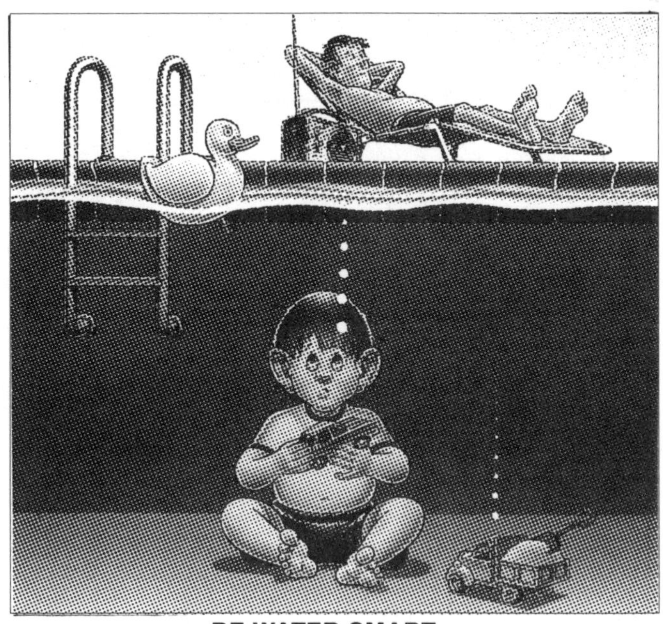

BE WATER SMART.
TODDLERS REQUIRE ADULT SUPERVISION.

aquatic spinal injuries caused by diving into shallow or unknown water. A spinal injury is catastrophic and frequently results in life in a wheel chair. Lifeguards can educate everyone who swims at the pool or beach that:

- diving into shallow or unknown water is a risk
- diving into shallow or unknown water can result in a broken neck or serious head injury
- no one should dive into shallow or unknown water, including experts.

SIGNAGE

The most common use of signage to educate the public is in the preparation and posting of facility rules. (See *Developing Facility Rules* in Chapter 2.) Additional signage is used to explain and warn of specific hazards such as currents, drop-offs, or boating lanes.

FACILITY RULES AND PATRON BEHAVIOUR

Lifeguards should think of rule infractions, not so much as occasions for discipline, but as a chance to modify hazardous behaviour, suggest alternatives, and provide education concerning safe aquatic practices.

The lifeguard staff must agree on the boundaries of acceptable behaviour in the facility, and all lifeguards must communicate a clear and consistent message to patrons about what constitutes safe behaviour in and around the water. Patrons will respect lifeguards for a professional and consistent approach. Because lifeguards can educate patrons only when patrons listen, lifeguards must:

- Conduct themselves maturely and professionally.
- Show friendliness and concern for patrons.
- Be consistent in enforcing policies.
- Show politeness, confidence, and some flexibility in correcting behaviour or when responding to emergencies.

Communication with patrons will be necessary when an individual is:

- Engaged in an activity which is or can become dangerous: pushing another swimmer into the pool or under the water, using or wearing equipment which could cause injury to other swimmers, encouraging a weak swimmer into deep water, throwing sand, etc.

Signs should both warn and educate.

- Doing something which can cause injury to himself or herself: running on the deck or dock, diving into shallow water, or hyperventilating before attempting a swim, etc.
- Disturbing or annoying other patrons or the staff: verbally abusing other patrons, pushing or shoving, distracting the lifeguard from watching swimmers, or playing with rescue equipment.
- Damaging property belonging either to the facility or to other patrons: damaging rescue equipment, removing or defacing signs, removing flags, stealing or throwing personal property of others into the water.

Approach the offender(s) to seek cooperation by explaining specifically the rule being broken or the risk created. Be courteous but firm, positive. and specific. Explain and correct. Avoid abusive (harsh) language and swearing. Never be provoked into striking the offender.

Signal the individual with a whistle or hand signal if it is not possible to approach the offender immediately. If the offending behaviour continues, go to him or her after alerting other guards to cover your area. Warn the offender firmly if no heed is taken of your instructions. Refer the individual to the head lifeguard (or vice versa if necessary) if cooperation is not forthcoming.

The head lifeguard should use the same courteous but firm manner. He or she can ask the uncooperative patron to leave the premises. If unacceptable behaviour persists, the head guard can involve the police. Calling the police is a last resort for minor problems.

The tone and manner of your communication should be appropriate for the individual. For example, a preschool child obviously cannot read warning signs or rules. A child (and some adults) may not remember or understand explanations. Also, young children cannot always connect disciplinary action with the dangerous behaviour which prompted it.

Lifeguards stationed at ground level are in an excellent position to interact with the public from moment to moment, and therefore must be sensitive to the positive public relations effect they can have with very little effort. Public education opportunities will present themselves much more often to the ground-level lifeguard, than to lifeguards supervising from a chair or tower.

APPRENTICE LIFEGUARDS

Apprentices (volunteer or paid) can be used to support public education objectives. Armed with handouts created by the facility staff, or pamphlets and brochures obtained from aquatic safety organizations, these individuals can distribute the material to the public throughout the day.

Apprentice lifeguards might be used to work on a specific problem – parental supervision, for example. An organized "Kid Patrol" might be designed to watch for children playing alone or unsupervised by an adult, with an aim to reunite child and parent.

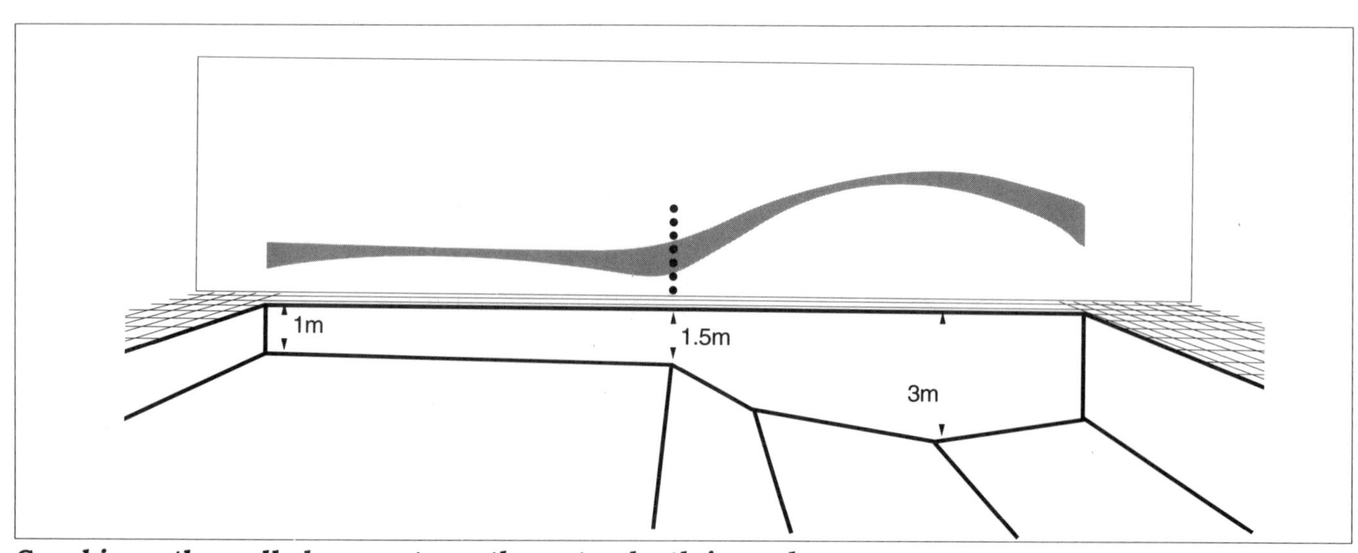

Graphic on the wall shows patrons the water depth in pool.

LITERATURE

Pamphlets, posters, and books on aspects of aquatic safety are published by a variety of organizations. Use these in bulletin board displays and as handouts at an appropriate location in the facility like the cashier counter or refreshment stand.

SPECIAL EVENTS

Lifeguard competitions, lifesaving demonstrations or competitions, open houses, barbecues are just four examples of special events which can be used to educate the public.

Consider a lifejacket or PFD "Check It Out" Day: patrons are encouraged to test their lifejacket or PFD at the facility.

PUBLIC ADDRESS SYSTEM

Use the facility public address system (with discretion) to educate the public about upcoming events, specific hazards, or a particular aquatic safety tip. Consider a regular "Tip of the Day" announcement, which gives patrons a tip on how to make their aquatic recreation more fun or safer.

COMMUNITY OUTREACH

Reach out into the community with public education messages by providing speakers for school visits, or community organization meetings or events. Contact schools early in the spring to draw maximum participation in May and early June. (Include in your program a promotion for developing a corps of apprentice lifeguards in the school.)

Consider making presentations with speakers using slides and films. Such presentations to politicians, service clubs, and related safety organizations are effective.

COMMUNICATION WITH THE MEDIA

The task of the media is to inform the public on subjects of current interest to the community. Always show courtesy by welcoming a reporter and providing helpful background information. Follow up with thanks for favourable publicity.

a) Program publicity.

The news media are eager for human interest stories. Take advantage of media interest in such stories as a child playing at a swimming facility to publicize your programs, educate the public about the job of a lifeguard, and attract new patrons.

Telephone the community desk of the local news media. (Make sure your employer gives approval for the project before contacting the media.) Local cable TV networks

Steps in Preparing a News Release

- In the upper left hand corner, write the full name, address, and phone number of your contact in case of questions. If material is for a daily paper, include a number for 7:00 am and a number for 10:30 am.
- Tell the essential story in the first few sentences. The rest of the release fills in the details. Include the Who, What, Where, When, Why, and How. Use relevant facts with a minimum of superlatives.
- Type the release double spaced on plain white paper. At the top, indicate either "For Immediate Release" or "For Release on Day and Date."
- Spell all names correctly. Newspaper style requires the first name or two initials. A. Smith is not enough.
- If the release carries the results of a special competition or event, draft the material beforehand based on what you think will happen. Adjust it after the event, if necessary. Deliver the release to the paper immediately following the event. Attach extra score sheets, results, brochures, or other information for accuracy.

often film longer segments of interviews or activities for repeated broadcast. Be friendly and well prepared with the information when making your contact. Know *what* you will say, *who* will say it, and *how, when, where* and *why* you will present the information. Invite reporters to photograph a recreational swim or a television crew to film the lifeguards during a simulated emergency.

b) Special events.

Many community news media provide a free "community calendar" service publicizing local events. Report your special activities well in advance to the news agencies. Write a news release of important facts.

TEST YOURSELF

1. *The lifeguards of Sunnydale Swimming Pool implemented plans for improving public relations. Develop some further plans which they could implement. While forming your plans, discuss your ideas with at least two experienced lifeguards.*
2. *Commission or make a poster publicizing the National Lifeguard Service. Arrange to have it displayed in a prominent location in your community.*
3. *With a partner, plan a public presentation either to help the public understand the role and training of lifeguards or to promote the programs available at your community swimming facility. You will make your presentation through the media – a newspaper article, a letter to the editor, a cable TV film clip, a slide show, or a radio interview. You complete your task with its actual presentation to the public through the media.*
4. *Draw up a plan for a special event which includes:*
   - *the theme or purpose of the special event*
   - *a schedule of the event outlining activities*
   - *how you will publicize the event*
   - *what materials you will need, when you will get them and how much it will cost*
   - *who is responsible for organizing specific portions of the events*
   - *a method of evaluating the success of the event*
   - *a letter of thanks to your sponsors.*
5. *Visit a swimming facility to observe how the staff promote good public relations. Make notes on your visit. Write a report suggesting methods for improving the public relations at that facility. Share your report with your NLS instructor or an experienced lifeguard for his or her comments.*
6. *With a partner, role play various situations which could include:*
   - *a patron complaining about the facility*
   - *a patron offering a suggestion about how to improve service*
   - *discipline of a patron*
   - *a patron exhibiting lewd behaviour.*

   Discuss these role plays to see how you can improve your public relations.
7. *List five pieces of equipment you could loan to patrons to enhance their enjoyment of your facility. Beside each item indicate where you could obtain it for little or no cost. Indicate how you could prevent its damage, theft, and unsafe use.*

Chapter 8

The Lifeguard and the Law

Chapter Focus

Lifeguards must be conscious of legal duties, obligations, and standards of behaviour expected of them. Usually a lifeguard's contacts with law enforcement personnel are routine, but occasionally lifeguards are questioned in connection with an investigation. In the case of an accident resulting in death, serious personal injury, or property damage, lifeguards, because of their specific knowledge of the situation, might be involved in a legal process as witnesses. In some situations, because of their specific legal responsibilities, lifeguards may become defendants in a lawsuit.

Think About After an Accident

"Two years ago when I was lifeguarding, I noticed a young boy who appeared to be in trouble in the water. I got to him as quickly as I could and he was under water for only a few seconds, but he was choking and having difficulty breathing. Then he stopped breathing altogether. We did everything we were trained to do, but he turned blue and stayed that way. By the time the ambulance arrived, his heart had stopped. He was revived in hospital, but died there a few days later."

"We felt awful. But I'm sure we did everything properly. Later the police came and asked a lot of questions. A few months later, there was an inquest, and I really felt that people blamed the lifeguards. Now I've been named in a lawsuit. It seems that someone told the family that I wasn't watching the water, and they say the rescue breathing wasn't done properly."

"I know there were lots of people who witnessed the incident, but we don't know their names. I'm sure I was watching, and I'm sure we did our best to revive him, but I'm not sure what the other guards were doing. It's been so long now I'm not sure I remember all the details. How do we prove the facts?"

THE LEGAL SYSTEM

Both the law and the legal system are concerned with the enforcement of obligations or standards of behaviour. Most legal obligations apply to all members of society, but there are some specific obligations peculiar to lifeguards. In addition, lifeguards are concerned with the standard of behaviour expected of them in their capacity as lifeguards.

The distinction between obligations (which are legal principles), and the required standard of behaviour (which is the interpretation of the principle for specific circumstances), is important. The following distinctions may help to explain certain aspects of the law:

- There are differences in kinds of law based on the source of the legal obligation.

- There is a difference between civil law (obligations between people), and criminal or quasi-criminal law (obligations between people and the state).
- There is a difference between the civil law of Quebec and the common law in other provinces.

DIFFERENT TYPES OF LAW

There are three types of law:

- written laws made by governments (statutes)
- written or oral laws made between individuals by agreement (contracts)
- principles of civil liability developed by the courts in common law provinces (torts) or in Quebec, enshrined in the Civil Code (delicts)

These different types of law interact, and each places different demands on the lifeguard and the aquatic facility.

An awareness of the different types of law can alert lifeguards to situations which impose legal obligations. With an understanding of legal principles, lifeguards can minimize legal risks and prevent a situation with potential legal repercussions from deteriorating.

a) Statutes.

The major types of statute encountered in Canada are:

Statute	**Jurisdiction**
The Constitution	Canada
Federal Acts and Regulations	Canada
Provincial Acts and Regulations	Province
Municipal By-laws	Municipality
By-laws or Regulations of Special Purpose Bodies	Specifically defined area

Besides federal, provincial, and municipal laws, special jurisdictions such as provincial and national parks, Canadian forces bases, or schools can be governed by special regulations. In each instance, lifeguards familiarize themselves with any laws governing aquatic supervision in each facility.

In general, statutes are of concern to lifeguards because they do one of two things:

- Regulate and punish those who fail to comply (criminal or quasi-criminal).
- Define, limit, or change rights between individuals.

From the lifeguard's perspective, it is important to know the following things about statutes:

- Statutes which govern behaviour or the operation of an aquatic facility will involve the lifeguard directly. Lifeguards are obligated to adhere to the laws that affect them.
- Legislatures can pass laws which change, repeal, or codify both private contracts and general civil obligations between individuals.
- The law may be different from one jurisdiction to another.
- Except for laws specifically affecting civil liability, laws such as the swimming pool regulations have nothing directly to do with liability.

b) Contracts.

Contracts are agreements between individuals which give rise to legal rights and obligations. Lifeguards are affected by contracts, often without realizing it. Contracts of employment, buying a ticket for admission to a facility, facility rentals, purchase of equipment, insurance, and waivers are all types of contracts. Contracts can be oral, written, or partly oral and partly written. The lifeguard needs to know two things about contracts:

- Contracts can create or expand legal rights between individuals.
- Contracts can eliminate or limit these rights.

An example of an expansion of rights by contract might be in representing to patrons that an aquatic facility is "completely safe." Patrons might be able to sue for accidents which are not the fault of the staff.

A waiver is an example of a contract limiting liability. When an individual, who is over the age of majority, freely and with full knowledge of the assumed risk, signs a waiver, he or she has, by contract, waived the right to sue. There are well known limitations to the effectiveness of waivers but they are generally based either on whether or not the contract is enforceable or upon exactly what rights were waived.

c) Torts and delicts.

Tort (from the French "tort" meaning "a wrong") claims arise when an individual receives injury to person or property under circumstances in which the law dictates that the person responsible for the injury or harm must compensate the injured party. Delicts are the same thing under Quebec law.

Negligence is the most important tort or delict. Negligence involves a careless act or omission by a person who has a duty to take care. This is the usual basis for a civil lawsuit involving personal injury or property damage.

TYPES OF LEGAL PROCEEDINGS

a) Lawsuits – civil courts.

A lifeguard may be involved in a civil court as a witness when someone else is being sued, or as a defendant when he or she is being sued. Civil courts decide liability and award compensation. The plaintiff must prove the facts alleged against the defendant and, if successful, the court orders the defendant to pay a sum of money to the plaintiff as compensation for the injury received.

b) Prosecutions – criminal courts.

A lifeguard can be required to attend a criminal court to give evidence as a witness or to appear if charged with an offence. Criminal courts decide whether an accused person is guilty of an offence. If found guilty, the accused is sentenced in accordance with the statute creating the offence.

c) Inquests.

An inquest or hearing is commonly called in deaths at supervised aquatic facilities, and lifeguards could be obligated to attend and to testify. Inquests are hearings convened by the coroner (usually a physician) or other official who is appointed to investigate deaths. The inquest determines who a deceased person was and how, where, and by what means the deceased person came to his or her death. Inquests can make recommendations to prevent similar future occurrences. The law of inquests is different in each province.

Although the inquest is not a trial (there is neither an accused nor a defendant), and does not determine liability, the inquest resembles a trial. The parties to a potential

Types of Law

Obligations and rights may be statutory, contractual, or by the law of torts and delicts. Remembering how each type of obligation is created and its purpose will help the lifeguard understand what is expected.

Statutes

From government	■ create offence ■ change rights	■ punishment ■ affects civil liability

Contracts

By agreement or promise	■ change rights ■ create rights	■ affects civil liability ■ compensation for breach

Torts/Delicts

Principles of law	■ create liability	■ compensation for injury

lawsuit can use the inquest as an opportunity to discover what evidence is available and to observe witnesses.

In some provinces, there is a coroner's jury. In Quebec there is no jury but the coroner hears from the parties involved and makes recommendations. The statutes vary in each jurisdiction but all provinces provide for some form of inquiry in cases of deaths whose cause is unclear.

PARTICIPANTS IN THE LEGAL SYSTEM

a) Police.

The police interact with lifeguards in the following circumstances:

- Lifeguards can summon the police to eject an unruly patron who refuses to leave the premises or to charge a patron who is a danger to others.
- In the case of a fatality, the police obtain statements, preserve evidence, and investigate the incident to eliminate homicide as the cause of the fatality and report their findings.
- If a lifeguard is accused of assaulting a patron or otherwise committing an offence, the police investigate and can lay charges or arrest the accused lifeguard.
- The police can require the lifeguard's evidence if the lifeguard was a witness to an incident under investigation.
- Should the police be the first emergency service to respond to an accident, they take steps to assist with the preservation of life, if necessary, and to maintain order.
- The police investigate vehicular accidents, enforce boating regulations, and take steps to confine a dangerous situation.

b) Inspectors and by-law enforcement officers.

These officials have powers of investigation and are responsible for enforcing certain statutory provisions. They do not have wide general powers like the police, but the lifeguard is likely to encounter some of the following:

- Pool inspectors ensure compliance with regulations; they warn or close the facility in the case of non-compliance.
- Health inspectors may evaluate water quality at public beaches; they may

Criminal Versus Civil Cases

The differences between criminal law and civil law are only important to lifeguards because the legal system deals with each in different ways. The following illustrates how criminal matters (offences) are dealt with differently from civil matters (breach of an obligation).

Criminal Offences	Civil Liability
charges laid by officials (police or inspectors)	action commenced by injured party
prosecution by government	prosecution by the injured party
in court, issue is "guilt"	in court, issue is "liability"
proof required "beyond a reasonable doubt"	proof required on a "balance of probabilities"
court imposes defined range of punishment	court awards compensation
no specific harm or damage is necessary	specific harm or damage must be proven

order the beach closed if it is found to be polluted or unfit for swimming.

- Fire inspectors investigate such items as fire alarm systems, emergency exits, fire doors, and facility design. Non-complying facilities can be closed.

c) Crown attorney or prosecutor.

The crown attorney is the government lawyer responsible for prosecuting criminal offences. The crown attorney can have a role in other proceedings such as inquests.

d) Judge.

The judge is the presiding official in a court. The judge is responsible for making findings of fact if there is no jury and for making the decision as to what law applies to the facts. The judge decides the sentence in criminal cases.

e) Jury.

A jury is composed of people from the community selected by lot. The jury makes findings of fact based on the evidence and, under the direction of the judge, decides whether the accused is guilty (criminal cases) or liable (civil cases). Coroners' juries may be responsible for finding the cause of death and can make recommendations. In some provinces, notably Quebec, juries are not used in civil court cases.

f) Insurance adjusters and investigators.

If an insurance company may have to pay an accident claim, the insurer appoints an adjuster to investigate and evaluate the claim. An uninsured defendant can do the same; a plaintiff or his or her lawyer or insurance company can also appoint an investigator or an adjuster.

Because a number of people can ask questions, lifeguards must know to whom they are talking and why. Before speaking to anyone, discuss your situation with your superiors and with your lawyer (in cases of possible personal liability).

The following situations can occur:

- The insurance company for the lifeguard's employer or the employer's lawyer (or both) need a statement from the lifeguard. You are obligated to cooperate with these people who are obtaining information in order to advise the defendant (lifeguard/employer). Written statements given to these people or notes of oral statements usually are provided to the plaintiff at some stage and can be used in court. Statements of any kind should be factual not speculative.
- Investigators for a plaintiff or potential plaintiff can interview the lifeguard. You must be cautious because you do not know if you will be sued. In addition, if you provide a statement, you will certainly be used as a witness.
- The lifeguard is under no obligation to provide information to a potential plaintiff. Any information you provide, especially if it is adverse to your interests, can be used in court; there is no duty to warn of this fact. Give no information or statements without discussing the matter with superiors and without obtaining legal advice, when appropriate.

g) Lawyers.

The plaintiff's lawyer is responsible for prosecuting a civil action and recovering damages on behalf of the injured person.

The defendant's lawyer is the lawyer hired to defend a court action. This lawyer requires full and detailed information from the defendant and key defence witnesses. All conversations between client and lawyer are privileged; therefore, discussions can be free and frank. A few situations can arise in which a lifeguard requires his or her own lawyer, separate from that of the employer.

h) Plaintiff.

The plaintiff is the person seeking compensation in a civil lawsuit.

i) Defendant.

The defendant is the person who is being sued in a lawsuit.

NEGLIGENCE

Negligence is the most likely allegation in a lawsuit. Negligence means carelessness, or the failure to behave in the manner expected by the community when dealing with others. The Quebec Civil Code (Article 1053) describes the obligation to take care as follows:

> *Every person capable of discerning right from wrong is responsible for the damage caused by his fault to another whether by positive act, imprudence, neglect or want of skill.*

The key concern is determining when "fault" exists in the legal sense. In a negligence claim, the plaintiff must prove three things:

- That the defendant owed a *duty of care* to the plaintiff.
- That the defendant, through a careless act or omission, fell below the *standard of care* which should be expected of a reasonable person under the circumstances.
- That the defendant's act or omission *caused damage* to the plaintiff's person or property.

Courts determine fault (find negligence) in the particular circumstances, and apply the principle of taking reasonable care equally to activities which are similar. Thus the situation at issue will be compared to similar situations in order to judge the conduct of the plaintiff and defendant. For example, boaters can be compared with motorists, pool operators with amusement park owners, and lifeguards with other kinds of supervisors.

DUTY OF CARE

Everyone has a duty not to injure other people during day-to-day activities. There may not *normally* be any duty to rescue a person from danger which the rescuer has not created. Whether a greater or more specific duty of care is owed is determined by the relationship between the injured person and the person alleged responsible for the injury. The relationship between parties creates obligations/duties/rights. A duty of care is created when operators and lifeguards open a facility to patrons.

STANDARD OF CARE

Having established that a duty exists between the defendant and the plaintiff, a court determines what standard of care the duty imposes. Because the expected standard of care varies with the circumstances, most legal argument arises in this area.

The standard of care has been described as the standard of "the reasonable person" or, in Quebec, as the standard of "the good father of a family." The standard means a person is obligated to take such care as a reasonable person, having due regard to the consequences of his or her actions, would take in the circumstances. The following could be used to establish an appropriate standard of care:

- the evidence of experts
- what other people or organizations do
- the amount of training the person has and what he or she is trained to do
- policies, procedures, rules, or standards set by the employer
- textbooks
- recommendations by training agencies or professional organizations
- standards set in similar fields
- the information about the risk which was available to the defendant
- requirements set by statute
- standards set by statute

The lifeguard who adheres to principles set out in textbooks and training courses and who adheres, at a minimum, to the standards set by the employer will likely be performing above the standard of care.

The standard of care is constantly evolving as recommendations, knowledge, and training change. If conflict exists among recommendations of employers, textbooks, and training courses, bring this dangerous situation to the attention of your employer.

CAUSATION

The plaintiff's injury must be directly linked to the defendant's activity. The injury must be considered by the court to have been generally "foreseeable" by a reasonable person.

DAMAGES

In negligence cases, a defendant found liable is responsible for compensating the plaintiff to the full extent of the damages suffered. This includes damages for pain and suffering and loss of enjoyment of life. As well, direct economic consequences, such as lifetime loss of income, medical expenses, and nursing care are compensated. Although Canadian courts tend to limit the amount available for pain and suffering claims, loss of income and medical expenses in a severely crippling injury can result in a judgment for millions of dollars.

DEFENCES

Even though negligence can be proven, there are defences available. One of these is contributory negligence. If the accident was, in part, the fault of the plaintiff, the judgment can be reduced by an amount corresponding to the injured person's own fault.

Another defence is voluntary assumption of risk or waiver. If the court finds that the plaintiff voluntarily engaged in the activity knowing of the risk of the injury which took place, there could be no right of action (similar to the contractual waiver). In both instances, (either written waiver or assumption of risk), the defence can succeed only if the person is old enough to appreciate the risk, if the risk is an obvious, normal risk of participation in the activity, and if the operator or supervisor of the activity has not been grossly negligent.

Written waivers which often are used in high-risk activities should not give a false sense of security. A waiver or a known high risk of injury voluntarily assumed does not eliminate the possibility of a negligence action. The courts have held that the waiver must show a clear intention to waive, and assume legal as well as physical risks.

JOINT RESPONSIBILITY

a) Shared responsibility.

In many cases, more than one person is responsible for an injury. Since the intention is to compensate the plaintiff, the plaintiff is generally allowed to recover the judgment awards from any one of the defendants who has money. The defendant forced to pay can attempt to recover from the other defendants. Thus, even five or ten percent liability can be very expensive.

b) Employer's liability.

A lifeguard's employer is affected by the principle of vicarious liability which makes the employer responsible for any negligence committed by an employee. This does not mean that the employee is not responsible. If forced to pay a judgment, the employer can attempt, in theory, to recover from the negligent lifeguard. The organization supplying the lifeguard normally is held responsible if the lifeguard is negligent. This principle is applied whether or not the lifeguard is being paid. In Quebec law, Article 1054 of the Civil Code states that a person is responsible for damage caused by the fault of persons under his or her control. This principle applies widely in all jurisdictions.

EXAMPLES OF DUTY OF CARE AND STANDARD OF CARE

In the examples which follow, the principles applied are more important than the specific decisions for the following reasons:

- Every case is different because the facts are never identical.
- Due to appeals, new decisions or government intervention, the law can change rapidly.
- If a case reaches trial at all, it means that the issues are not clear; therefore, the case can be lost.

a) The lifeguard.

No statute or legal principle clearly defines the lifeguard's duty of care owed to swimmers. Few cases in Canada or elsewhere have dealt with this issue directly.

Vigilant, attentive and alert.

The two core areas of responsibility inherent in lifeguarding are supervision and rescue. Because lifeguards have responsibilities in addition to these core responsibilities in various circumstances, the demands these responsibilities place on the lifeguard may vary.

Defining the duty of care may be easier than defining the standard of care. A case which dealt with the standard of care inherent in supervision was decided in Ontario in 1988. In *Crupi* v. *Royal Ottawa Hospital*[1] and others, a waterfront lifeguard on duty with a small number of swimmers in the water did not see a child who had slipped under the water and had submerged immediately. The water was murky which often is the case at waterfronts. The lifeguard could not see a person under water.

The court held that the standard of care for a lifeguard required that the lifeguard be alert, vigilant, and attentive, but not that the lifeguard witness every incident. In other words, the lifeguard must actively scan the water; simple failure to witness an incident without evidence that the lifeguard was inattentive, did not constitute a breach of the standard of care.

b) Occupiers of land.

Occupiers of land have an obligation to those coming onto the premises. The obligation is high to children, who may not appreciate the nature of a danger. A significant amount of negligence litigation in sports and recreation results from accidents which occur because of the condition of land or premises. In many jurisdictions, the occupier's liability is codified by statute. Such a separate codification does not exist in Quebec, since section 1053 of the Civil Code, examined above, is interpreted very broadly and covers this area.

Failure to take reasonable steps to protect users of land from danger is a major cause of civil liability. What risks should an owner of land foresee to patrons, trespassers, children, spectators?

One case which illustrates how the occupier's obligation can affect lifeguarding was decided in Ontario in 1982. In *Wessell* v. *Kinsmen Club of Sault Ste. Marie*[2] a raft anchored in the defendant's park came loose from its anchor. At the end of the day, the lifeguard (who had reported the problem) pulled it up on shore. After hours, the raft was pushed back into the water by several teenage swimmers and the plaintiff's son drowned when attempting to swim back to shore from the raft which had drifted out. Although it reduced the damages by 25 percent for contributory negligence, the court held the defendant liable because the unanchored raft constituted an unusual danger.

A similar decision was reached in *Bisson* v. *Corporation of Powell River*,[3] a 1967 British Columbia decision upheld by the B.C. Court of Appeal. In this case, a person who was a lifeguard and swimming instructor examining the Powell River swimming program accepted the word of local lifeguards concerning water depth. The plaintiff was paralysed as a result of diving from a diving tower and there were no signs warning of tidal conditions, or water depth. The Court of Appeal reduced the damages on the basis that the plaintiff was 20 percent to blame for his own accident. More recently, cases in British Columbia and Ontario[4] have held that the owners of an aquatic facility were not liable for spinal injuries which took place while the premises were unsupervised. These latter cases have been based on whether or not the danger was "concealed" or hidden from the injured person and whether it should have been so obvious to the land owner that the owner ought to have prevented it.

In *Unger* v. *The City of Ottawa*,[5] the Ontario High Court found no liability on the City because the accident was not "foreseeable". In the *Unger* case, which related to a preseason accident in early June, a young man broke his neck when he dived from a lifeguard chair which was situated with its front legs in shallow water. The court held that the City had a positive duty to take reasonable steps to protect persons from dangers it should have known to exist. Nevertheless, the judge concluded that it would not have been foreseeable that a person would dive from the lifeguard chair. The fact that a danger was not foreseeable as such is a defence to negligence, but clearly it is a defence upon which it is difficult to rely. A second incident at the same facility or even a similar subsequent incident at another facility could hardly be said to be unforeseeable.

c) Duty of an expert.

Canadian courts now recognize that negligent advice given by an expert whether or not it is paid for, gives rise to a cause of action.[6] The test is whether the "expert" ought to have known that the person to whom advice is given would rely upon that advice. Frequently, recreation programs dispense advice on all manner of things from construction of playgrounds to water safety. Great care should be exercised to ensure that the advice given is sound and is within the sphere of expertise of those offering it. Refer a person to literature or a source of advice. Give advice only with reasonable care and due thought to the consequences should your advice be wrong.

d) Duty of a supervisor of children.

Teachers in schools are held to a higher standard of care than average because the duty assumed is to exercise "parental" supervision. The teacher is held to the standard of care of the reasonable parent. This standard is also applied to other supervisors of children, such as camp operators, trip leaders, and playground supervisors who assume a parental role of direct supervision.[7]

While the lifeguard does not exercise direct supervision over children, the standard of care in the supervision of children is greater than in the supervision of adults. The law recognizes that children have a lesser degree of knowledge, judgment, and responsibility for their actions than adults do.

e) Duty of instructors.

A 1981 decision of the British Columbia Supreme Court relates to the duty of instructors. In *Smith* v. *Horizon Aero Sports Ltd.*[8] it was held that an instructor of a dangerous activity (sky diving) had assumed a high duty of care to an adult student, which the court equated with the duty owed by teachers to children. In this case, it was held that the instructor owed a duty not only to teach safety precautions but also to ensure that the student remembered them before allowing the student to jump from a plane. It is likely that the standard of care required of swimming instructors, especially if teaching children, is higher than when lifeguarding. The instructor is engaged in direct supervision while teaching an activity with risks known to the instructor but not necessarily to the students.

f) The duty to rescue.

At common law, a person has no duty to volunteer regardless of the level of training he or she may possess. This is not true in all jurisdictions, notably Quebec, where the Quebec Charter of Human Rights and Freedoms imposes a duty to rescue if the rescuer can do so without risk. A duty to rescue may be imposed by circumstances. For example, as described below, the operator of a boat has been held to have a duty to take reasonable steps to rescue a person who falls overboard. A person also assumes a duty to act in accordance with the standard of reasonable care if he or she voluntarily initiates rescue attempts. Obviously, a lifeguard who has assumed responsibility for swimmers in a defined area, has a duty to take reasonable steps to rescue any person in distress in the defined area.

The Quebec Charter of Human Rights and Freedoms imposes upon Quebecers the duty to assist others as follows:

> *Section 2: "Every human being whose life is in peril has a right to assistance.*
>
> *Every person must come to the aid of anyone whose life is in peril, either personally or calling for aid, by giving him the necessary and immediate physical assistance, unless it involves danger to himself or a third person, or he has another valid reason."*

g) Standard of care expected of rescuers.

Should a rescuer be expected to use the best available technique? In the case of *Horsley* v. *McLaren*,[9] a boat operator was held to have a duty to take action when a friend carelessly fell overboard into the icy May waters of Lake Ontario. The issue of the standard of care arose because the evidence disclosed that the operator did not use the best or recommended rescue technique. In this case the Supreme Court of Canada upheld an earlier appeal that overturned the trial judge's finding of negligence. The Supreme Court found that the operator's actions did not amount to negligence since the steps he took were reasonable.

h) Duty to subsequent rescuers.

In *Horsley* v. *McLaren*, the plaintiff was not the family of the passenger who fell overboard but the family of another passenger who died trying to save the victim when it appeared the operator's rescue attempt was ineffective. The Court left no doubt that, had the operator been negligent, liability would have existed towards the subsequent rescuer. This applied a principle expounded by the English jurist Lord Denning in *Videan* v. *British Transport Commission*[10] in which he held that liability for negligence extended to cover persons who were injured trying to rescue a victim from the consequences of the defendant's act or omission. In *Modde-Jonge* v. *Huron Country Board of Education,*[11] the Ontario High Court held that a non-swimming teacher who took a group of students to swim at an unsupervised beach with a drop-off was liable, not only in respect of the first student who drowned, but also for a second student who drowned when swimming out to rescue the first.

i) Duties of event organizers.

Organizers of events owe a duty of care to ensure that the event is set up and run safely. Reasonable precautions must be taken and reasonable care exercised. In *Crocker* v. *Sundance Northwest Resorts,*[12] the ski resort organizers asked the plaintiff, who was under the influence of alcohol, not to participate in an event. The plaintiff was not prevented from participating however, and the court found the resort liable for the paralysis resulting from an injury the plaintiff suffered after he insisted on participating.

The Ontario Court of Appeal overturned this decision, holding that the plaintiff was solely responsible for his own injuries. In considering this decision, the Supreme Court of Canada reinstated the trial judge's verdict but assessed contributory negligence at 25 percent and reduced the damages accordingly. The event organizer was responsible for 75 percent of a large sum of money.

j) Waivers and voluntary assumption of risk.

In the *Crocker* case and the *Horizon Aero Sports* case, although the plaintiff had signed a waiver, it was not held to protect the defendant. If there is negligence, a waiver does not often protect the defendant from liability.

The principle of voluntary assumption of risk has similar limitations because the injury can result from a risk which was either greater than known to the patron, or could not have been known to the patron.

A waiver was effective in a 1983 decision of the British Columbia Court of Appeal. In *Delaney* v. *Cascade River Holidays Ltd.,*[13] although death resulted from a defective lifejacket, no recovery was permitted. The waiver, which was clear and unambiguous, excluded liability for negligence, was executed prior to payment, was read, understood, and clearly formed a binding contract.

ASSAULT AND BATTERY

An assault (threatening a person with physical harm), or battery (touching the person without his or her consent), gives rise to civil liability. Since these are intentional acts, the principles of negligence are not involved. If a lifeguard threatens or strikes a patron or a fellow staff member causing damage, both criminal charges and a civil lawsuit can result.

a) Consent in first aid.

The implication of battery for first aid is less obvious. Before rendering first aid, lifeguards must identify themselves and ask the individual's permission. In life-threatening emergencies, the lifeguard should assume consent. The consequences of your acting to save an individual are not likely to result in harm and a lawsuit.

Injuries such as fractures, eye injuries, burns, and severe (but not life-threatening) injuries present a more difficult situation. For example, if you splint a fracture in accordance with your first aid training, it is unlikely that you would be held negligent should some unforeseen difficulty cause harm to the limb. However, liability for damage can result if you give the same treatment to an injured person who requested that no splint be applied. When first aid is rendered without the patient's permission, reasonable care is not a defence.

Obtaining consent in every situation is impractical particularly where children are involved. Technically, if they are below the age of majority, and certainly if they are very young, the consent could not be valid. Ideally, the lifeguard should have the consent of both parent and child.

There is no simple answer to this dilemma. Controlled programs, such as day camps or swimming lessons often obtain blanket parental consent forms and waivers which are of limited use if serious harm is caused by a first aid procedure without specific permission. Lifeguards must be alert to the problem caused by such specific first aid treatments if unnecessary under the circumstances.

The notion of "assault and battery" does not exist in Quebec civil law. In cases of injury or attack, it is either the sections of the Civil Code regarding civil responsibility (section 1053 & ff.) or the relevant sections of the Criminal Code that apply.

INSURANCE

Most employers carry liability insurance which protects them in the case of legal action, but does not necessarily protect the employees against liability while on the job. However, in many instances, an employer who is sued for the negligence of its employee defends on behalf of both.

Lifeguards need to know the extent to which they are protected and if they must pay legal costs of their own. In the rare instance when the employer believes the employee was in dereliction of duty and does not stand behind the employee's action, the lifeguard must retain counsel.

A lifeguard defended by an insurance company must cooperate fully with the insurer and is defended by a lawyer selected by the insurer. The insurer can also choose to settle the action rather than continuing with the defence.

STATUTE LAW AND LIFEGUARDING

Legislation can specifically affect the lifeguard's job responsibilities. A statute could:

- Require the lifeguard to do something or refrain from doing something.
- Prohibit or regulate certain patron activities or behaviours.
- Impose conditions of operating a facility or program.

In addition, the standard dictated by statute may be evidence of a minimum standard of reasonable care in a civil action for negligence.

There is little point in detailing statutory provisions in a textbook because laws change from time to time. Statutes are also different in different jurisdictions. The following are examples of provisions which affect lifeguards.

FEDERAL LEGISLATION

The Criminal Code and the Canada Shipping Act directly affect lifeguards.

a) The Criminal Code.

The Criminal Code of Canada is the general statute defining criminal offences. The lifeguard, like any other person, is subject to this code and entitled to its protection. Offences, such as assault or criminal negligence applicable to everyone, concern the lifeguard.

Assault, in the criminal context, is striking or attempting to strike a person with the intent to do harm. Criminal negligence is a negligent act or omission with wanton disregard for the safety of a person or persons.

Thus, actions which are the basis for a civil action also can be crimes. Criminal negligence charges are normally laid in cases of gross and extreme negligence when an unacceptable safety hazard is created.

A variety of criminal offences relate to alcohol consumption including the offence of operating a boat or other vessel under the influence of alcohol or other intoxicants. If convicted, a person can lose the right to operate a vessel just as he or she can lose the right to operate a motor vehicle if convicted of drunk driving.

Boating sections of the Criminal Code make it an offence to waterski or otherwise be towed by a vessel after sunset or to operate a vessel in a dangerous manner, and require boaters or operators of vessels involved in an accident to stop, to render assistance, and to provide names and addresses of those involved.

Section 262 of the Criminal Code makes it an offence to interfere with an attempted rescue as follows:

> *IMPEDING ATTEMPT TO SAVE LIFE*
>
> *262. Every one who*
>
> *(a) prevents or impedes or attempts to prevent or impede any person who is attempting to save his own life, or*
>
> *(b) without reasonable cause prevents or impedes or attempts to prevent or impede any person who is attempting to save the life of another person, is guilty of an indictable offence and liable to imprisonment for a term not exceeding ten years.*

Lifeguards guilty of a criminal offence can be charged and can find themselves a defendant in a criminal trial. A lifeguard who knows that certain patron activities constitute a crime should call the police in dangerous situations.

b) The Canada Shipping Act.

Federal regulations dictate the standards of operation for various types of vessels and boats. These include use of lifejackets or personal flotation devices, number of passengers, size of motor, safety equipment, lighting, and rules of navigation.

Waterfront personnel are familiar with police enforcement of small vessel regulations. These apply to lifeguard rescue boats and other lifeguard craft which must be operated to conform with the regulations (and comply with water safety standards as well).

Through application by the provincial government, the Federal Minister of Transport is empowered to approve speed limits and can place restrictions on vessels or other limitations on use of vessels. At a waterfront where boating constitutes a hazard to swimmers, special regulations can be enacted, posted, and enforced by police marine units.

PROVINCIAL LEGISLATION

Every facility should make copies of the legislation governing that facility available to the lifeguards, who should familiarize themselves with the requirements and scope of such regulations or laws.

a) Lifeguard qualifications.

Most provinces dictate the minimum qualification for lifeguards in particular environments. Each province has different regulations; large numbers of facilities are unregulated.

b) Staffing.

In many facilities, the minimum ratio of lifeguards to swimmers is dictated by regulation; nevertheless, many facilities are unregulated.

c) Facility operation.

In most provinces, construction and operation of man-made aquatic facilities such as pools and waterparks are regulated. Levels of chemicals, filtration, water tests, and number of swimmers also are regulated.

d) Trespass.

Trespass legislation in some provinces gives to the occupier of land or the person in charge of a facility the power to expel a patron and permits the patron who refuses to leave to be charged with an offence. Lifeguards must clearly understand their rights. Establish the procedures to be followed with local police.

e) Record keeping.

The law requires that certain records be kept. (See *Record Information* below.)

f) Employment standards.

Employment standards and occupational health and safety legislation in most jurisdictions set out minimum standards for all employees. Minimum wage, pay equity, work hours, entitlement to overtime, breaks, and the right to refuse to work in a highly dangerous situation are included.

These rights are given by the law. The employer must comply, but standards vary with the jurisdiction, the nature of the employer, the number of hours worked, and other factors.

g) **Collective bargaining.**

In most jurisdictions, employees, both part-time and full-time, have the right to form a union and to bargain collectively.

A lifeguard can work in a unionized or non-unionized environment. In the unionized environment, the collective agreement defines working conditions. The employee and the employer cannot make separate contracts. A unionized lifeguard has access to a grievance procedure if his or her rights under a collective agreement are infringed. Typically, there can be protection from dismissal except for cause.

While collective agreements can mean more protection for the employee, the rigidity imposed by it prevents changes with ease. In some circumstances, training, qualifications, staffing, compensation, and hours of work are defined by the agreement; change becomes difficult because it is negotiated between the union bargaining team and the management bargaining team in an adversarial environment.

LEGAL "FIRST AID"

As with medical first aid, the guiding principle of legal first aid is to preserve the situation and to prevent it from getting worse until professional help can be obtained. Information about the incident is plentiful at the time of occurrence; later this information can become evidence in a legal proceeding.

ESTABLISH LEGAL RESPONSE PROCEDURES

As a defensive measure, expect legal consequences to result from injury to participants in recreational activity. Specific procedures which should be followed to deal with possible legal ramifications include:

- immediate notification of superiors
- gathering and controlling information
- support and assistance for staff
- accident analysis and evaluation

IDENTIFY RISKS

When an incident occurs, identify the probability of a consequence. This relates directly to the seriousness of the accident, but also depends on the cause. Immediately report accidents involving equipment, staff members, condition of the premises, an instructional or structured setting, and any situation in which staff response might be questioned or in which resuscitation measures or hospitalization were required. Preserve the evidence.

RECORD INFORMATION

The first priority is victim care. Then staff should:

a) **Identify witnesses, get statements and preserve the evidence.**

Diagrams or photographs of the accident site are extremely useful; accuracy is absolutely essential because all records created can become evidence. Ideally, a trained person should do this.

b) **Follow up with staff and witnesses to obtain statements and detailed recollection of events.**

Do this before people have a chance to discuss the situation (which can change their recollection of events). If possible, have an expert do this.

c) **Complete all required documentation thoroughly and accurately.**

Since you cannot know in advance what records are significant, this applies to everything from daily log sheets to accident report forms. Logs and forms should contain all important and relevant information.

d) **Maintain a professional, competent approach.**

A decision to sue is sometimes influenced by the perception of apparent unprofessional or incompetent lifeguard behaviour. An individual is more likely to commence an action if he or she feels personally aggrieved at the organization. Never admit or imply fault.

CONTROL THE SITUATION

Do not make the situation worse. Minimize discussion. Initially, the people involved have strong opinions or feelings regarding an occurrence. Advising the victim that "I'm sorry it was all my fault. The city should have fixed that months ago" or otherwise releasing opinions can trigger unfounded legal action.

Gather and control all information to ensure that complete analysis takes place before statements are released to an accident victim's family, the media, or others. Return the facility to normal operation if appropriate.

OBTAIN PROFESSIONAL ASSISTANCE

The exact assistance required, whether it is an investigator, an insurance adjuster, or a lawyer, is determined by the circumstances. Although this decision is not the lifeguard's, the sooner made, the better. Prompt notification is important.

ENSURE FOLLOW-UP AND EVALUATION

Evaluation of information obtained following any accident is a key component both in preventing future accidents and in guarding against liability. Two or three similar accidents should alert staff to hidden risks. Failure to prevent the fourth or fifth accident can be negligent whereas failure to prevent the first occurrence would not.

Often, important data lies hidden in accumulated accident reports because no one analysed or documented the information. A graphic, simple way to track accidents is to mark each one on a map of the facility coded to distinguish different types or causes (e.g., patron activity, medical emergencies, slippery floors).

TEST YOURSELF

1. *Governments pass statutes to regulate behaviour. Distinguish this from the main purpose of civil liability.*
2. *What are the three things a plaintiff must prove to make a case for negligence?*
3. *List three reasons why waivers or exclusions of liability may not be effective.*
4. *Why are careful, accurate records important?*
5. *List four tools which may be used by a court to establish the standard of care.*
6. *List as many practical steps as possible which an aquatic staff might implement to reduce the likelihood of liability.*
7. *How can communication and coordination with police be of assistance to lifeguards?*

REFERENCES

Barnes, *Sports and the Law in Canada*, Butterworths, 1983

Linden, *Canadian Tort Law*, Butterworths, 1988

Marshall, *Canadian Law in Inquests*, Carswell, 1980

Rainaldi, ed., *Remedies in Tort*, Carswell, 1987

Robertson, *Selected Cases on Negligence Liability in Parks, Recreation and Sport*, Recreation Resource Centre of Nova Scotia, 1987

Robertson, *Sport and Recreation Liability and You*, Self Counsel Press, 1988

CASES

The following cases are referred to in this chapter. Readers unfamiliar with Canadian legal citation, should be able to locate the original reports with the assistance of a law librarian.

1. *Carmelo Crupi* v. *The Royal Ottawa Hospital et. al.*, 1988, unreported, file no 43667/85, Ottawa (Ontario District Court).
2. *Wessell* v. *Kinsman Club of Sault Ste. Marie*, (1982) 37 O.R. (2d) 481 (Ontario High Court)
3. *Bisson* v. *Corporation of Powell River*, (1967) 66 D.L.R. (2d) 226; affirmed at 68 D.L.R. (2d) 765 (British Columbia Court of Appeal)
4. Unreported jury verdicts in which The Royal Life Saving Society Canada gave expert testimony.
5. *Unger et. al.* v. *Corporation of The City of Ottawa, et. al.* (1989) 68 O.R. (2d) 263 (Ontario High Court)
6. Generally known in Canada as Hedley-Byrne liability from the English case of that name *Hedley-Byrne & Co.* v. *Heller & Partners Ltd.* [1964] A.C. 465 (House of Lords). See *Spiewak et. al.* v. *251268 Ontario Ltd. et. al.* (1987) 43 D.L.R. (4th) 554 (Ontario High Court), an example of liability for advice given by a real estate agent to a purchaser with whom he had no contractual relationship.
7. Numerous cases relating to teachers and schools establish this principle. See for example *Thornton et. al.* v. *Board of Trustees for School District No. 57 (Prince George) et. al.* (1978) 83 D.L.R. (3d) 480 (Supreme Court of Canada). The duty "of the reasonable parent" was applied to a ski instructor although the instructor was ultimately found not to have been negligent in *Taylor et. al.* v. *The Queen in Right of British Columbia et. al.* (1981) 124 D.L.R. (3d) 415 Supreme Court of Canada), indexed as *Taylor* v. *Ankenman.*
8. *Smith* v. *Horizon Aero Sports Ltd. et. al.* (1981) 130 D.L.R. (3d) 91 (British Columbia Supreme Court)
9. *Horsely* v. *McLaren*, (1971) 22 D.L.R. (3d) 545 (Supreme Court of Canada)
10. *Videan* v. *British Transport Commission* [1963] 2 Q.B. 650
11. *Modde-Jonge* v. *Huron County Board of Education* (1972) 25 D.L.R. (3d) 661 (Ontario High Court)
12. *Crocker* v. *Sundance Northwest Resorts* (1988) 51 D.L.R. (4th) 321 (Supreme Court of Canada)
13. *Delaney* v. *Cascade River Holidays* (1983) 44 B.C.L.R. 24 (British Columbia Court of Appeal)

Chapter 9

Administration and Management

Chapter Focus

As employees, lifeguards work within an administrative framework and under certain management policies and procedures. In addition, lifeguards undertake administrative tasks (e.g., reports) and often organizational and management responsibilities as well. This chapter outlines the principles of planning, implementing, and evaluating which are important to the lifeguard's role in the development and improvement of an aquatic facility's program.

Think About this Request

MEMO TO: Head Lifeguard

FROM: R. Warren

RE: Letter of Complaint

According to the attached letter, the pool was opened fifteen minutes late last Tuesday. Those waiting to get in were apparently told that the lifeguards were "not ready yet." The writer remarks that this is the second time this has happened in the last six weeks.

With reference to the staff manual concerning facility opening, staff hours and punctuality, please review this letter with the lifeguards under your supervision, and report the cause of the problem and your recommendations in writing to me. In addition, I would appreciate it if you would prepare a response to the letter (which my office will type).

PROGRAM PLANNING AND ORGANIZATION

At any level, it is important that staff understand the "big picture" and come to see themselves as stakeholders in achieving the goals and objectives of their employer. If statements of mission or purpose, or goals and objectives do not exist, there is an opportunity for staff input in creating them. If they already exist, staff need to learn what they are and become committed to them.

PLANNING

Planning is preparation on paper. The adage, "plan the work, then work the plan" illustrates the goal of planning. Learn to think about opportunities, tasks, and problems from many perspectives, and anticipate the effects your plans and methods will have on co-workers, the program, and the public. Whether planning for one special project or an entire aquatic program, consider the following:

a) Input.

Ask others what they think are important goals, methods, and activities. When others share in planning, they take on ownership which commits them to the results.

b) Goals.

Establish clear objectives. For example:

"I want my special event to..."

- involve families
- help people learn about the lifeguards
- keep people active
- stimulate fun

The action words help you visualize exactly what should happen. Goals must be *manageable* and *realistic* enough to be successful. They must be *appropriate* to meet the needs of the participants.

c) Method.

Decide, with the input of other knowledgeable individuals, the best way to accomplish your goals. Reviewing records of similar events helps you learn from previous experience, avoid previous mistakes, and borrow successful methods.

d) Timing.

Successful planners decide when events will occur and in which order. Establish a "critical path" (timeline) which divides a large project into smaller parts. Timelines give you confidence that you are making progress and that all will be ready on time. Always allow a generous amount of time to carry out the plan to avoid last-minute rushing.

e) Atmosphere.

Create a working environment that helps co-workers to enjoy tasks and to feel a sense of accomplishment. Although individuals have their assigned roles, involve them in a cooperative, creative way wherever possible. Allow some flexibility in how they accomplish tasks and remember to thank them for their assistance.

When planning a meeting or special event, ensure that the participants will be comfortable. Consider parking, location, seating arrangements, lighting, handicapped access, ages of participants, and refreshments.

f) Budget.

Take the available resources into account money, time, expertise, materials, and equipment. Ensure that there are enough resources to complete the project. Decide on the priority tasks and allocate resources to the project priorities.

IMPLEMENTING

Valid and realistic goals, a good plan, committed and motivated people, adequate timelines, and sufficient budgets all make a plan work. However, your most valuable asset can be assistance from others. Consider how you can best tap co-workers' abilities to contribute to the project's success.

a) Delegating.

Assign tasks only to those capable of doing the jobs. Offer clear instructions that provide practical suggestions for completing the assignment. If your instructions are excessively detailed, co-workers can interpret your precise directions as lack of confidence. This also limits challenges to their creativity. Your recognition of their personal abilities and achievements is a first-rate motivator.

b) Reporting.

When several individuals work on the same plan, keep yourself informed of their progress. Schedule regular meetings to share what each person is doing, what problems are developing, and how the whole project is progressing.

c) Problem solving.

Encourage individuals who identify problems to suggest solutions since they might best understand the problem. In problem solving, include those who will be affected by the solution. Consider the following steps:

- Identify the main problem as specifically as possible.
- Gather facts and opinions, and identify relevant factors.
- Develop and analyse alternative solution(s).
- Select the most appropriate solution.

d) Evaluating.

All staff should be informed of how, when, and why evaluations will occur. Evaluate all aspects of the project or program including people involved, facilities, methods used, and the evaluation process itself. Either written reports or oral feedback are suitable providing the results are recorded.

Staff who are aware of the reasons for reports and comments will realize that their opinions are important for future developments. Differences in individual viewpoints should be probed thoroughly. Encourage frankness, objectivity, and specificity in evaluations.

Evaluations yield suggestions for improvement. Being part of a change for the better is exciting. Follow through on suggestions made.

Lifeguards also perform administrative duties.

STAFF ORGANIZATION

LINES OF AUTHORITY AND RESPONSIBILITY

If individuals are to do their best work, they must clearly understand their specific responsibilities. The size of the community, the number of facilities, and the nature of the programs determine which methods of staff organization are most suitable.

Each level in an organization carries specific duties. Management levels approve rather than prepare suggestions and recommendations. Lifeguards should continually evaluate the operation from their perspective and direct comments to those in higher authority. When ideas for improvement are not flowing upwards, less desirable (and sometimes uninformed) policies can flow downwards.

In most organizations, lifeguards have a job description of their responsibilities and lines of authority. When problems arise, follow the appropriate chain of command in seeking solutions.

a) Head lifeguard.

The head lifeguard is responsible for ensuring the overall safe supervision of the aquatic facility. He or she usually reports to the facility manager or aquatic director or supervisor. The head lifeguard should be a well qualified and experienced lifeguard, and a mature individual with a responsible and professional attitude. The following responsibilities are commonly found in the head lifeguard's job description:

- Determine (or make recommendations concerning) lifeguard staff size (full- or part-time), organization, supervision, and evaluation.
- Be familiar with and carry out facility opening and closing procedures.
- Supervise and be responsible for the behaviour of lifeguards and participate in disciplinary action if necessary.
- Be responsible for cleanliness and maintenance of areas and equipment.
- Establish, assume responsibility for, and participate in, pre-season and inservice training.
- Establish a schedule of lifeguard duties.
- Be familiar with the emergency and search procedures of the facility.
- Restrict the use of or close the facility when dangerous conditions exist.
- Be responsible for all records and reports.
- Be responsible for maintaining a good public image for the facility and for maintaining good public relations.
- Be familiar with all aspects of the aquatic program.
- Ensure that the lifeguarding provisions of government regulations are respected at all times.
- Wear designated uniform while on duty.
- Perform related duties as may be assigned.

b) Lifeguards.

- Hold appropriate qualifications.
- Be responsible to the head lifeguard.
- Operate all recreational and safety equipment.
- Safeguard patrons using the facility.
- Perform rescues in accordance with the emergency procedures of the facility.
- Assist in cleanliness and maintenance of the area and equipment.
- Maintain good physical condition through practice and participation in in-service training.
- Enforce rules and regulations.
- Wear designated lifeguard uniform while on duty.
- Remain on duty as assigned until relieved.
- Remain within call when on breaks.
- Perform other related duties as assigned.
- Foster a good public image of the facility and maintain good public relations.

c) Instructors.

- Hold appropriate qualifications.
- Comply with regulations of the facility.
- Prepare lesson plans for all classes.
- Be responsible for all records and reports on progress of pupils as required.
- Wear designated uniform while on duty.
- Participate in training sessions provided.
- Foster a good public image of the facility and maintain good public relations.
- Perform other related duties as assigned.

d) Cashiers.

- Be honest and reliable.
- Be accurate with figures.
- Maintain good public relations.
- Be familiar with the facility, its program, policies, and procedures in order to answer questions.
- Be responsible for specified records and reports.

e) Maintenance engineer.

- Be qualified to operate facility.
- Complete reports as required.
- Be responsible for the safe operation of equipment.
- Carry out necessary inspections of facility.
- Request ordering of supplies and materials related to maintenance.

SELECTION OF STAFF

When recreation directors and aquatic supervisors seek candidates for staff positions, they:

- Advertise the available positions in newspapers, schools, universities, and employment centres.
- Include the required prerequisites, general job description, approximate wage, hours of work, and how to obtain an application form.
- Interview applicants based on the needs of the program offered, qualifications, and completeness of the application form.

  Applicants for lifeguard or lifeguard-instructor jobs should learn the answers to the following questions

  - Who is the employer (agency, city, town, camp, or other)?
  - To whom will you be responsible?
  - How will you fit into the total scheme of the operation?
  - What are the specific duties related to the job?
  - What is the term of employment? Start and finish dates?
  - What is the schedule of hours, days off?
  - What is the wage/salary?
  - What are the employee benefits: vacation, sick leave, accident, disability insurance?
  - Is there a training, orientation, or probationary period? When?
  - Is a medical examination report required?
  - What are the details concerning uniform? Supplied or purchased?
  - What are the policies of the employer regarding liability insurance? How are you covered and for what dollar value?
  - What are the policies and procedures and where are they written down?

The interviewer should give some indication of the applicant's position following the interview; that is, hired, rejected, or to be notified.

Employment Application Form and Interview Guide

It is the legitimate right of employers to obtain the most qualified and suitable candidate for a particular job. Often recruitment practices, though not open or intentional, are discriminatory. Employment decisions should be based on criteria relating to the applicant's eligibility and ability to do the job, rather than on factors that are unrelated to job performance. Therefore employers should ask only those questions on application forms and interviews that relate to job requirements.

A. The following list illustrates the type of questions that are appropriate or inappropriate on application forms and at employment interviews. It is not exhaustive and employers should remain current with employment-related legislation..

1. Questions on birthplace, ancestry, ethnic origin, race, colour, religion are inappropriate. Inquiries as to colour of eyes, hair or photographs are also inappropriate. It is appropriate to ask "Are you legally entitled to work in Canada?" and an applicant may be asked to provide proof of eligibility to work in Canada.

2. Questions on sex, sexual orientation, marital status, family status are inappropriate. It is also inappropriate to inquire about height and weight, children and dependants or information about a spouse. After hiring, inquiries which are pertinent to an employee benefit plan may be made (e.g. marital status or dependants).

3. Questions about age are inappropriate on application forms; it is appropriate to ask "Are you legally entitled to work?" and at an employment interview, an applicant may be asked about his or her age if it is a genuine requirement for the job.

4. Questions about health and disabilities are inappropriate on application forms. At employment interviews, enquiries which are directly related to an applicant's ability to perform the duties of the job are appropriate.

5. Questions on job-related education and training such as diplomas and certifications obtained, and courses of study are appropriate. At employment interviews, job-related inquiries designed to determine the merits of an applicant's qualifications, including verification of certifications, are appropriate.

B. The following sample questions are appropriate to use on an application form for employment.

1. **Personal Data**

Name . . . .

Address . . . .

Telephone number(s) . . . .

Are you legally eligible to work in Canada? ❑ YES ❑ NO

Preferred work location . . . .

Are you willing to relocate? ❑ YES ❑ NO

2. **Education**

Secondary school

- highest grade or level completed . . . .

Community college, Trade school

- Name and length of program . . . .

- Certification or Diploma obtained ❑ YES ❑ NO

University

- Name and length of program . . . .

- Degree obtained ❑ YES ❑ NO

3. **Aquatic Certifications**

- Name and length of program . . . .

- Certification obtained ❑ YES ❑ NO

4. **Employment**

Name and address of previous employer . . . .

- Job title . . . .

- Duties

- Period of employment From . . . . To . . . .

- Name of Supervisor . . . .

- Reason for leaving . . . .

5. **Activities**

- Civic, volunteer, etc. . . . .

- Work -related experience, training, etc. . . . .

I hereby declare that the foregoing information is true and complete to my knowledge. I understand that a false statement may disqualify me from employment or cause my dismissal.

Signature . . . .

Date . . . .

Provincial governments require that all employers meet specific employment standards. These standards include hours of work, minimum wage, overtime pay, vacation pay, severance pay, holidays, equal pay for equal work, and termination of employment. You can find this information through the provincial government and seek information from your employers regarding details of the standards. (These provincial regulations do not apply to federal government employees or to a variety of other occupations.)

The Federal Charter of Rights and Freedoms declares that every person has a right to freedom from discrimination in several areas, including employment, but exemptions do exist. Employers are aware of this legislation. Lifeguards who question their employers' policies should check the legislation and regulations of their provincial governments.

HOURS OF WORK

Employers generally expect lifeguards to work daytime, evening, and weekend hours. With incentive (overtime) pay, lifeguards may work a forty-eight hour week for a short time (summer season only). Fatigue reduces vigilance, patience, physical endurance, and emotional stability. Employers and lifeguards must consider the possibility of reduced effectiveness caused by overtime incentives. Employers should count inservice training time as part of lifeguards' working hours.

Many agencies and recreation departments employ part-time aquatic staff as lifeguards and instructors. Part-time staff should:

- Have standards and personnel policies different from the full-time personnel that recognize the contribution of part-time staff to the total program.
- Be encouraged to participate in meetings, and to contribute to the evaluation and development of the facility's programs and activities.
- Participate in organized professional development opportunities which relate to the goals and objectives of the facility and its programs.
- Be provided with recognition and staff "perks."

STAFF RELATIONS

a) Employer-employee relations.

When an employer shows confidence in the staff by offering them additional responsibilities, along with the training and tools to be successful, the staff responds positively, even eagerly. Money need not be the only effective incentive. When an employer inspires trust and confidence in employees, they usually complete new tasks successfully and creatively, learning a great deal from the experience.

Employers need to get out from behind their desks to meet their staff on a friendly basis. Appearances at the pool or beach show interest, offer opportunity for informal dialogue, and a chance to understand problems and concerns arising from the employee's job.

b) Relations among fellow employees.

As with relations between lifeguards and the public, internal relations among lifeguards require mutual respect, cooperation, and concern. When people work closely together over extended periods, interpersonal conflicts can develop. They must be resolved without jeopardizing the effectiveness of the lifeguard team. If lifeguards are unable to function effectively as a group, they create a safety hazard. The supervisor, or head lifeguard, should be alert to such situations and immediately take steps to correct the problem. Suggestions for good internal staff relations include:

- Respect one another's privacy. Working in a busy, confined area can cause stress. Be considerate when sharing space in a staff room and to respect the privacy of personal lockers and equipment.
- Help keep the staff room tidy. Clutter and garbage produce an unattractive atmosphere. Assess your personal habits noting how they affect others.
- Respect fellow lifeguards who have worked hard to earn their position. All deserve courtesy and understanding. If you sense conflict, be patient and charitable. Above all, separate your personal relationship from your professional relationship when you run into conflict.

- When professional differences arise, follow the appropriate channels to settle the dispute. On matters of lifeguarding technique or patron discipline, inform your manager or head lifeguard of the situation.
- Get to know your fellow lifeguards. Take time to learn their interests and personal needs. Spending time as a staff away from the work place can promote better relations among the staff. Try arranging staff barbecues or outings in relaxed settings which allow for better personal communication.
- Practice your skills with your fellow lifeguards. During emergencies you will count on one another, possibly for your lives. Treat errors as opportunities to learn from one another.

Head lifeguards, supervisors, or managers will also:

- Make certain all lifeguards understand the importance of their jobs, and include an evaluation of ability to get along with co-workers in performance evaluations.
- Encourage inventive programs which require lifeguards to concentrate on principles, yet allow flexibility in methods.
- Always compliment staff on tasks well done.
- Deal with an employee problem immediately to resolve concerns.
- Provide additional assistance to staff members needing individual training and help.
- Involve every staff member in planning sessions.

STAFF EVALUATION

Patrons, employers, and fellow employees evaluate lifeguards on and off the job. The general public evaluates lifeguards even when they are off duty. Opinions are formed from what lifeguards say and what they do. (See Chapter 9, *Public Relations and Public Education.*)

Effective evaluations offer encouragement and direction. Employers must thoroughly explain the evaluation process to employees at all levels in the organization. The evaluation methods explained here are initiated by the employer.

Lifeguard supervisors complete written evaluation reports which they discuss with the individual lifeguards. Supervisors discuss these evaluation reports with the employer who may adjust the ratings (employer and supervisor may review the evaluations together). The final report submitted to the employer bears the signatures of both supervisor and lifeguard indicating that both have read it. Keep written reports on file for future reference.

The format can change for each evaluation. Investigate methods which produce positive results and rely on these. Seek new ideas used by other employers in aquatics and other fields.

A continuous evaluation process promotes excellence. Ideas which improve efficiency and reduce costs of operation will come forward. Often, management rewards lifeguards who have offered significant and useful recommendations. Such schemes encourage evaluations from all employees that results in improvements to the facilities.

COORDINATION OF STAFF IN A RECREATION COMPLEX

Where a swimming pool is one part of a large complex, a lifeguard might be called to another area of the facility to assist in a special circumstance or in an emergency. Many communities include in one recreation complex a pool, arena, gymnasia, racket sports courts, food services, exercise rooms, and library. Each area has its own staff with designated roles to provide service to users of that area.

In an emergency, all staff need to know the plan for the entire complex. Lifeguards need to understand their role in this larger picture. See *Staff Manual* (below) for suggested content of the facility operations manual.

All staff should rehearse these emergency procedures on a scheduled basis. New staff must be schooled in these procedures very early in their employment.

Written reports following these practices are extremely important since there are few real emergencies. The system, once tested, will either be valid or need revision. If changes are written into the operations manual, the revised guide must be distributed to all staff and the improved emergency procedures rehearsed.

STAFF MANUAL

Every facility should provide its staff with a manual or guide which includes all operation procedures and policies. The manual is essential to the lifeguards' understanding of their role in every aspect of their job. The information also gives them an appreciation of the roles of other employees and how each group interacts and cooperates. The complexity of the operations manual will depend upon the facility.

Lifeguards and senior personnel should contribute to the preparation and ongoing revision of the material in the manual. The content should be evaluated at least annually and revised as necessary.

Suggested content includes:

- ❑ **Purpose**
  - Organization mission or purpose statement
  - Facility goals and objectives
  - Program or activity goals and objectives
- ❑ **Physical set-up**
  - Diagrams, maps, or outlines of the full facility including descriptions of normal conditions and known hazards or conditions peculiar to each area
  - Information on how the public obtain access to each area
  - The control of the number of patrons admitted to the facilities
  - The locations of alarms, exits, emergency vehicle access, specialized equipment, such as self-contained breathing apparatus and fire-fighting equipment
- ❑ **Lifeguarding procedures**
  - Bather load restrictions and lifeguard-to-bather load ratios
  - Use of equipment (boats and vehicles)
  - Signals (whistles, flags, lights, arm, and verbal)
  - Communications operation (radio, telephone, and public address systems)
  - Public relations with patrons and the media
  - Routine procedures for opening and closing
- ❑ **Emergency action plans**
  - Routine aquatic emergency procedures
  - Emergency requiring police, ambulance, or fire department intervention
  - Fire (in any location) in the facility
  - Bomb threat
  - Power failure
  - Overcrowding in an area
  - Chlorine leak (or other toxic substance)
  - Structural failure
  - Serious injury or death
- ❑ **Report policies**
  - Required reports
  - Reporting procedures
  - Sample forms
- ❑ **Personnel policies and procedures**
  - Job descriptions of duties and responsibilities
  - Hours of work, overtime, sick leave, vacation pay, pay procedures, employee benefits, insurance policy, employee evaluation)
  - Uniforms
- ❑ **Personnel directory**
  - Identification by name and title of members of the department or agency
  - Identification of the person(s) in charge of each sector of a multi-facility complex

RECORD KEEPING AND REPORTS

IMPORTANCE OF ACCURATE RECORDS

The importance of accurately recording and retaining written facts cannot be underestimated. Records are used by lifeguards and facility management to document trends and spot recurring problems, both of which may call for a change in policy or procedure. Moreover, serious aquatic accidents are investigated by the authorities and all written details are carefully examined. Such records are referred to and used in evidence at inquests and court cases, often a considerable time after the incident. Data that should be kept include records of:

- **Facility operation and maintenance**
  - Water quality and temperature checks
  - Maintenance checks and repairs
  - Weather conditions
- **Facility use**
  - Patron attendance figures
  - Rentals, special groups
- **Incident reports**
  - Water rescues
  - Emergency care responses
  - Incident reports (e.g, vandalism, theft, fights)
- **Staff**
  - Emergency policy and procedures
  - Staffing schedules
  - Staff qualifications
  - Pre-season and inservice training programs including staff attendance

ANNUAL REPORTS

An annual report is prepared at the conclusion of the season or at the end of the year. Usually, the head lifeguard, aquatic director, or waterfront director has the responsibility for this task. The annual report includes the following:

- Facility report
  - » Beach, pool, or waterfront area
  - » Equipment
- Recreational program
- Instructional program
- Accident and rescue report summaries
- Special programs
- Staff evaluation
- Financial report
- Recommendations
- Appendix of relevant data for example, daily reports, program statistics, accidents, budgets, and inventory of equipment and supplies

A cumulative report over several years provides statistics on record-keeping, accident reports, program analysis, and lines of communication that help improve the effectiveness of the facility's program.

TEST YOURSELF

1. *Role play a job interview with a partner. One of you plays the role of aquatic manager; the other takes the role of a new lifeguard being hired for the job. Discuss the experience. Perhaps a third person can observe your interview to give you feedback on how well you performed. Did you get the job?*
2. *Ask a friend or colleague to give you an assessment of your work habits and skills. Discuss any differences between his or her assessment and your own perception of your ability.*

Chapter 10

Pre-Season and Inservice Lifeguard Training

Chapter Focus

Initial lifeguard training introduces lifesavers to the basics of safety supervision, accident prevention, and lifeguard emergency procedures. However, ongoing training and development is necessary to keep recognition, reaction and rescue skills ready, to apply the principles of emergency procedures to the characteristics of specific aquatic facilities, and to maintain good physical condition. In addition, techniques and procedures change over time and lifeguards need to keep themselves abreast of these developments.

This chapter underlines the importance of inservice and pre-season training and provides suggestions for the content, process, and means of a lifeguard's continuing education.

Think About Getting Better

Certification as an NLS lifeguard is not the end of a lifeguard's education, but rather the beginning. After initial training, lifeguards have to stay good and get better at what they do. To stay good, they practice skills, apply knowledge, and use problem solving, decision making, and judgment. They remain up-to-date with current developments in the lifeguarding field.

To get better, lifeguards seek out opportunities to learn, grow, and develop both personally and professionally. Many lifeguards pursue challenging careers which grow out of a subject or activity that caught their interest during inservice training programs. It will be no surprise to learn that former lifeguards end up in leadership roles in their careers and in their communities. Thousands of former lifeguards now enjoy success in careers that depend on leadership, sound judgment, ability to handle stress, determination, teamwork, people skills, and a personal commitment to continue learning.

Think about staying good...and getting better.

ONGOING TRAINING AND DEVELOPMENT

A lifeguard's job requires a high degree of judgment, knowledge, skill, and fitness in both day-to-day guarding and in the stress of an emergency. Inservice training helps sustain the lifeguard's confidence in his or her ability to prevent accidents and to respond competently when they do occur.

PRINCIPLES AND PRACTICE

Lifeguards and employers both must recognize the need for and encourage regular and ongoing lifeguard training and development opportunities. Physical and mental preparation are equally important; inservice training programs should include, but go well beyond, practice sessions in the water.

After their initial certification as lifeguards, staff need:

- To learn the specific requirements, policies, and procedures of the employer.
- To practice and develop individual lifeguarding and rescue skills and knowledge.
- To learn how to work as members of a team.
- To learn about new techniques and developments.
- To maintain mental and physical fitness.

a) Pre-season training.

Pre-season training allows new staff to learn and returning lifeguards to review facility-specific supervision, rescue, and public relations skills. Training does not stop, however, when the first swimmer visits the facility.

b) Inservice training.

Inservice training activities should be planned, held regularly, and scheduled as part of the lifeguard's job responsibilities. Inservice training hours should be recognized as paid time. Every lifeguard should be required to participate.

The training schedule should be posted or circulated to all staff members well in advance. Inservice programs should be evaluated by the participants and employer on a regular and ongoing basis.

❑ **New staff orientation**

Design specific orientations for staff who join an aquatic facility after pre-season training is over, and then integrate them into the ongoing inservice program.

❑ **Year-round versus summer:**

Inservice programs designed for summer-only beach or swimming pool lifeguards will be different in schedule, emphasis, and scope from those planned for full-time employees of a year-round swimming pool or waterpark. Pre-season training is likely to be concentrated and demanding in summer-only programs.

❑ **Motivation**

Build incentive and motivation into the inservice training programs. Lifeguards train very hard to prepare for accidents and events they hope will never happen. In excellent facilities, major emergencies are extremely rare, making it more challenging to keep inservice training motivations high.

❑ **Record participation**

Record participation in inservice sessions for both personal incentive and possible evidence in the event of an inquest, inquiry, or legal case. In some aquatic programs, it is common practice for participants in each inservice session to sign a sheet recording the items completed.

COMPONENTS OF PRE-SEASON AND INSERVICE TRAINING

The essential components of ongoing lifeguard education are:

❑ **Orientation**

- Introduction to fellow staff members.
- Exploration of lifeguard job description responsibilities.
- Introduction to and evaluation of hazards and risks in the facility, and a review of facility rules and policies concerning them.
- Review of personnel policies and procedures.
- Specific job-related training required to familiarize staff with the facility's programs, activities, operation and maintenance, and policies and procedures concerning supplies and equipment.

❑ **Facility-specific emergency procedures**

- Evaluation and practice of emergency procedures designed for the aquatic facility.

❑ **Lifeguard skills and procedures**

- Review and practice of supervision, recognition, and rescue intervention skills.
- Practice use of lifeguard equipment.
- Review of supervision policies and procedures including number of lifeguards per patron formula and guidelines for patron and staff conduct.

- Reporting and evaluating procedures.

❑ **Resuscitation and aquatic emergency care skills**
- Review and practice of first aid response procedures including use of first aid equipment and supplies.

❑ **Communication and teamwork**
- Practice of communication signals, use of communication equipment.
- Team building.

❑ **Physical fitness**
- Initial and periodic assessment of physical condition.
- Training program to improve and maintain physical fitness.

RECOMMENDED AREAS OF EMPHASIS

FACILITY EMERGENCY PROCEDURES

Each facility, whether a beach, waterfront, pool, or waterpark has unique danger areas, design features, staff complement and structure, and community emergency services. A competently managed aquatic program has emergency plans and procedures developed specifically for its needs.

When lifeguards are hired they should receive, read, and understand the staff manual before pre-season training begins. If you are returning to the same facility for a new season, your employer should draw your attention to new or altered sections of the staff manual. (See *Staff Manual* in Chapter 9.)

LIFEGUARD SKILLS AND PROCEDURES

Inservice training provides lifeguards with the opportunity to sharpen rescue skills and apply knowledge which can grow rusty with inattention or disuse. Practice with the equipment provided in the facility is essential if these items are to be employed efficiently in an emergency (e.g., boats, paddleboards, rescue aids, first aid kits).

In addition, new equipment and new techniques will need to be tested and brought into service from time to time.

***Diving board activity requires specific safety rules which should be established during preseason training.* (See Diving Boards *in* Chapter 2.)**

RESUSCITATION AND AQUATIC EMERGENCY CARE

First aid and resuscitation procedures and skills are rarely used by lifeguards outside practice sessions. Ironically, these are some of the skills which lifeguards must practice most often because the consequences of a life-threatening aquatic emergency can be catastrophic.

COMMUNICATION AND TEAMWORK

In an emergency, lifeguards must be able to communicate with each other accurately and rapidly. The development and practice of effective communication signals and practice with communication equipment is an important aspect of ongoing training.

In addition, lifeguards are most effective when they work as an integrated team of professionals who understand and trust the skills and abilities of fellow team members. Effective teamwork results from superior communications, an appreciation for individual strengths and weaknesses, and the trust that is developed through practice and team building.

PHYSICAL FITNESS

Physical fitness is a cornerstone of a lifeguard's job responsibilities, enabling the lifeguard to remain vigilant, attentive, and alert to signs of potential trouble, and to respond both safely and with confidence in an emergency.

Physical fitness efforts are concerned with improving and maintaining coordination, flexibility, agility, cardiorespiratory endurance, and muscular strength and endurance. Characteristics of physical fitness include:

- Strength for everyday routine and for emergencies.
- Stamina (endurance) to perform necessary tasks without undue fatigue.
- Cardiorespiratory endurance for sustained effort.
- Agility to perform a wide range of movement.
- Speed to move rapidly.
- Control to skillfully coordinate body movements.

All recreation leaders and supervisors, as well as lifeguards, need to set goals for personal fitness. Employers who understand the values of physical fitness will inspire their lifeguards to work toward achieving it.

OPPORTUNITIES, METHODS, AND RESOURCES

SIMULATED EMERGENCIES

Practice and evaluation of performance in simulated emergencies is an excellent way to improve judgment, knowledge, skill, and fitness. (See *Practicing Emergency Procedures* in Chapter 3.)

a) Low-stress learning.

Initial learning and practice of rescue skills and emergency procedures should be undertaken in a low-stress and low-risk environment. Early practices should be private; later they might be opened to the public as a public relations initiative.

Individual skills should be practiced in isolation before they are used in a rescue response. Early practices should be designed to encourage learning and to avoid punishing errors. As lifeguards become more familiar with the procedures, equipment, and skills, additional factors are added to the simulations until all subsequent simulated emergencies are as realistic as possible. Ultimately, simulated emergencies might be called during an actual public swimming session.

b) Simulated emergencies during public swims.

Simulations by patrons trained for the purpose can be arranged during public recreational swimming periods – but with caution, and great planning. Consider appropriate timing; avoid the busiest times or when the staff is under stress. Ensure additional personnel are available to assure constant supervision and to talk to patrons about the simulation. Inform the public that they are watching a simulation. Ensure that the staff member responsible for contacting emergency services understands that the emergency is simulated. Consider that the lifeguards who respond may become upset by any mistakes they make, and may not be ready to return to duty immediately.

LIFEGUARD SKILLS

An endless variety of skill drills can be custom-designed to suit the training needs and priorities of any staff or staff member. The steps in training skills are simple: design a drill or exercise which provides an opportunity for the staff to practice it repeatedly. Then follow the standard learning principles of practice-feedback-practice. (See the RLSSC *Instructor Notes* for more information.) Some examples are:

a) Skill stations and circuits.

Organize circuit training stations around the pool or beach. Perform a different skill or procedure at each station. For example:

- Station 1 – Rescue non-breathing victim
- Station 2 – Rescue spinal-injured victim in deep water
- Station 3 – Launch rescue boat or paddleboard
- Station 4 – Perform eggbeater kick

b) Recognition and reaction drills.

Many drills can improve scanning and perception skills. For example:

- A coloured ball is released in a zone. The lifeguard must see it within ten seconds and be holding it within 20 seconds.

Holes might be made in the ball, so that it will sink within 30 seconds.

- Balls of two different colours are tossed into the water. One colour represents a minor emergency, the other a major emergency. The lifeguard is timed on how fast he or she notices the ball, signals other lifeguards appropriately, and retrieves the ball.
- Swimmers simulate a major or minor accident. The lifeguard is timed on speed of recognition and reaction to the point where the victim's head is supported above the surface.

c) Stop-action rescues.

Use stop-action drills to focus on specific parts of a rescue response (e.g., entries, approach, victim recovery from a depth, tow, carry, removal, rescue breathing). Lifeguards respond to a rescue emergency only up to the point of application of the skills being worked on.

MANAGEMENT APPRENTICESHIP

Staff members may be invited to apprentice (for a day, week, month or longer period), with senior personnel. Lifeguards could apprentice with the head lifeguard, supervisor, or facility manager for example. The exact nature of the apprenticeship will vary with the circumstances, but the goal is to provide the apprentice with an opportunity to gain a broader perspective and deeper understanding of the management function.

STAFF OR INTER-FACILITY COMMITTEES AND MEETINGS

Committees can be established to take care of certain aspects of aquatics during the season such as public relations, staff training, social events, public education, or promotion. The planning and organizing involved improves judgment and leadership. Committees also enable lifeguards to contribute to the policies and administration of the program.

Regular staff meetings inform everyone about what is happening at the facility and can be used to address specific job-related subjects for discussion or report. Individual staff members might be assigned a different topic or issue to present each week.

CUSTOM CLINICS, WORKSHOPS, AND SEMINARS

Training in specific job-related subjects can be presented in clinics, workshops, or seminars specifically designed for the purpose and delivered by knowledgeable staff or outside experts. Examples of suitable subjects include:

- victim-rescuer relationships
- critical-incident stress
- legal responsibility
- water chemistry
- oxygen therapy
- public relations
- communications

CONFERENCES

Use community resources to attain and maintain staff skills during pre-season and inservice training. But go beyond local community resources from time to time to gain a broader perspective.

Employers should provide funds to send staff members to local, regional, national, and international aquatic conferences. Individuals selected to attend must be capable of sharing their new knowledge with other staff members.

Such conferences which take place frequently are publicized well in advance. Therefore, plans to assign delegates can be made early in

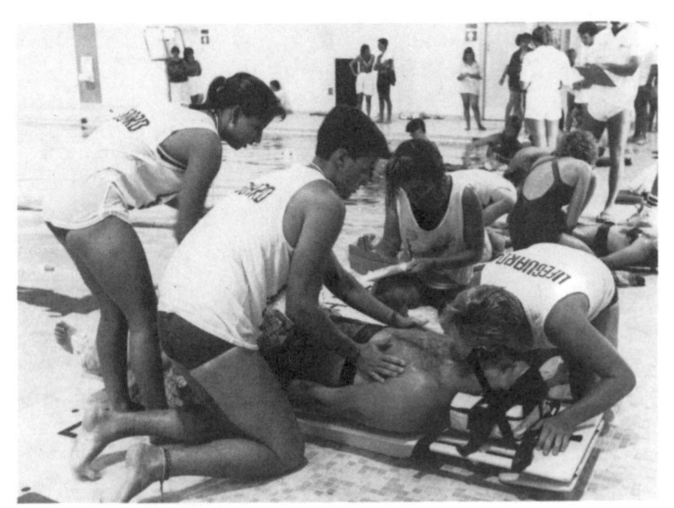

Lifeguards and employers must both ensure regular inservice training.

the year. An individual attending a conference receives a great deal of information from the formal sessions; however, he or she learns as much or more in information-sharing during informal discussions with other participants.

COURSES AND CERTIFICATIONS

Aquatic and other job-related courses provide skill acquisition or skill development opportunities, many combined with physical fitness.

If posted and advertised, points for aquatic awards can provide an incentive for lifeguards to continue training. A sample point system might allot the following values:

	Points
Distinction Award	25
Diploma Award	100
Instructor Award	50
National Lifeguard	50
Aquatic Emergency Care	50
Instructor Trainer	100

COMPETITIONS

Competitions offer superb opportunities to meet new people, have fun, exchange ideas, and be exposed to new techniques and procedures.

a) **Lifesaving competitions.**

Competitions which focus on lifesaving skills rather than lifeguarding skills and procedures can be organized for both staff and the public at large. Participants in lifesaving training courses and graduates of these courses find lifesaving competitions a challenging and fun incentive. Often, lifesaving competitions are designed to fulfil both an inservice training need as well as public relations, public education, and potential staff development objectives.

b) **Lifeguard competitions.**

Local inter-staff and inter-facility competitions allow lifeguards to observe the skills and methods of fellow lifeguards within the organization or city. Many municipalities host regional competitions at which lifeguards share and compare skills and knowledge with peers in nearby cities or municipalities.

The Royal Life Saving Society Canada (RLSSC) in cooperation with one or more of its provincial affiliates organizes provincial (and sometimes inter-provincial) lifeguard competitions. Lifeguards from across Canada compete in the annual RLSSC Canadian Lifeguard Championships; the location changes each year. Canadian lifeguard teams also compete in international competitions.

SPECIAL EVENTS AND PROJECTS

In the process of organizing special events, staff members practice planning, delegating, supervising, communicating, and evaluating. Public education projects for example, might include writing a newspaper article, designing posters, organizing simulated emergencies rescues during public swims, conducting learning activities for patrons, or speaking at schools or to community groups.

RESEARCH

A single organization or agency cannot presume to have all the knowledge and expertise within its sphere. Administrators should encourage staff development by providing incentive, time, and acknowledgement to those lifeguards who demonstrate creativity and innovation.

Lifeguarding techniques, procedures, and equipment are all possible areas for research.

RESOURCE CENTRE

Within the well organized pool office or waterfront staff room, administrators should include newsletters, monographs, books, magazines, photographs, coloured slides, and pamphlets.

Important articles and information should be circulated to lifeguards and instructors as required reading. Reactions to the information could become the focus of a staff meeting or workshop. Local college and university libraries are an excellent source of books, films, and video tapes.

PHYSICAL FITNESS TRAINING

Design fitness programs based on the FITT principles of training:

- Frequency (How often?)
- Intensity (How hard?)
- Time (How long?)
- Type (What kind?)

Detailed information is presented in *The Canadian Lifesaving Manual.*

a) Plan workouts.

Plan a program that will improve fitness without creating harmful stress or excessive fatigue. Develop individual workouts of 15 to 30 minutes duration to perform from three to five times a week. In each workout include:

- ❑ **Warm-up**
  Begin with three to four minutes of light activities to prepare the body for the more vigorous exercise to follow.
- ❑ **Stretching**
  Stretching exercises increase flexibility and range of motion in the joints which are essential to swimming and rescue skills.
- ❑ **Strength and power**
  Certain amounts of muscular strength and power are essential to fitness. Choose exercises in this portion of the workout that strengthen muscles.
- ❑ **Endurance**
  Activities that increase endurance are most important to developing and maintaining physical fitness.
- ❑ **Cool down**
  Gradually end the workout with three or four minutes of cool-down activities that are less strenuous than the workout.

b) Measure progress.

It is important for both training and motivation that physical fitness improvements be measured. Use heart rate target zone (see *The Canadian Lifesaving Manual*) to adjust how hard you need to work to benefit from the workout.

The 12-minute test is another way to track progress. Participants swim as far as they can in 12 minutes keeping their heart rates in the target zone for the duration. Record the distance (laps or metres). Since the heart becomes stronger as fitness improves, each heartbeat is more efficient. As fitness improves, participants will swim longer distances on successive 12-minute tests providing their heart rates remain in the target zone. Comparison of successive trials shows improvement in fitness. Measure progress at two-week intervals.

c) Sample activities.

A competitive swimming model workout incorporating rescue skills and strokes is one useful framework for physical fitness development. However, there are a wide variety of other activities which can be used to improve and maintain fitness:

❑ **Competitive-style workouts**

An early season training workout might be structured as follows:

Warm-up

2 lengths freestyle – easy

2 lengths flutter kick with board

Stretching and strength

Push-ups

Shoulder and hamstring stretch

Endurance

2 lengths head-up crawl – maximum speed. Rest until heart rate drops into target zone.

2 lengths head-up breaststroke – maximum speed. Rest until heart rate drops into target zone.

2 lengths freestyle – maximum speed. Rest until heart rate drops into target zone.

2 lengths freestyle – maximum speed. Rest until heart rate drops into target zone.

3 lengths dolphin kick with board.

Cool-down

1 length backstroke

1 length breaststroke

1 length freestyle

❑ **Musical bricks**

All lifeguards tread water in a circle passing one (or more) diving bricks around the circle while the instructor provides musical background. When the music stops, the person holding the brick sits out by treading water inside the circle. Guards are added to the centre until only one lifeguard, the winner, is left outside.

❑ **Rescue drag**

Swim 100 m dragging one or more victims with a rescue tube. Handicap the stronger swimmers with more victims.

❑ **Half in a row**

Place half of the lifeguards in the water 5 m to 7 m off shore. Each shore lifeguard rescues all the victims, one at a time, as rapidly as possible. This very strenuous drill works well with as many as 40 lifeguards.

❑ **Tea cup tread**

Give each lifeguard a plastic cup and saucer full of water balanced in each hand. The winner is the lifeguard who keeps the cup and saucer full of water, above the surface and balanced the longest. Bumping is allowed.

❑ **Chain swim**

Put 3 or 4 lifeguards in a chain. The first lifeguard swims with arms only and grasps the next lifeguard by the neck with his or her feet. The second lifeguard swims with one arm while holding the feet of the first lifeguard with his or her other arm. This continues to the last lifeguard who provides the kick. (Encourage flip turns.)

❑ **Games**

Organize your fellow lifeguards into a game of waterpolo, volleyball or underwater hockey. All are fun conditioning games.

❑ **Swim the lake**

Set up a chart scaled to distances between your favourite geographical points, for example, Lac St. Jean. Let each lap of the pool or waterfront represent kilometres on the map. Individuals and teams can accumulate kilometres. A variation of this activity is to arrange a competition with a neighbouring pool or beach.

❑ **Circuit training**

Plan a circuit including various activities such as running, jumping, swimming, lifting, and diving.

TEST YOURSELF

1. *Plan a training program to improve your physical fitness after consulting an experienced, knowledgeable person. Set a reasonable goal for yourself.*
2. *Draw up a list of reasons to present to an imaginary employer that explains why the employer should include inservice training as a part of the lifeguards' working day. What advantages will an employer reap from such a policy?*
3. *Set a goal for yourself involving your professional development. Make a contract with a friend or fellow lifeguard to achieve the goal within a specified time. When defining the goal:*
   - *make it concrete*
   - *develop a plan (How will I do it?)*
   - *identify a measuring criterion (How will I know when I have achieved it?)*

   For example: "I will learn more about first aid within the next three months by enrolling in an Aquatic Emergency Care course with a qualified instructor. Earning AEC certification will indicate that I have achieved my goal."
4. *Attend the next regional, provincial, or national lifeguard championship as a spectator or competitor. List in priority order, all that you learn from the competition.*
5. *Choose and complete some of the suggested activities in this chapter.*

Chapter 11

Swimming Pool Operation and Safety

Chapter Focus

Lifeguards have a responsibility to help provide a safe and inviting atmosphere for recreational and instructional activities offered in their aquatic facility.

While many recreation organizations employ people who are experts in chemical, operational, and maintenance duties required to maintain clean, balanced water and efficient pool equipment and mechanical systems, lifeguards are often assigned the responsibility for the safety, operation, and cleanliness of smaller facilities.

This chapter provides lifeguards with the basic information on swimming pool operation and maintenance necessary to help them enhance patron comfort and safety.

Think About the Lifeguard's Role

"When Mrs. Clayton called to say she was calling the health inspector, I should have known it was not going to be a good day. The Clayton twins both had ear infections and their doctor had suggested that swimming lessons were to blame. The weather was iffy at mid-morning, but by noon there was not a cloud in the sky. By one o'clock the parking lot and the pool were packed. We had to call in extra guards."

"At two o'clock Kathy and her girlfriend came to the office to say that the water was turning their hair green and couldn't we please turn off the chlorine. By three o'clock, the health inspector had come and gone. And by four o'clock, the water was starting to cloud slightly - a milky white colour.

"When the ten-year-old who'd slipped on the melted chocolate bar while running on the deck came to the first aid room, I was ready to call it a day."

POOL OPERATION

A pool operations manual or guide should be developed for every swimming pool. This guide includes the mechanical aspects of the operation of the pool, procedures for the chemicals used, water quality and other tests and when these are to be performed, how tests are recorded, and those responsible for each item. Become familiar with the local and provincial regulations governing public and semi-public pools.

CLEANING THE POOL WATER (Filtration)

In most swimming pools, water is drawn from drains at the deepest point in the tank and from surface skimmers or overflows located around the sides of the pool. Surface skimmers trap floating debris such as leaves, threads, and miscellaneous bits from bathing suits. Large particles such as hair, lint, threads, bandaids, and leaves are held by hair and lint traps. The traps contain a basket or strainer which should be emptied frequently. Drain covers trap debris which has sunk to the bottom of the pool.

Pool filters remove other foreign matter such as algae, make-up, dirt particles, and other suspended solids. When pool water is forced through the filter (pressure system) or pulled through the medium (vacuum system), the suspended particles are held in the filter media. Periodically, the media must be cleaned of this particulate matter.

The efficiency of a filtration system depends upon the level of operation, the correct size for the demands, and the maintenance procedures practiced. The time between backwashing varies with the filter type, the number and characteristics of swimmers, and with the surrounding environment (e.g., a nearby dusty field or parking lot).

Filtration systems are named according to the filtration media and whether the system is pressure or vacuum.

a) Sand and gravel filters.

The pressure sand and gravel system forces water into the top of a large enclosed tank. Usually a flocculent (gelatinous layer, usually alum), on the surface of the sand traps and holds finely suspended particles. The water then passes through layers of sand and gravel which trap larger particles from the water before returning to the pool.

As the filter media becomes clogged with accumulated debris, water flows through more slowly, pressure builds up (indicated by flow and pressure gauges), and the filters must be cleaned or "backwashed." During backwashing, the water flow is reversed forcing water from the bottom of the filter tank to the top stirring up the trapped debris. The murky water created by this action flows out the top of the filter tank as waste. When the debris in the filter is removed and the water flows clear once again, the backwash is complete.

High-rate sand filters are similar to sand and gravel filters but use only sand as the filtration medium.

b) Pressure diatomaceous earth filters.

Water forced into the bottom of a closed tank passes through fine screens of nylon, polyethylene, or stainless steel coated with diatomaceous earth. The diatomaceous earth traps the dirt particles and allows the filtered water to pass through.

When the build-up of dirt is extensive, the screens need to be cleaned. The method of cleaning varies with the model of filter. Diatomaceous earth is held on the screens by the pressure of the water flowing through the tank. When the pump is shut off most of the diatomaceous earth falls off, and the remaining diatomaceous earth is sprayed off. After cleaning, the filter screens are "pre-coated" with fresh diatomaceous earth before normal filtering processes begin.

c) Vacuum diatomaceous earth filters.

Pool water is drawn through an open tank containing filter elements coated with diatomaceous earth.

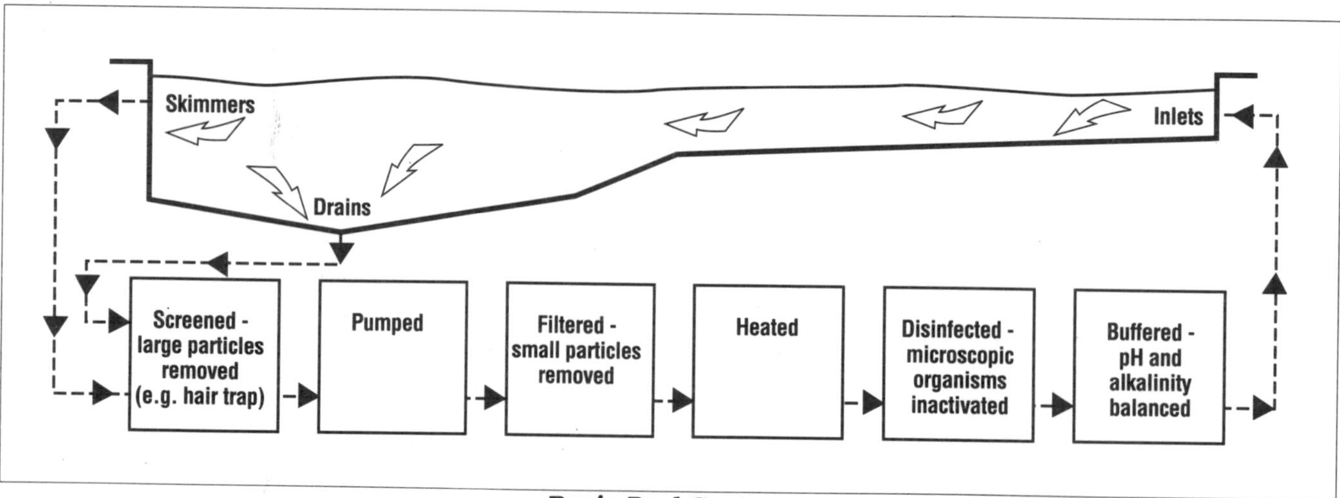

Basic Pool System

Water is continuously drawn from the tank, treated and then recycled back into the tank.

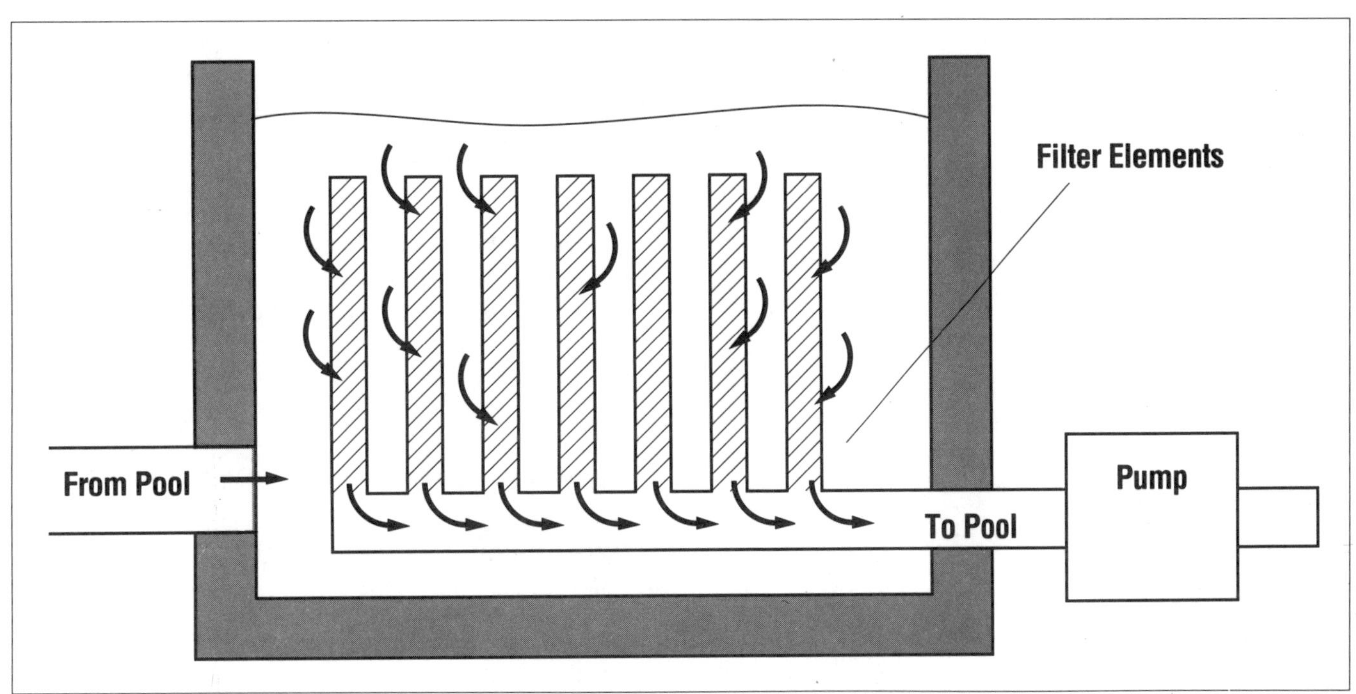

Vacuum Diatomaceous Earth Filter

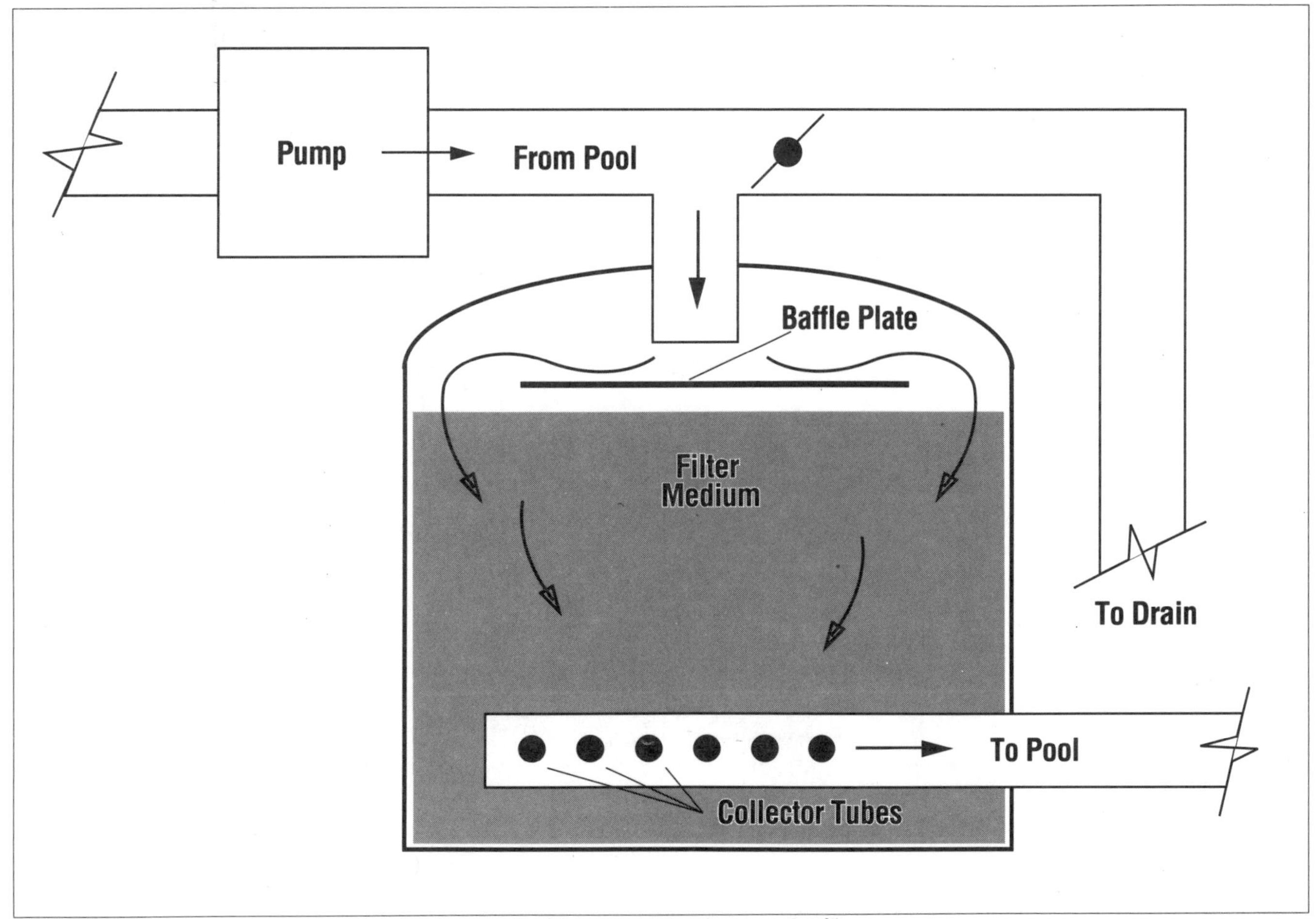

Sand Filter or Sand-gravel Filter

The vacuum diatomaceous earth system is simple to clean since the tank is open and easily accessible. Shut off the water pump and close the water line from the pool. Spray the filter elements and drain the debris to waste. Then fill the tank with pool water and pre-coat the screens with fresh diatomaceous earth before starting the normal filtering process again.

Wear an approved dust mask when handling diatomaceous earth. The fine particles which often cloud in the air can be inhaled. The dust may be harmful to other equipment in the area.

d) Cartridge filters.

This system, which may be pressure or vacuum, consists of a tank which surrounds a cartridge made for specially manufactured filtration media. Clean media by shutting off the pump, removing the cartridge, and hosing the cartridge surface.

HEATING THE POOL WATER

The filtered water can be heated before being returned to the pool. Thermostats control the heaters. Heaters can be separate from the pool water system or part of the building heating system (indoor pools only). Most heating systems operate on natural gas or fuel oil although solar heating is becoming a possibility.

CHEMICAL TREATMENT OF POOL WATER

In addition to the physical screening of suspended debris and dirt by the filters, pool water must be chemically treated to kill microorganisms and algae. Common problems associated with poorly maintained swimming pools are eye, ear, nose and throat infections, skin rashes, plantar warts, athlete's foot, and stomach and intestinal illness.

a) Destroying bacteria and plant growth.

Chlorine and bromine compounds are the most common chemicals used to destroy disease producing organisms and to prevent algae growth in pools. Chlorine and chlorine compounds are used most frequently. Note that chlorine gas is a deadly compound and regulated by several laws in Canada.

b) Maintaining comfortable water.

Water, when forced by chemical or physical pressures and stresses, breaks into hydrogen ions (positive charge) and hydroxyl ions (negative charge).

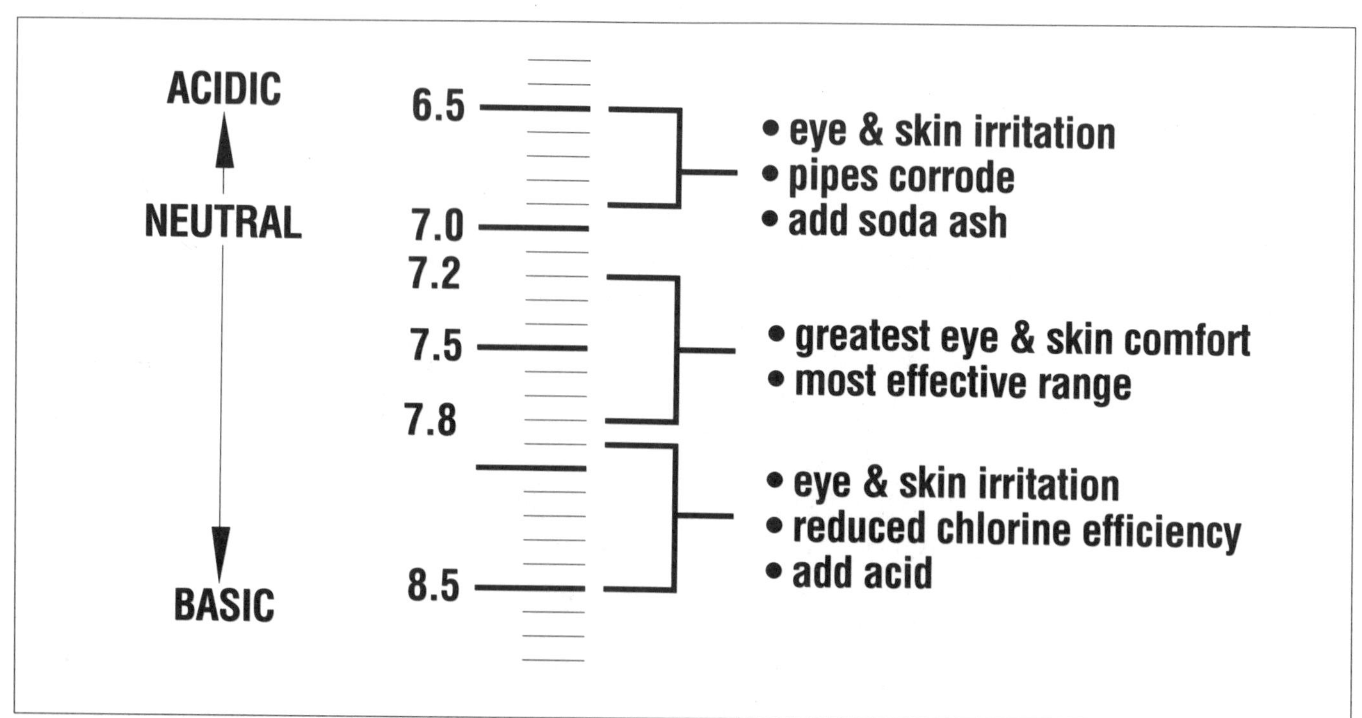

Water pH Levels

The pH of pool water is an important factor in swimmer comfort, the effectiveness of disinfectants, and in the maintenance of pool equipment.

The pH of a solution is a numerical expression of ionization in that solution. If a solution has more positive ions than negative, it is termed "acidic." If a solution has a higher proportion of negative ions, it is "basic" or "alkaline." Water in its pure form is considered neutral – neither acidic nor alkaline.

The pH value of pure water is 7.0. Acidic solutions have a pH between 1.0 and 7.0 (1.0 is a very strong acid). Basic solutions have a pH between 7.0 and 14.0 (14.0 is very strongly alkaline).

The pH of the water has important consequences for swimmers. The ideal pH of swimming pool water is between 7.2 and 7.8. Problems arise outside this range. A high Ph can cause discolouration of the water, and a gritty, itchy irritation of swimmers' eyes. Low pH causes corrosion of pipes and metal fittings, such as ladders, inlets, and drains. Acidic water can change the colour of hair that has been dyed and causes a stinging irritation of swimmers' eyes. In addition, pH levels outside the 7.2 to 7.8 range reduce the efficiency of chlorine and bromine.

If the pH is too high, add an acid to neutralize the alkalinity. The preferred and common acid used for this purpose is muriatic acid. (Some spas and therapy pools prefer sodium bisulphate which, dissolved in water, is a weaker acid and easier to handle as it is granular in form.) If the pH is too low, add alkaline substances such as soda ash (sodium carbonate) to neutralize the acids.

Lifeguards and pool operators must regularly check the pH and other chemical levels. A word of caution – do not over-react to a high or low pH reading by dumping in excessive amounts of acid or soda ash. Make all adjustments slowly when no swimmers are present and check the revised readings until the appropriate normal value is reached.

c) Testing pool water.

The amount of chlorine (or bromine) required to destroy the bacteria in the water is called the chlorine demand. A residual amount of chlorine is needed in the water because chlorine is destroyed in the battle with bacteria, by sunlight, and as a result of water agitation.

The most effective part of the residual is called free available chlorine residual. (The least effective part of the residual is called combined residual.) The free available chlorine residual must be replenished regularly by adding chlorine. Free available chlorine residuals should be maintained at 0.8 to 1.5 p.p.m. of water molecules. Free available bromine residuals should number 2.0 p.p.m.

Some pools are equipped with devices which monitor and automatically adjust the pH and disinfectant levels. However, additional testing and recording of the test results still is required. When test readings show that the equipment is not operating correctly, immediately notify the appropriate personnel.

Test for chemicals using the following methods:

- **Free available chlorine (chlorine residual)**
  The Palin method employs diethyl-p-phenylenediamine (D.P.D.) as the indicator. Various tablets, when dissolved in a sample of the pool water, produce a water colour which is compared with a desired standard colour to assess the pool water.
- **pH**
  The indicator is added to the water sample vial and the resulting colour is compared and measured against a series of standards. Phenol red, the most common test, measures pH values from 6.8 to 8.4, changing colour from yellow to red. Bromthynol blue measures pH from 6.2 to 7.6 changing from yellow to blue as alkalinity increases.
- **Alkalinity**
  The total alkalinity of pool water determines the variations in pH when an acid or an alkali is added. High alkaline levels are reduced by adding muriatic acid and low levels increased by adding bicarbonate of soda (baking soda).
- **Bacteriological test**
  Health department personnel routinely test pool water for the presence of coliform bacteria. (Fecal coliforms are

Chemical Safety Precautions

Chemical	Description	Safety Precautions
Clorine (gas or liquid)	■ normally contained in steel tanks (cylinders of gas or liquid) ■ heat causes rapid expansion ■ gas has a sharp, penetrating odour ■ gas is heavier than air ■ liquid chlorine is clear amber in colour which immediately turns to gas at room temperature	■ store tanks upright indoors in fire-resistant, well-insulated building ■ store chlorine tanks and equipment in a separate labelled room complete with efficient mechanical ventilation ■ chain or strap tanks to rigid supports to prevent falling ■ keep a self-contained breathing apparatus stored outside the chlorine room ■ check tanks daily for leaks using chlorine detectors ■ record emergency numbers outside but near the chlorine storage in case help is required ■ emergency signalling device
Calcium Hypochlorite (dry, white granular substance)	■ relatively stable compound of chlorine and calcium ■ normally a coarse powder or in tablet form ■ dangerous if spilled or scattered in moist area or when in the presence of oxidizable material since lumps may explode when wet	■ store in a cool, dry, dark area in well-sealed, opaque containers ■ use only clean equipment for handling ■ avoid contact with easily oxidizable material (rags) ■ always add the compound to water, never vice versa ■ avoid contact with acids (forms lethal chlorine gas)
Sodium Hypochlorite (liquid bleach)	■ liquid compound of sodium and water ■ safer to use than other forms of chlorine but more expensive	■ always add chemicals to water ■ use clean, dry, plastic vessel if measuring liquid ■ avoid contact ■ will corrode equipment ■ store safely to avoid spillage ■ do not spill on skin or clothes ■ never mix with acids (forms lethal chlorine gas)

Elemental Bromine (liquid bromine)	■ heavy red to dark brown liquid (natural form of bromine) ■ aggressive oxidizing agent ■ fumes are toxic, irritating to eyes and respiratory tract	■ storage rules similar to chlorine ■ avoid spillage or inhalation of fumes ■ avoid contact with rags, dirt, or other easily cobustible objects
Organic Bromine (Hydantoin or stick bromine)	■ slowly dissolving solid most commonly found in tablet or stick form ■ twice as heavy as calcium hypochlorite	■ less hazardous than elemental bromine ■ follow directions for use
Ozone (gas)	■ pungent odour and irritating to the eyes, nose and mouth ■ less stable than chlorine- and bromine-dissolved compounds	■ for safety precautions see chlorine
Muriatic Acid (liquid)	■ industrial form of hydrochloric acid ■ used to scrub decks to kill algae ■ used to adjust pH and Total Alkalinity ■ very corrosive	■ avoid contact with chlorine products (forms lethal chlorine gas) ■ use in water solution ■ avoid spillage ■ store in cool, well-ventilated area away from direct heat and other chemicals

Many common swimming pool chemicals are toxic and dangerous. Exercise extreme caution in the storage and use of these chemicals. See *Working with Hazardous Pool Chemicals* in Chapter 11.

bacteria of fecal origin, i.e., feces in the water.) This group of bacteria have the potential to cause disease. The count of coliforms present is a common water quality indicator; their presence indicates insufficient chemical disinfection of the pool water. This test requires laboratory analysis and results commonly take two or three days.

❑ **Cyanuric acid test**

Some outdoor pools use a stabilizer like cyanuric acid to limit the breakdown of free available chlorine caused by sunlight. Cyanuric acid is a white granular substance which is dissolved in water to form a weak acid before being added to the pool.

Common product names are "dichlor" and "trichlor." The ideal level of cyanuric acid in the pool water ranges between 15 and 30 p.p.m. with a target of 20 p.p.m. Test monthly for cyanuric acid levels using the specific test kit. Concentrations of cyanuric acid can be reduced only by dilution; therefore too high a level requires draining some water and refilling the pool from the fresh water supply.

Do not use a stabilizer in an indoor pool.

To make certain that samples taken are representative of the pool water, select a location that contains well-mixed pool water (away from water inlets or outlets) and sample at a depth of at least 12 inches below the surface.

Read tests as soon as the samples are taken and carefully record results on the data sheet. Dispose of the liquid in the test vials to waste. Do not throw the liquid back into the pool.

Clean equipment is essential in carrying out these tests. Do not use your finger to cover the inverted vial as it is mixed.

Follow the manufacturer's instructions in performing all tests. If unusual problems or readings occur, consult a local pool supplies company and/or health units. Select the same type of kit that the local health officials use.

Purchase reagents (indicators) in reasonably small quantities since they deteriorate over time. Start each new season with fresh reagents if you are operating a seasonal program. Use only reagents which the manufacturer of the standards supplies.

The accuracy of readings may be affected by temperature, the type of light through which the standards and sample are viewed, and other or unusual chemicals in the pool water.

d) Testing temperature.

Take the temperature of the pool water at least three times per day. Temperatures vary with facility use but usually range between 23 and 28 degrees Celsius. At indoor pools, air temperature is usually maintained higher than the water temperature.

e) Checking water clarity.

Many provinces have specific guidelines for acceptable water clarity. Lines on the pool bottom and the pool drains should be clearly visible from the pool deck. A black disc, 12 cm in diameter, can be used as a visible check for clarity.

If the water becomes murky or turbid, immediately take steps to rectify the problem. When visibility is so impaired that you cannot see the bottom easily, do not permit swimming. (Check local regulations affecting pool closure.)

MAINTENANCE

DAILY DUTIES

The following checklist outlines some typical tasks performed by lifeguards on a daily basis when opening and closing the pool.

❑ **Opening**

- Check emergency telephone.
- Check emergency lighting.
- Check first aid kit.
- Test pool water for chlorine or bromine residuals, pH, temperature and clarity (record results).
- Check and put into place all safety equipment, such as gas masks and reaching assists.
- Test and check circuits for underwater lights. (Ground fault indicators will indicate even slight leakage of current.)

- Remove debris from water bottom, surface of the pool, skimmers, and gutters.
- Add make-up water to the pool if required.
- Check security of float lines, boards, ladders, guard chairs, and slides.
- Check for loose tiles or cracks in the deck.
- Read pool log entries from the previous day.
- Check cleanliness of change rooms, washrooms.
- Check facility for over-night damage (vandalism).

Lifeguards who use skin diving equipment while inspecting the pool have an advantage. Before the pool opens to the public and while the water is relatively still, check the adequacy of vacuuming operations using a facemask for good visibility. An underwater search may indicate cracks developing in the walls or pool bottom. Check ladders for signs of wear and loose anchoring brackets and fasteners. Check the pool bottom for small metal objects such as bobby pins, coins, and safety pins which rust and leave stains on tiles and painted surfaces.

❑ **Closing**

- Turn chlorine or bromine supply down or off unless automated.
- Sweep, disinfect, and hose down change rooms, deck, bleachers, benches, and filter room (not pumps).
- Check windows and doors for cleanliness and security.
- Supply towels, soap, toilet paper as necessary.
- Place clothing or other articles in "lost and found."
- Collect and store tote baskets.
- Empty garbage receptacles.
- Check supply of chemicals.
- Place orders to replace used inventory and supplies.
- Hang up wet equipment to dry.
- Tidy the pool office, file records, hang clothes neatly.
- Make a daily summary entry into the daily log or journal.
- Turn off lights, lock doors and gates.

PERIODIC ONGOING DUTIES

Many provinces require, by law, written records. Maintaining complete and accurate records allows the staff to monitor the pool operation over long periods of time. These records are valuable evidence if lifeguards become involved in a legal situation. (Refer to *The Lifeguard and the Law*, Chapter 8.)

Additional periodic duties include:

- Vacuum pool bottom as necessary.
- Clean hair and lint traps.
- Brush and scrub pool walls, bottom and deck areas when needed.
- Complete additional water tests as required.
- Inspect painted surfaces and recommend repainting if necessary.
- Periodically review past reports and records to evaluate ongoing trends and common accident locations.

COMMON PROBLEMS AND SOLUTIONS

a) Algae.

These single-celled plants multiply rapidly under ideal growth conditions, especially moist sunlit places. Algae commonly grow on walls, the deck, and bottom of outdoor swimming pools although they do grow in indoor pools. Algae can cause dangerous slippery surfaces as well as detract from the appearance of the facility.

Continuous vacuuming, sweeping, and chlorination of the pool help avoid algae problems. If algae take hold, superchlorination (to chlorine residual levels of about 10 p.p.m.), can eliminate them.

Chemicals called algaecides, while effective in controlling or killing algae, can create a mild foam and cause an increased chlorine demand.

Algae growth can be detected early. Look in small cracks, on surfaces not reached by the vacuum cleaner head, and on walls behind ladders.

b) Murky water.

Turbid pool water can indicate a need to backwash the filters. In extreme cases, shut down the filters while they are inspected.

Turbid water might also indicate the need for vacuuming.

If murky water prevents an easy visual scan of the pool bottom, clear swimmers from the water until the problem is corrected.

c) **Coloured water.**

If the pH falls below 7.2 and gaseous chlorine is added, a greenish colour can appear. Correct the problem easily by adding a basic substance such as soda ash or sodium bicarbonate. Metals which are precipitated can colour the water. Copper causes a blue to blue-green colour, iron a brown colour, and manganese a dark brown colour. Seek professional advice to correct the problem(s).

d) **Foulings.**

Occasionally swimming pool water is accidentally fouled by children (or others). Because defecations create a health risk, ask swimmers to leave the water. Close the pool long enough to perform vacuuming and superchlorination procedures. Refer to the local health unit for further guidelines.

e) **Infections.**

Keep people with obvious infections out of the pool. Do not admit individuals with open sores, skin rash, pink eye, boils, impetigo, athlete's foot, or colds.

If swimmers or staff members suffer a rash of infections, call the health department for bacteriological samples. Review the pool chemical records. An insufficient supply of chlorine or bromine could be the cause, although some bacteria become resistant to chlorine and bromine and thrive even when the pool chemical records indicate water treatment has been adequate.

f) **Rain.**

When heavy rain makes visibility poor, especially visibility of the pool bottom, clear swimmers from the water.

WORKING WITH HAZARDOUS CHEMICALS

Lifeguards must be aware that many pool chemicals are dangerous if not handled with extreme caution. Too often, people become accustomed to handling pool chemicals carelessly, and forget the potential dangers until an accident occurs.

Employers are required to provide for the safety of employees at work. The specific wording of standards of good practice vary; however the goal is to prevent accidents, subsequent injuries, and the consequences.

Employers must provide the training and employees must demonstrate their ability to perform their job in a safe manner. Lifeguards involved in any aspect of the pool's chemical system, must have appropriate training. The employer is responsible to:

- Obtain from manufacturers a Material Safety Data Sheet (MSDS) for each chemical product utilized in the facility.
- Ascertain, from the MSDS, the hazards involved with each product. Manufacturers will label the product containers accordingly; if material is subdivided it should be labelled by the employer.
- Determine hazards resulting from the interaction of chemicals whether such mixing is intended or not.
- Develop suitable procedures for the use, handling, disposal and storage of all hazardous products.
- Train all employees in the hazards, instructions for safe use, and measures to be taken should an accident occur (for first aid, spill clean-up, and follow-up evaluation).
- Rehearse emergency drill on a scheduled basis.

Because MSDS are supplied by manufacturers and because there are many different products, listing all information for pool staff in this text is impractical. Learn the specifics applicable in your situation from your employer. (See *Chemical Safety Precautions* and *Chemical Safety Equipment* in Chapter 11.)

Chemical Safety Equipment

Chemical	Effects of Exposure	Safety Equipment
Chlorine gas	■ low concentration (1.0 - 3.0 p.p.m.) causes irritation to eyes, ears, nose, throat, lungs, skin. ■ above 5 p.p.m. causes coughing, difficulty breathing ■ above 25 p.p.m. risk of suffocation resulting from lung damage ■ reacts with water to form acids	■ detectors for presence and pressure of chlorine gas ■ eye-wash facility to irrigate eyes, safety glasses and face shields to prevent gas or liquid entering the eyes ■ self-contained breathing apparatus (e.g. Scott Air Pac) required to enter a contaminated area ■ protective suits available for persons engaged in controlling chlorine leaks
Hypochlorite	■ produces chlorine gas if mixed with acid ■ when dissolved in water in high concentration, produces hydrochlorus and hydrochloric acid (which are not harmful when diluted in pool water, but are harmful if concentrated acids come in contact with skin, eyes, nose, and mouth)	■ see chlorine gas ■ flush acid burns with copious amounts of fresh water
Bromine (sticks)	■ the solid sticks in contact with acid produce bromine and chlorine	■ see chlorine gas
Diatomaceous earth	■ respiratory hazard	■ wear an approved dust mask and eye protection (goggles or facemask)
Algaecides	■ concentrated chemicals can burn skin	■ flush affected areas with copious amounts of fresh water
Cleaners Muriatic acid	■ burns skin ■ vapour irritates eyes, throat and lungs	■ wear eye protection and gloves (if contacted, flush with fresh water)
Alkali (e.g., lye)	■ causes caustic burns more severe than acid burns	■ wear eye protection and gloves (wash affected area with copious amounts of fresh water)

SPAS, HOT TUBS, AND WHIRLPOOLS

Lifeguards at facilities which include hot tubs, spas, and whirlpools must be aware of the following unique aspects.

WATER TEMPERATURE SAFETY

Water temperature should be a maximum of 40 degrees Celsius (excessively warm water may cause skin burns). Even water at only 40 Celsius can cause a problem for people under the influence of drugs or alcohol, for those on anticoagulants (heart patients), tranquilizers, or antihistamines (allergy sufferers). The effects of these substances can cause the patron to faint, slip, fall asleep, and ultimately submerge. Children under five years should not be exposed to temperatures greater than 34 - 37 Celsius.

Usually, pregnant women are advised by their doctors NOT to take hot tub baths. Persons with heart problems and/or high blood pressure should not remain in warm water for long periods. For all patrons, the duration of stay in a hot tub, spa, or whirlpool should be a maximum of 15 minutes.

MECHANICAL

The need for a high rate of water circulation can cause a strong water current to the drain. Individuals with long hair should be warned to keep their heads above the surface.

BACTERIAL CONTAMINATION AND OTHER INFECTIONS

Adequate chlorine/bromine levels (3.0 - 5.0 p.p.m.) must be maintained. In water above 28 Celsius, twice as much chlorine is required to maintain adequate free available chlorine residual levels. Chlorine/bromine is used up faster in warm water due to increased body contaminants. Increased water circulation provided by jets and bubblers causes more rapid oxidation of free available chlorine.

A number of factors, including less water volume than in a swimming pool, provide an environment for significant bacterial growth. Pseudomonas is the most common bacteria in spas; it survives the high temperatures and causes skin and urinary tract infections. Shower after using a spa.

Bacteria causing Legionaire's disease and Pontiac Fever have also been found in spa water samples.

MAINTENANCE

Increased solid wastes and high bather loads in spas demand frequent cleaning of the filter. The water must be discarded frequently and replaced with clean water. In a swimming pool, water turnover is usually required four times per day. In spas, the recommended number of daily turnovers is far greater. Consult local regulations for guidance.

Balancing the water chemistry is more difficult in a hot tub than in a swimming pool due to temperature, volume of water, and bather load. The probability of pipe and equipment corrosion (caused by low pH) and of scale formation (caused by high pH) is higher in spas than in pools.

Attention to spa maintenance ensures that patrons are safe and comfortable during and following their use of the spa.

SWIMMING POOL DESIGN

SAFETY

The trend in pool design is to build recreational facilities which cater to the leisure needs of their communities. New pools are designed with special populations and age groups in mind. In older facilities, patrons adapt their activities to suit the standard design. In the construction of leisure facilities, pools are adapting to patrons' needs and desires.

Contemporary pools come in a variety of shapes. Designers organize them around playground themes with islands, slides, pulley rides, waterfalls, and hot tubs. Fitness and exercise areas are becoming standard features. Tarzan ropes, inflatables, inner tubes, floating mats, and blocks are some of the multitude of accessories found in such facilities.

Whether the facility is new or old, lifeguards must understand its design and conduct regular inspections to ensure cleanliness and a safe, pleasant environment. Loose ladders, slides, diving boards, and swings; fraying safety lines and swinging ropes; rough edges, and deck and bottom surfaces are all potential sources of an accident.

BARRIER FREE POOLS

The National Building Code of Canada, supplement No. 5 states, "One in every seven Canadians has an infirmity associated with aging or a permanent physical disability." Too often these persons are prevented from enjoying the leisure opportunities available at public swimming pools because the design of these facilities present difficulties for the disabled.

Review the checklist to determine how well your facility meets the needs of the disabled in your community.

❑ **Pool Accessibility Checklist**

This checklist provides some ideas about how to change behaviour and how to adapt your facility to ensure that all members of your community can enjoy safe, enjoyable recreational swimming.

- Is the accessibility symbol posted at accessible facilities?
- Are parking spaces allocated for handicapped persons and conveniently located near the entrance?
- Are senior citizens and handicapped persons aware of leisure programs available to them?
- Are cashiers and receptionists trained to meet the special needs of individuals? For example, do they escort senior citizens and handicapped persons through the reception area?
- Are guide dogs permitted entry into the facility?
- Do lifeguards make contact with and offer assistance to disabled or aged individuals?
- Are pool policies posted with print large enough to be read easily by senior citizens or those with visual impairment?
- Are signs printed with dark blue or black lettering on a white background, or vice versa?
- Are raised or recessed letters used to identify rooms or offices, 1.35 m to 1.65 m from the floor?
- Are doors to non-public areas kept locked?
- Are corridors and walkways free of protruding signs or clutter?

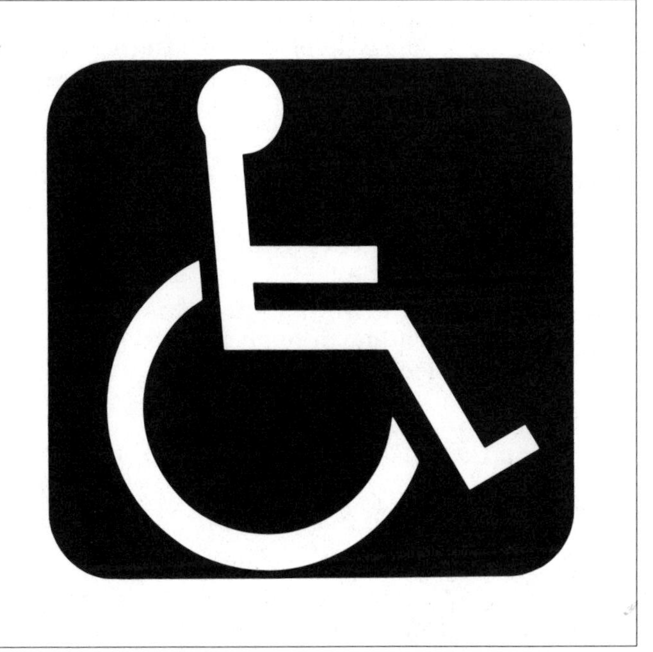

This symbol indicates the facility is accessible to people with physical disabilities.

- Does your lifeguard-to-patron signal system include both visual and sound signals?
- Are there privacy curtains or partitions in your change rooms and washrooms?
- Are water and air temperature compatible for use by handicapped or aged patrons?
- Does at least one staff person know the manual alphabet?
- Do staff members indicate by their attitude that they welcome the patronage of senior citizens and disabled individuals? Are special needs populations part of the staff's pre-season or inservice training?
- Are snow and ice regularly removed from entrances and ramps in winter?
- Are plate glass doors and windows marked?
- Are walkways at least 1.2 m wide? (British Columbia has a .9 m minimum width.)
- Are walkway grades no greater than 5%?
- Is there at least one ground level entrance to the facility? If not, is there a ramped entrance?
- Do ramped areas have non-skid surfaces and are they under 1 in 12 gradient?

- Are doors wide enough and readily opened for easy access? Are there thresholds and obstructions that block wheelchairs?
- Is there elevator access to other floors?
- Are there handrails available for use in the pool?
- Are washrooms accessible to handicapped patrons?
- Are mirrors, drinking fountains and dispensers at a low enough level to be used from a wheelchair?
- Are there steps, ramps, or lifts available for access to the water?
- Are telephones accessible from a wheelchair? Are booths wide enough? Are phones low enough?
- Do floors have non-skid surfaces?
- Are showers and shower controls accessible to persons in wheelchairs?
- Are there benches in the deck area?
- Are trash receptacles accessible to the disabled with an opening no more than 1.0 m off the ground?

TEST YOURSELF

1. *Arrange for a tour of a local facility. Check the filter system to see if you can identify the type of system and its basic operation. Locate lint and hair traps or other features that lifeguards need to maintain.*
2. *Experiment with samples of pool water in buckets. Set up stations. At one station, test the sample for chlorine or bromine residual. At another, test for pH. Practice lowering or raising the pH levels in your samples by adding acid or soda ash. Try various test kits observing the best conditions for reading the results.*
3. *Plan an emergency procedure for a chlorine leak during a public swim, and for an accident involving pool chemicals. Check your answers with* Preparing for Emergencies *in Chapter 3 and* Accident Response Plan *in Chapter 6.*
4. *Spend a day at a local facility. Help the lifeguard staff with their daily maintenance chores. Learn how they keep their pool clean, safe, and inviting.*
5. *You are lifeguarding the pool and adjacent whirlpool at a private club. List what you must watch for in patrons using the whirlpool.*
6. *Inspect a nearby facility and report on how well it meets safety standards and guidelines. (As a matter of courtesy, introduce yourself and explain to the staff the nature of your visit.)*

Chapter 12

Surf and Waterfront Operation and Safety

Chapter Focus

Beach lifeguarding requires knowledge and skills which are different from swimming pool or waterpark lifeguarding. Waterfronts or beaches are established in a variety of environments including ponds, rivers, quarries, lakes, the Great Lakes, and ocean beaches. Each area has its own particular characteristics: some public facilities are greatly modified by man and others are in a natural state.

Lifeguards have a responsibility to know their area better than anyone, to be comfortable in it, and to understand and respect its characteristics and its dangers. The lifeguard's choices in how the area will be patrolled are key to preventing accidents, as well as effectively responding to them in the event they do occur.

Think About the Reporter's Question

"A newspaper reporter picked the busiest afternoon of the summer to come down and interview John and me for a feature in the paper – everyone else was on duty. She asked us a bunch of questions about what it was like to lifeguard a beach on a crowded day, what were our biggest problems, who caused the most trouble, how many rescues we had done so far this season, and could she take our picture for the article."

"I said the biggest single problem we had was people who didn't know anything about swimming at a beach. And John said too many people thought they were in a swimming pool. The reporter laughed and then she stopped and said, 'Why is that a problem?'"

ASSESSMENT AND PLANNING

An assessment of the features and characteristics of the area enables lifeguards:

- To identify problems and hazards and therefore minimize or eliminate risks.
- To determine the most effective way(s) to supervise the area and educate swimmers of hazards.
- To determine appropriate rescue procedures.

The purpose of the facility should be clearly established before decisions are made on the design of the waterfront. Consider the activities in which people will be participating, and how people will get to the area. The site should allow for the seasonal influx of summer visitors with adequate areas for parking and picnicking. Plan the area so that lifeguards can control access to some extent. Prohibit cars, bicycles, and motorcycles in the beach or dock area.

Evaluate the following before establishing a supervised area and prior to each season:

SHORELINE

Evaluate the shore area considering the beach or the dock facilities which are available or necessary. The water's edge should be free of rocks and weeds. Where it is impossible to remove stumps or rocks, you may build docks over or around them if possible, or mark the area off. Clear the beach area of trees, shrubs, and logs which interfere with the lifeguard's line of sight and create problems when rescue is required.

If possible, set up the shore area in such a way that only pedestrian traffic has access through one or two entrances.

The shore areas adjacent to large beaches and waterfronts must be wide enough to accommodate parking lots, washroom facilities, perhaps changing areas, and lifeguard administration and equipment areas. Emergency vehicles must have road access to the entrance. Keep this access clear at all times. Fence, or otherwise indicate the area which patrons use as the beach.

BOTTOM CONDITIONS

Large shallow water areas are preferable at public beaches and waterfronts. Ideally, these have a clean sandy bottom with a gentle slope. Attempt to stir up the bottom when making your evaluation; clay and muddy bottom conditions are a real challenge to both guard and search. Consider rejecting them for public use if you can find a better spot.

This harvester provides an environmentally friendly method of controlling plant growth. Photo Richard Huint.

A bottom consisting of small pebbles or rocks is adequate although less comfortable on the feet. If possible, remove large rocks, otherwise mark them with brightly coloured buoys.

In general there is no need for a swimming area to be deeper than three or four metres. Depending on the facility, a greater or lesser depth may exist. Obtain a complete picture of water depth in the entire area by wading or using a sounding line from a boat.

An area with a sharp drop-off is hazardous. It is necessary either to keep swimmers from going into this area or to mark it clearly. (The marker should be placed a few metres before the drop-off.) Post appropriate signage to educate swimmers and non-swimmers concerning this danger.

Swimmers dislike the feel and thought of weeds. They can panic from the fear of becoming caught and trapped under the surface. In these cases the fear and subsequent panic are the real dangers rather than the entanglement.

Because swimmers inexperienced in waterfront conditions anticipate a uniform bottom, they frequently walk into water beyond their depth. Patrons need to be informed of changing bottom conditions, inshore holes, and streams. Mark these areas to help safeguard and educate patrons.

Remove any glass, bottles, cans, and other refuse from the bottom. Include in the assessment provision for this clean-up. People have carelessly thrown, driven, pushed, and poured refuse into our waterways for many years. Often boaters, hunters, and anglers use beaches after the swimming season. They make fires and might leave behind cans and bottles or other garbage. This material needs to be cleaned before the beach opens. A thorough inspection of both the beach and the bottom is required.

WATER PURITY

Contact local public health personnel to determine who is responsible for water testing and to learn the procedures for reporting changes in water quality. Ensure that water samples are checked during your evaluation and assessment process. This sampling is normally done by local public authorities.

The potential for pollution of the water area is a concern in the evaluation. Pollution can result from sources both within and outside the area: contamination from swimmers and from power boats will both contribute.

From time to time, conditions exist which result in sudden temporary pollution caused by a variety of factors including breaks in sewer or water lines, leakage from industrial plants, boating accidents which create oil or gasoline spills, and chemical insecticides from runoff. While planning a waterfront or beach swimming area, consider the possibility of such accidental pollution. Perhaps you can move the swimming area to a less hazardous location.

If local health authorities do not do so, ensure that tests of water quality are made frequently throughout the swimming season. Rashes or infection are a signal to lifeguards to consider closing the swimming area until healthy conditions are restored. Ailments caused by high bacteria levels include stomach disorders, diarrhoea, stuffy noses, sore throats, and ear problems. Immediately report outbreaks of these conditions to the local health authorities.

SEASONAL CHANGES IN WATER LEVEL

To make assessments of a waterfront area, you need information concerning the water depths and conditions at all seasons of the year. Dams and locks control some lake and river depths at fairly constant levels throughout the year, but they also allow sudden dramatic changes. Most natural waterways are subject to seasonal change (as well as year-to-year changes), which the facility planner should investigate. Because water depths usually decrease over the summer, hazardous conditions can result. Patrons may think they are jumping or diving into 2.3 m of water which, by summer's end, is only 2 m in depth. The same hazard applies to docks and rafts and to their anchors. Anchors and rocks can become underwater hazards late in the season because swimmers are unaware of the change in water depth; they are now familiar with the area and are less timid than earlier.

CURRENTS AND NATURAL WATER FLOW

Waterfront and swimming facilities on rivers bring mixed blessings. The movement of water which maintains clean water also brings floating debris and waste into the area.

Currents are hazardous to weak swimmers – extreme caution in planning to avoid these areas is advised. If possible, prepare the area in a sheltered inlet or bay where there is minimal or no current.

PREVAILING WIND

The direction and average strength of the prevailing wind is an important factor in planning a waterfront facility. Wind conditions influence the positioning of docks, rafts, floatlines, and the methods of anchoring these items. The strength and distance over which the wind blows determines the type of wave motion. Position permanent docks to quell the effect of the waves within a swimming area, thus reducing the size of the waves. Such docks also limit the clearing of surface debris through wind action.

Place anchors for floating rafts and floatlines in two directions; one anchor into the direction of the prevailing wind, the other at ninety degrees to this direction.

DIRECTION OF THE SUN

The sun's position is a prime consideration because glare from the sun on water can seriously affect the lifeguard's vision. In the ideal situation, the sun will be behind the lifeguards during hours of supervision. Lifeguards should be equipped with polarized sunglasses and peaked hats, and frequently shift their positions during the periods of greatest glare. In addition, lifeguards should be protected by a roof or umbrella, and high SPF sunscreen. (See *The Sun* in Chapter 2.)

WATER TRAFFIC

Boating, boardsailing, and surfboarding activity can be a hazard to swimmers and a distraction for lifeguards. Protect swimming areas from boaters' intrusions. Whatever the design of the facility, a method of keeping boaters away from swimmers is essential. Either provide for or prohibit the mooring of vessels.

Boating restriction regulations under the Canada Shipping Act make it possible to impose speed limits on designated waters and to restrict specific craft in certain waters. Application can be submitted to provincial governments for investigation of the merits of a proposal from various levels of government, by the public, private bodies, or individuals. With Federal authorization, place signs notifying boaters of the restrictions regarding noise, nuisance, danger to other craft or swimmers, and erosion of shorelines due to the "wash" from passing boats.

Lifeguards interested in boating activities should obtain further information from knowledgeable sources.

WINTER CONDITIONS

The formation of ice and movement of ice at breakup is an important factor in facility design. Docks must be constructed to contend with the force of the ice in the spring. Wind conditions at breakup can increase damage as a direct result of ice formation. As the surface water is cooled, ice forms around the structures and builds over the winter. Once the warmer weather returns, the ice honeycombs, cracks, and large pieces of ice float on the water surface. Wind pushes the ice into piles often with one flow stacked on top of another. The huge blocks are like giant bulldozers plowing everything in their path; wood and concrete are pushed aside like match sticks.

Once the ice is out, carefully check equipment and structures prior to opening the swimming area for the season.

MARINE LIFE

The ocean beaches of Canada have very few hazardous plants and animals. From time to time, jellyfish may float on the water surface and cause painful stings, and sometimes anaphylactic shock when swimmers touch them. Clams and other shelled creatures in both salt and fresh waters can cut the feet of swimmers who step on a broken or open shell. Lifeguards working on ocean beaches are encouraged to learn about local marine life hazards.

WEATHER

See also *Weather Concerns* in Chapter 2.

a) Haze and fog.

Solid particles like carbon, smoke, and dust act as seeds upon which water vapour in the air condenses. This condensation results in clouds, fog or mist. All can produce rain.

Continuing haze indicates rain. Fog forms when vapour-laden air is cooled. Because formation takes place from the ground upward, the water or land must be colder than the air next to it. A wind shift which moves a mass of warm air over a cool ocean produces fog. On coastal beaches where the wind shifts are rapid, fog forms quickly. Fog remains in periods of calm wind. It severely reduces visibility.

b) Waves and wind.

The wind's direction and strength affects wave motion. If the wind is perpendicular to shore, larger incoming wave crests are pushed up onto the beach. Wind coming at an angle to the beach creates cross waves and rough, choppy water. Resulting rips endanger swimmers.

A wind moving from shore to sea reduces the strength of medium-size waves. High

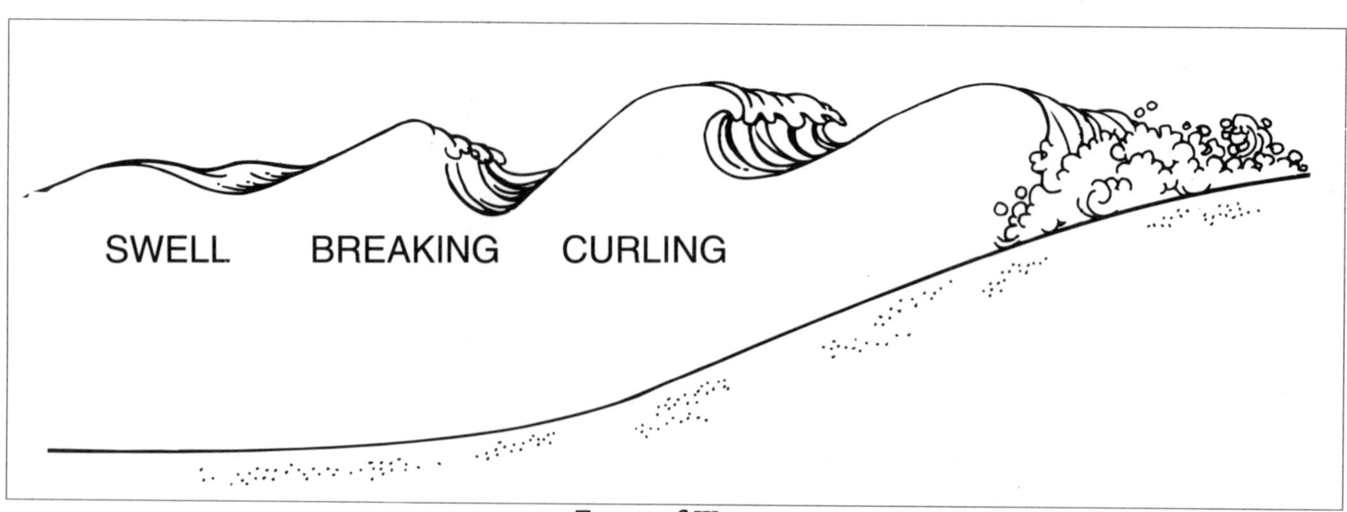

Types of Waves

surf and offshore winds result in "dumpers" which are waves that pound onto shore rather than roll up the beach. Offshore winds present a hazard especially to those in boats and on inflatable equipment. Although the waves move them shoreward, the powerful wind forces them out to sea.

Long, high swells and calm winds indicate that winds have created the wave motion a long distance away. Note how those winds affect local weather conditions.

SURF CONDITIONS

Large waves, currents, and their resulting breakers create the surf conditions. Although normally associated with ocean beaches, surf conditions can exist in other locations where wind generates large waves on large bodies of water. The Great Lakes and other large inland lakes are also subject to surf conditions to some degree.

WAVES

Wind moving across the water surface causes waves. Small ripples create angled surfaces against which moving water puts pressure. Increased wind velocity moving more water builds the waves higher until crests become tall enough to "break" and spill forward. Swells (waves before they break) can travel thousands of miles before breaking on a distant shore.

As swells reach shallower water, they slow down. When waves approach the shoreline, their length decreases, their height increases, and the speed at the bottom of the wave decreases. Faster moving water at the crest spills over the slower moving water at the bottom. The waves, now parallel to the beach, break and are called surf. The remaining water or "uprush" runs onto the beach until it spends its energy. Then, the water driven onto the beach falls back into the sea returning to its natural level.

If the bottom surface holds a steep underwater slope or reef, the waves striking it break quickly, causing air and water to mix and form foam or "white water." White water, which provides little buoyant support for a swimmer, is dangerous.

An ocean bottom that slopes gradually upward into shallow water forms a wave that spills gently. These "spilling" waves create less sound than the "plunging" waves caused by steep slopes. "Surging" breakers are foamy waves at a very steep beach. Wave sounds, in darkness or fog, indicate four things to lifeguards:

- the type of wave that is breaking
- the power or force of the surf
- the location of the main break in the surf
- the approximate width of the surf zone

Large waves which move sand as they strike the bottom can expose previously buried rocks or debris, form holes in the bottom, create drop-offs, and alter the positions of sand bars. Large waves which keep swimmers close to shore or out of the water altogether actually assist lifeguards; however, during lulls (calm periods between waves), many swimmers ven-

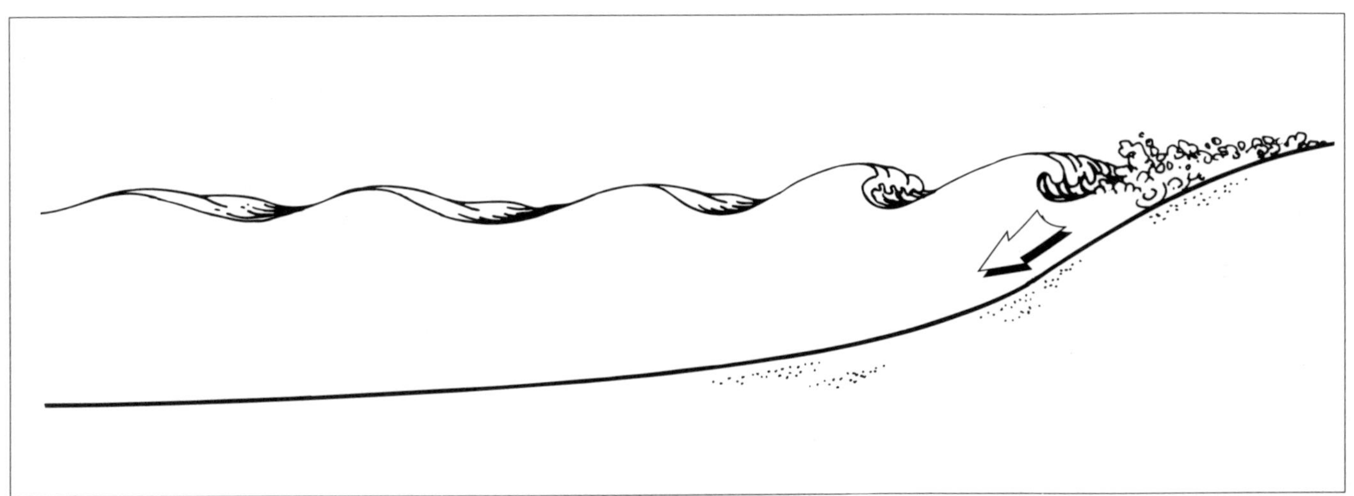

Undertow Current

The strength of the undertow is determined by the size of the wave and the slope of the beach.

ture further into the surf than they safely should only to be swept off their feet when the big waves return.

Wave motion continues long after the wind has died. Thus the waves still pound onto the beach even though the wind is light or offshore.

For surf conditions to occur, at least one of the following conditions is present:

- an onshore wind
- a storm at sea or on a large lake
- a sudden tidal variation

Surf may be choppy (1 m - 3 m in height) or large and rolling (1.5 m - 10 m in height). After water has hit the beach, it creates dangerous currents as it returns seaward.

INSHORE HOLES

Inshore holes, often near shore, are depressions (which can measure several metres in diameter), dug into the sand by wave action at any depth. A small child easily can step from ankle deep water into depths over his or her head. These holes also are hazardous to lifeguards running to make a rescue.

UNDERTOW OR RUNBACK

An undertow or runback is a current created by the volume of water moving back to sea after striking shore. The term undertow commonly is used to describe the feeling of the water movement rather than the scientific basis for the current itself.

Since water seeks its own level, the volume of water forced onto shore by wind and waves returns to sea. The strength of the runback is influenced by the wave's size (therefore the wind's strength), and by the slope of the beach. The steeper the slope of the beach the stronger the runback.

The runback or undertow is a serious hazard to swimmers especially to those unaware of its presence or to those who do not know how to manage it. The flow beneath the surface dislodges the sand causing swimmers standing near shore to lose their footing. Swimmers feel as if their feet are being pulled out from under them. The waves moving towards shore on the surface, combined with the undertow, knock swimmers over. Since the force is usually only present over a short distance, the solution for the swimmers is to allow themselves to be carried out by the current while moving diagonally to the surface. Once swimmers regain the surface away from shore, the strength of the runback becomes negligible and they can return with the next wave.

Non-swimmers caught in this situation, or weak swimmers who may exhaust themselves by fighting the current, require immediate assistance.

RIPS

Rips and runouts are the currents of water moving toward the sea caused by sandbars or reefs located parallel to and off shore. These currents are less evident during a storm; however the swell following the storm brings on strong rips.

Water volume increases between the sandbar and shore because winds sweep the waves on shore over the bars. After sufficient water volume is built up, the water seeks to return to sea. The rip is the current of water formed as the returning water breaks through the weakest point in the bar and flows to sea. The current is weakest at shore, strongest at the break-through point, and quickly dissipates after passing the break.

When a rip occurs along a sandy shore, it forms gullies or channels in the sand as the water carries the sand away from shore.

A rip moving out to sea also follows a depression or elevation on the bottom. Where there are hollows or elevations in the ocean floor, incoming waves move faster over the hollows and slower over the elevations. The result is waves bent into a convex or concave shape. In a hollow, the wave energy is dissipated while at an elevation the wave energy is increased. The large concave wave breaks to either side of the ridge and the water flows seaward. The smaller convex wave draws water from the shallow area into the hollow and then seaward.

The strength of these currents varies depending on the cause, but they can move the swimmer into a dangerous situation (usually out to sea, sometimes into a pier or piling). The larger the surf, the stronger the rip current becomes.

Wind and wave conditions which cause an unusual build up of water result in rips as the excess volume of water returns to sea. The water within the rip may come from one or both sides. Rip currents may be identified in:

- Water which appears darker than the surrounding water because there is less wave motion on the surface of the current.
- An area of rough choppy water, perhaps foamy, in which current and wind seem to go in different directions.
- Lighter or muddy-coloured water resulting from suspended materials (sand, clay, pollutants) picked up from the bottom and mixed with the water.
- A break in the surf line where the waves are not as large.

Rip currents can be spotted more easily when wave motion is consistent than when wave motion is variable. Rips are consistently found in certain situations, and are common in areas where the shore and bottom conditions are rocky.

At points where such stationary objects as piers, jetties, or rocks are projecting into the ocean, rips frequently are present when wind conditions are of consistent strength and duration. Sometimes an unusual wind condition will create a "flash rip."

Rip currents which cause constantly changing bottom conditions are hazardous to swimmers. The water depth can change and the currents can create holes in the bottom or expose rocks. Swimmers caught in these currents should swim diagonally out of them or allow the currents to carry them out to a point where the rip disperses. Then, they should take a safer path back to shore.

LATERAL CURRENTS

Lateral currents (long-shore currents) move in a direction parallel to shore. If waves strike the beach at an angle rather than head-on, the water near shore moves in the same direction as the waves. These lateral currents can carry unsuspecting swimmers out of the immediate area into more dangerous waters.

Lateral currents also are formed near rip currents, as the water moves into the rip current and then seaward.

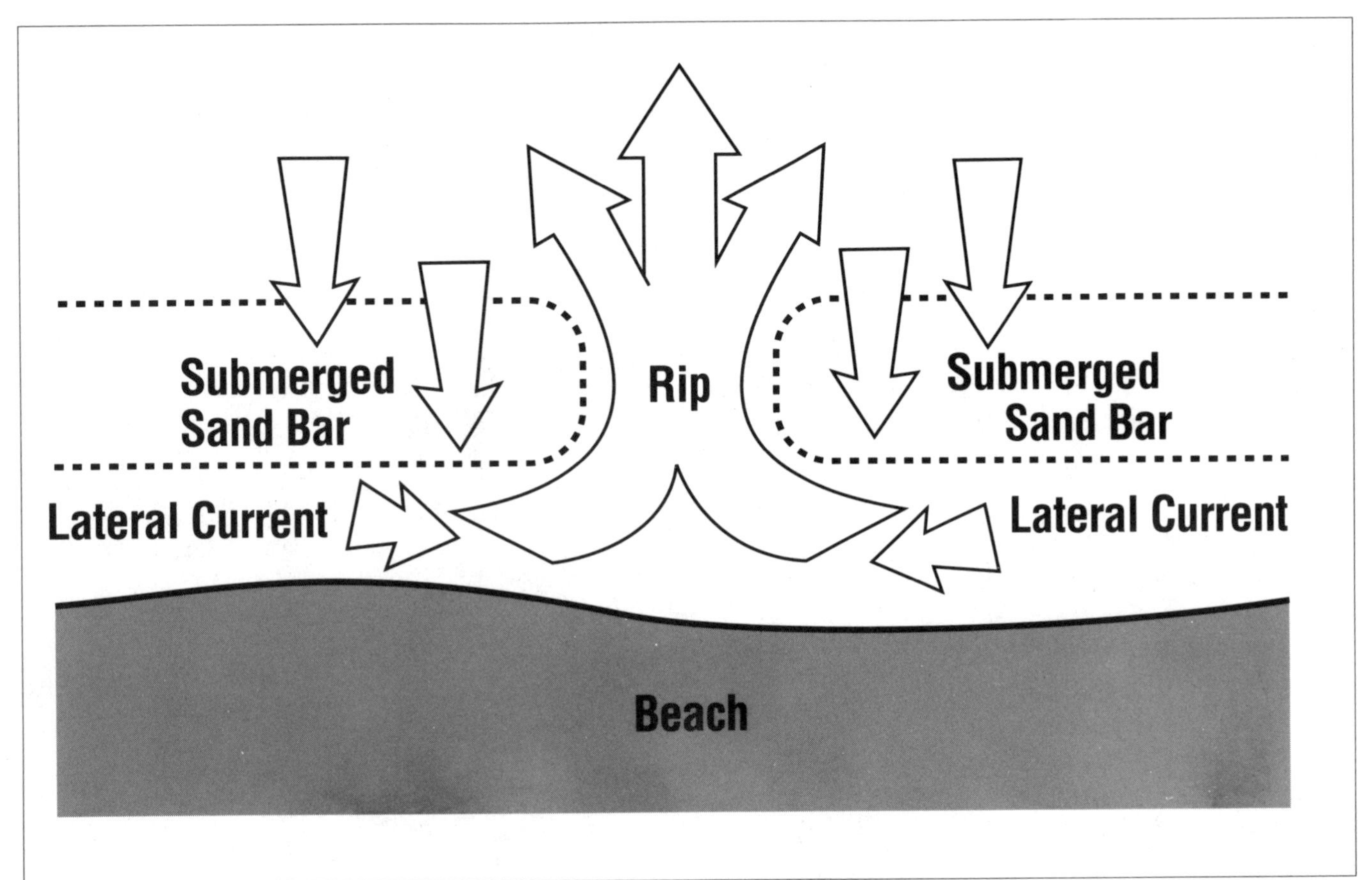

Rip and Lateral Currents

TIDES

The water on the earth's surface shifts as the earth's rotation is altered by attraction to the sun and the moon. At low tide, the water is pulled away from the shore and is shallower than at high tide. These tidal changes in ocean waters occur daily; however, the amount of tidal variation differs at each season of the year.

In tidal waters, swimmers can underestimate the water depth. A shallow area at one time becomes deeper a few hours later, and unsuspecting poor or weak swimmers can suddenly find themselves in difficulty in the same spot they safely played in earlier. Swimmers or waders playing on a sandbar can find, when returning to shore, that the water between sandbars is beyond their depth.

Tidal variations can create rips around piers and wharfs as the water moves toward or away from these structures.

Lifeguards working where tidal conditions exist should consult *Canadian Tide Current Tables* published yearly by the Canadian Hydrographic Service, Marine Services Branch in Ottawa. Information is contained in several volumes with each volume dealing with a specific area of Canada. You can determine the times of low and high tide and calculate intermediate tidal heights and times from these tables.

Tidal height variations in Canada range from negligible up to four metres. In isolated cases, tidal variations are significantly higher than these normals.

Sand bars, built as a result of wave action, move position. Swimmers should not anticipate a sand bar in its same location in tidal waters. Shoals or reefs of rock are more permanent. The action of waves against these obstacles can allow a swimmer to strike the bottom at low tide but not be a hazard at high tide. Rips that occur at the margins of sandbars or shoals are an additional danger.

Select areas that are least affected by tides and currents for your swimming area. Be wary of locations with the dangerous surf conditions of waves, undertows, rips, currents, and tides.

BEACH ORGANIZATION

DESIGNATING THE SUPERVISED AREA

The decision to supervise a beach (or not) and the degree of supervision to be provided will be based upon:

- the size of the area
- the number of patrons
- the budget available for staff and equipment
- the type of beach and shoreline
- the water (and land) activities enjoyed
- the water and beach hazards
- the situation and location of the waterfront or beach

- the influences of citizen demands, political considerations, commercial opportunities
- local/provincial regulations

Consideration and decisions are required concerning who will use the beach (e.g., local residents, visitors, tourists, disabled, seniors, school children). Many types or degrees of supervision are possible – from small groups each with their respective leader(s) as seen in summer camp programs, to broad expanses of beach with one lifeguard assigned to each fraction of a kilometre.

The decision to provide supervision may be a difficult one. If minimal supervision is provided by the beach owner or operator, the public must be educated regarding the degree of operator and lifeguard responsibility. This may require an ongoing education process. Lifeguards must clearly understand their responsibilities in terms of supervision expected of them. The employer is required to deal with the expectations of both lifeguards and patrons.

Clearly, the public has an expectation that lifeguards patrol to prevent accidents. When patrolling large sites with a limited number of staff, this can become difficult to the point that lifeguards can no longer effectively patrol for the purpose of prevention, but realistically, can only patrol to recognize and react to emergencies. In this case, there are several strategies lifeguards can use to augment their effectiveness:

- Use flags to reduce the patrol area to accommodate the staff available. Clearly indicate through signs that patrons swim beyond the flags at their own risk.
- Consider forming a lifesaving club to involve local teenagers as apprentice lifeguards in the preventive aspects of the job.
- Use signage to indicate that patrons are responsible for the supervision of their children, and that lifeguards are on duty in the event of an accident.

The supervised area should be designated to:

- give patrons the knowledge of where they should enter the water and how far to swim beyond the beach.
- make patrons aware of specific hazards which may exist.
- indicate to all water users the area defined for swimmers, boardsailors, surfers, or boaters.

The swimming area may be tightly defined like in a swimming pool, or it may be very broad and open. See *Safety Supervision* in Chapter 2, for information on the design of zones, positioning, and scanning.

DOCKS AND PIERS

Docks come in an infinite variety of shapes and sizes. Select a dock with concern for its purpose, the effect of currents and winds on it, and safety.

Permanent docks are built either on wood, cement or steel pilings or on a crib. Although the crib-type docks are more economical, they can be unstable in winter conditions or in supporting the weight of the structures moored to it or on top of it. Piers are constructed by building a platform over pilings and are used in heavy weather areas such as large lakes and at ocean beaches.

Portions of the dock can be semi-permanent (i.e., they remain in place), but they can also be adjusted for winter conditions and changing water depths. These stanchion construction docks have sections slipped over steel posts and adjusted with the water level. The post is either driven into the sand or mud, or rests on an iron baseplate on the bottom.

Many varieties of floating docks are now commercially available. They can be purchased in sections which allows waterfront personnel to design the size and shape of the area to suit individual needs and specifications. Small sections ordinarily require anchoring on two sides for stability. All synthetic materials are relatively maintenance-free. Because new methods and materials are constantly being developed, survey the market before making a decision to purchase.

Inspect docks daily for loose boards, protruding nails and slippery spots. Immediately remedy any problems.

Divers from elevated diving boards in swimming areas put swimmers at risk. If diving is part of the waterfront scheme, erect diving platforms and boards only on permanent docks or piers where water remains at a constant depth.

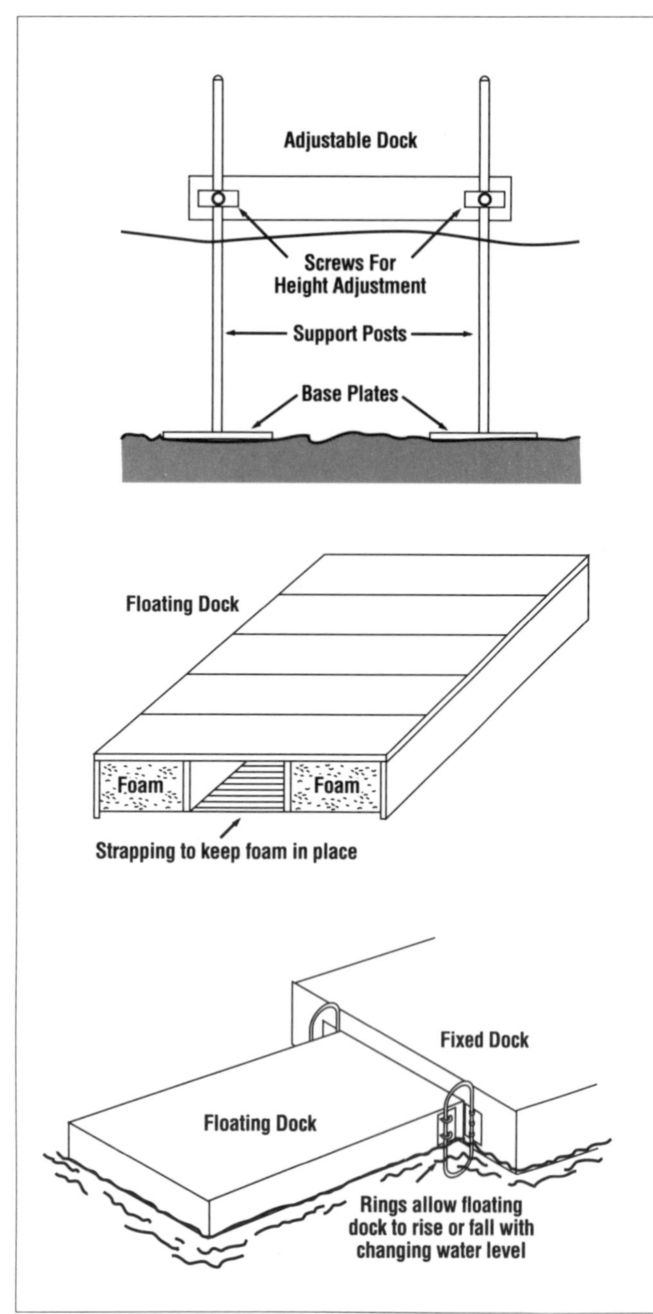

Docks for Changing Water Levels

FLOATLINES

Defining a swimming area with floatlines is sometimes possible in calm water areas. Ocean beaches and large lake settings require that the area be designated by flags or lifeguard stations on shore.

Construct floatlines by stringing polyethylene floats on polypropylene or plastic woven line. If cost is a factor, make floats from wood or empty plastic bottles. The latter look less attractive, but do an adequate job provided their buoyancy provides visibility. A bright colour – white, yellow, or fluorescent orange – gives floatlines the greatest visibility.

Splice the ends of floatlines onto rustproof swivel clips and secure them to anchor chains, posts, rafts, or docks. Extend posts at corners, well above the water surface and paint them brightly. Place anchors with the anchor lines angled into the direction of the prevailing wind.

BUOYS

Use a series of single buoys to designate the swimming area. Use large and easily visible markers. The number of buoys may vary; however, each requires a single anchor which is set, then removed at the end of the season.

Because sandy bottoms constantly change, lifeguards need to prepare a diagram of the area and note changes as they occur especially following storms or high surf. Keep these diagrams on file. They are necessary for an accident investigation and also for determining the supervision area from season to season.

If it is necessary to anchor floatlines, attach the floatline clip to a swivel shackle on a single skeg or a mushroom anchor. Use plastic bottles painted with fluorescent paint or commercial polyethylene or wooden floats as markers to indicate underwater hazards or shallow areas. Wood or polyethylene buoys should have a swivel clip to the anchoring line or chain.

Lifeguards at beaches and rivers adjacent to or on federal waterways need to be familiar with the Canadian buoyage system.

Lifeguards use a variety of knots and splices while working on a waterfront. You need to be adept at these and to be aware of the strengths and limitations of each one.

FLAGS ON SHORE

Indicate the supervised swimming area with flags on shore. Guard the water area between flags. Several countries use this system by planting two flags (red and yellow single horizontal stripes) on the beach.

The advantage of such a system is flexibility because it permits changing the flags' positions. The area is designated daily to avoid conditions, such as rips, within the guarded area. Use different coloured flags to assign areas for surfing, skin diving, and other ac-

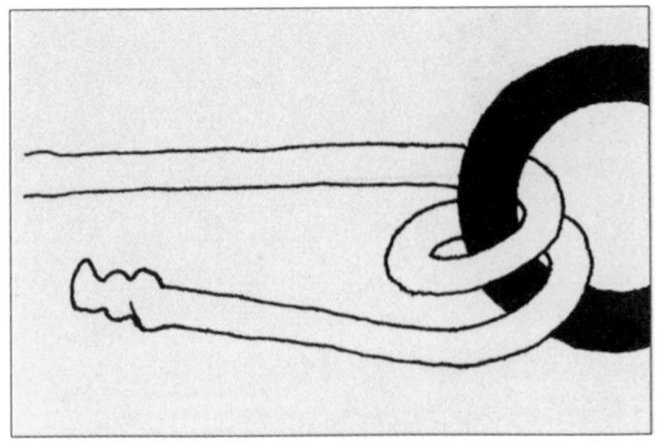

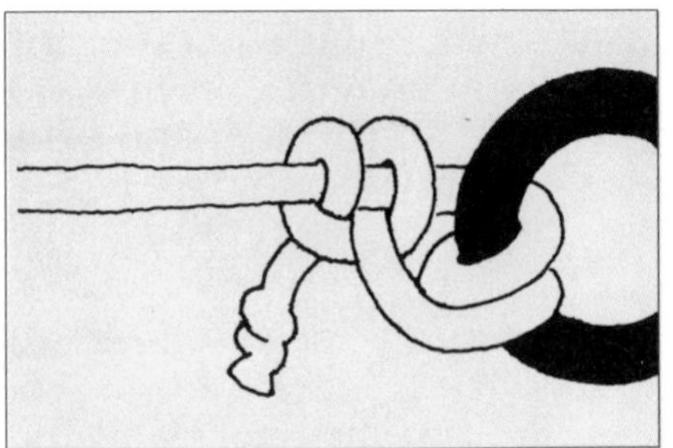

Round Turn and Two Half Hitches

To fasten a rope to another object, such as a ring or post, use a round turn and two half hitches.

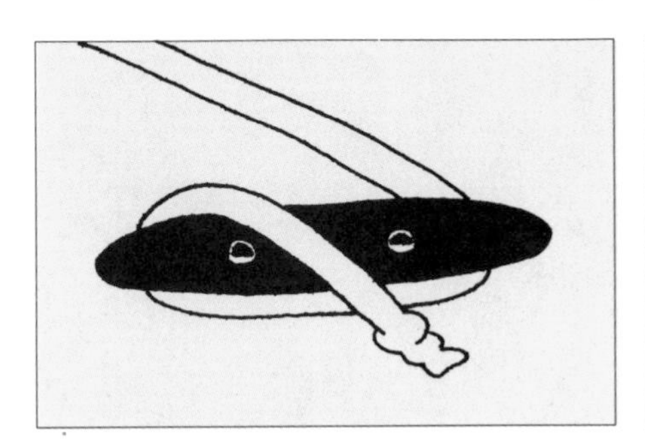
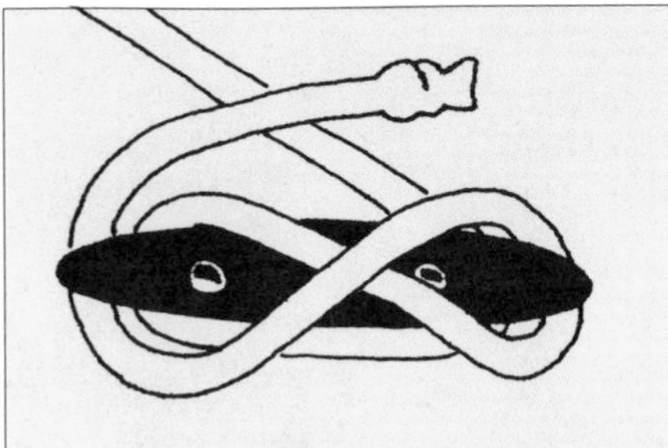
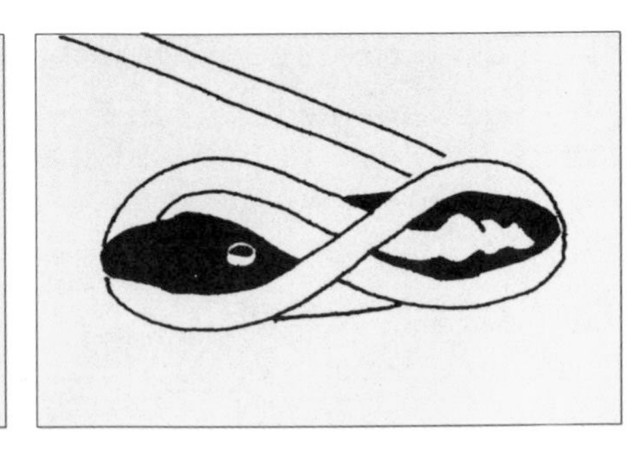

Fastening to a Cleat

To fasten a rope to a cleat, first make a round turn, then a figure eight, then add a single hitch.

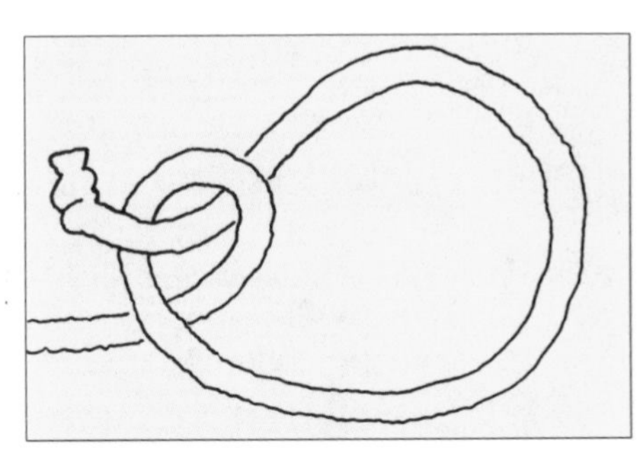
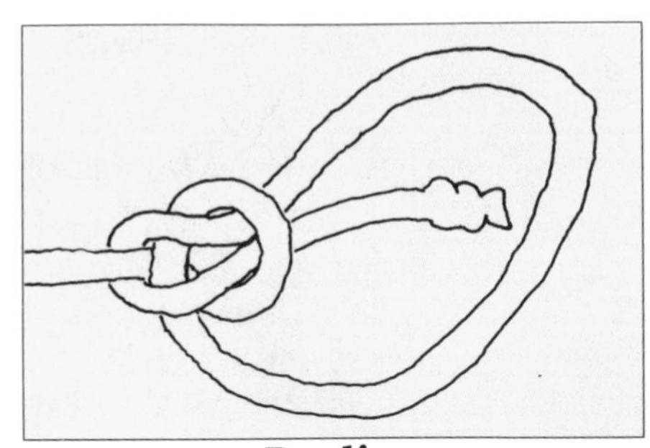
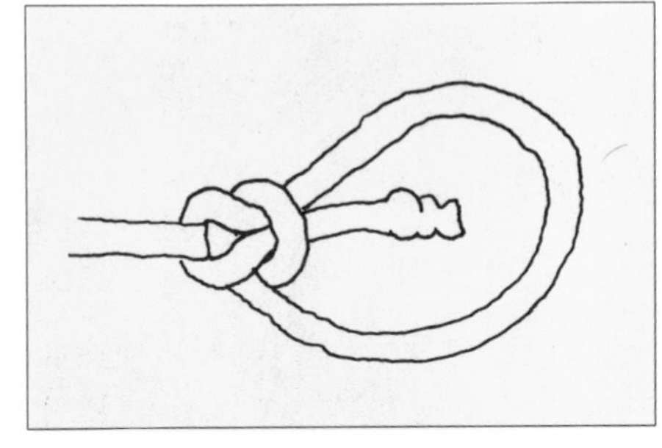

Bowline

A bowline is used to make a loop in a rope, to be placed around an object such as a post or person.

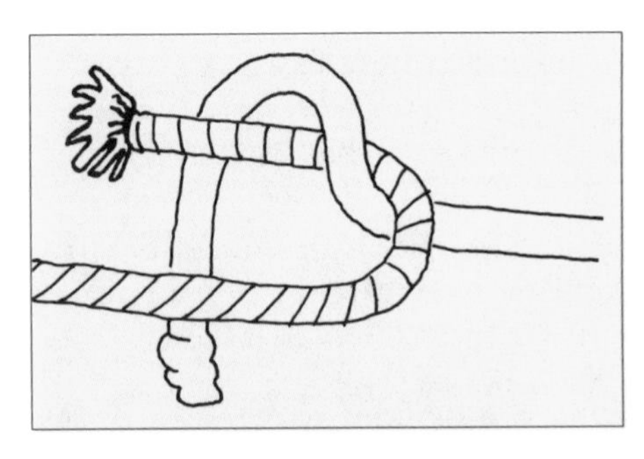
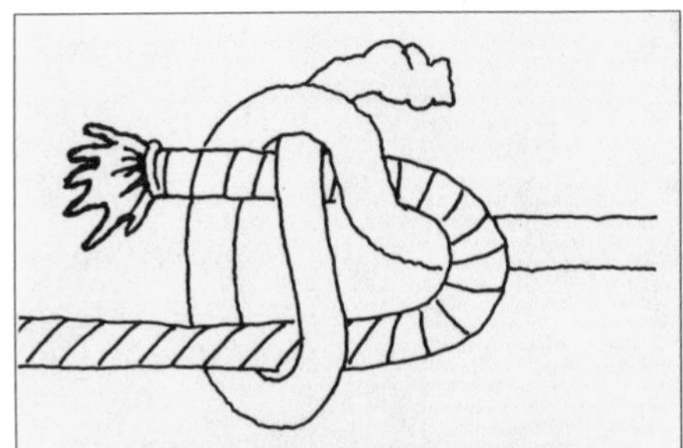

Sheet Bend

A sheet bend is used to temporarily unite two ropes. Use the sheet bend with two ropes of similar size and material. If it is necessary to join ropes of different diameter or material, make the knot more secure by : (1) Using a double sheet bend (pass the working end of the rope twice around the loop instead of once). (2) Using the smaller rope as the working end that is passed around the loop in the larger rope. (3) Using a stopper knot in the end of the smaller rope to prevent it from untying.

tivities not permitted in the swimming area. The limitation of this system is that you must teach it to all patrons, and swimmers must refer continually to shore to determine whether they are still within the guarded area.

Even with flags indicating the water's use, fly flags on the beach to indicate the present conditions. Use a large, central pole attached to lifeguard installations or mount them separately to posts. Flags indicating conditions are sized 0.5 m by 0.8 m and are of non-fading material.

Some countries use balloons rather than flags which can twist around their masts.

Lifeguards must educate the public regarding flag and balloon systems. Red, yellow, and green colours are appropriate. Sample flag signals:

Waterfront towers provide improved visibility, sun protection, equipment storage, and a communication centre.

- ❑ **Green flag**
  - Lifeguard on duty
  - Conditions good
  - Safe to swim
- ❑ **Yellow flag**
  - Lifeguard on duty
  - Conditions dangerous
  - Swimming risky or limited
- ❑ **Red flag**
  - Lifeguard on duty
  - Dangerous water/wind conditions
  - Swimming prohibited or limited

RAFTS

Use floating platforms or rafts in areas where a dock structure is impossible and at locations where you need to have a lifeguard or instructor stationed. Styrofoam plastic floats and steel barrels give the rafts buoyancy.

Because adequate anchoring of rafts is sometimes difficult in windy conditions, you could require three anchors. One method of anchoring rafts is to secure the mooring line at a point in the centre, underneath the raft. Steel chain and steel or aluminum woven cables are popular choices for anchor lines. Trampoline cord, which provides a fairly taut line yet has some flexibility in rough water, is used in some inland lake areas.

Docks and rafts must have a non-skid surface. Use pressure-treated lumber for construction. Allow spaces between boards to allow faster drying and improved grip.

Do not mount diving boards on floating rafts and platforms due to the risks created by the motion of waves and by persons walking or standing on the board.

Do not permit swimming under rafts because lifeguards cannot see patrons who get into difficulty. If water depth is insufficient, prohibit diving from the raft or dock.

Be aware that while rafts can increase the fun potential of a site, they may also tempt weak swimmers to go out beyond their abilities.

LIFEGUARD STATIONS AND CHAIRS

The height of lifeguard chairs and towers provides a scanning advantage for lifeguards. The desired height for a tower or chair depends on the environment in which it is located. The height should provide the lifeguard with adequate sight lines and visibility for the area to be supervised, in addition to efficiency and personal safety in responding to a rescue.

The size of lifeguard stations will be influenced by its function as an observation platform, communications centre, equipment storage place, etc. Permanent stations, which are useful in areas with sufficient patrons and equipment, should be located with consideration for seasonal changes in the water level.

An enclosed lifeguard station is almost essential on ocean beaches. It functions as the communication and basic first aid centre. These buildings are used for safe storage of equipment at night and for the telephone or radio equipment. Signs and a distinctive colour on the sides of the building indicate to the public the function and services available. Locate the building well back from the water for protection from winter conditions and high tide.

An open platform with a wood or canvas roof or an umbrella attached can serve as a lifeguard station.

Build a storage area into the tower unit for securing first aid equipment and special rescue equipment such as skin diving or scuba gear. Tower lifeguards need basic rescue equipment either with them or immediately at hand.

Portable lifeguard chairs may be useful on ocean beaches where they can be moved if necessary as the tide changes. The location of towers and chairs and the distance between them depends on:

- environmental factors
- size, shape, and nature of the area under supervision
- size of the crowd
- wave and weather conditions
- sight lines, visibility
- any special hazards
- local regulations

COMMUNICATION SYSTEMS

Lifeguard towers are usually the centres of communication at beaches. While whistles may be effective on small beaches, the waterfront lifeguard may receive limited patron response from a whistle due to the size of the area, the wind, and noise from waves or boats.

With any electronic or battery powered communication device, extra batteries and a back-up communication system should be in place.

a) Telephone or two-way radio.

Equip each lifeguard station with a telephone or two-way radio. The lifeguards must know the procedures for summoning emergency assistance. A direct line to ambulance dispatch may be provided. When the information is relayed from the lifeguard to an intermediate centre, give only the essential information to the operator, that is, the exact location and the nature of the problem. Code emergencies to minimize communication time, for example:

Code 3 Major accident: require ambulance and resuscitator immediately.

Code 2 Injury with situation under control: advise ambulance to proceed without undue risk.

Code 1 Require police assistance immediately.

Telephones and radios provide opportunity for communication between lifeguard stations or chairs. This may be useful especially when one lifeguard leaves the chair or station to deal with a specific opportunity to educate a patron or to perform minor first aid. Usually a combination of one or more permanent radio sets and a series of portable, battery-operated units are used. The frequency for the system is on citizens' band or public services' band (police or rescue work).

When transmitting and receiving radio communications:

- Identify the receiver's name (or number), and give your name (or number).
- Await acknowledgement.
- State message speaking slowly (50 to 60 words per minute) and distinctly.
- Await acknowledgement before signing off with your name (or number).

Since portable radio units are expensive, ensure their security and protect each unit from damage by water, sand and abuse.

b) Loud hailer, power megaphone, and public address system.

Although these tools are useful, rolling surf and constant background noise decrease their effectiveness. Hand held and battery operated models have an approximate range of 300 metres. Install the public address system at the central tower or administration building.

Lifeguards use a loud hailer or portable public address when attempting to locate parents or children on the beach, or when directing patrons within a limited area.

Restrict the use of a powerful public address system to crowd control and brief general announcements. In an emergency, calmly direct the patrons rather than command them. Speak directly into the microphone – slowly, distinctly, and politely. Use the public address system only for necessary announcements; otherwise patrons ignore its constant bombardment. Consider that you may need to communicate with patrons in more than one language.

c) **Sirens.**

A siren is a possible signal for a water emergency. A few public beaches use sirens as emergency signals. Recognize the possible psychological impact associated with a siren which may make this a fear-inducing device in public areas.

Distress Signals.

The following are visual and audible signals recognized internationally as indicating a vessel in distress.

- Arms outstretched to each side, raised and lowered repeatedly.
- A square flag or shape, having above or below it any ball or circle shape.
- A red flare, of parachute, star or hand-held types.
- An orange coloured smoke flare.
- A light, sound or radio signal of S.O.S. in Morse code (... – – – ...).
- The word "Mayday" repeated on radiotelephone (channel 16, VHF marine band).

d) **Hand signals.**

See *Communication Among Lifeguards* in Chapter 3.

RESCUE EQUIPMENT

LAND VEHICLES

On long stretches of supervised or partially supervised beach, a four-wheel drive vehicle has several useful functions. You can move a victim to the first aid centre, bring equipment and additional personnel to the site of an emergency, assist with crowd control, and perform general maintenance duties. Make your rescue vehicle easy to identify; equip it with a siren, flashing top light, and radio.

The personnel using the rescue vehicles are responsible for their daily inspection and maintenance. Rescue equipment in vehicles can include rescue cans or tubes, stretcher, blankets, spineboard, first aid kit, extra line, oxygen equipment, and items specific to the beach or terrain.

Operate the vehicles at low speeds. Restrict the use of lights and siren to serious emergencies. Because people are interested in the function of the rescue vehicles, they will crowd around in an emergency. Politely request onlookers to remain clear.

Most people are unaccustomed to vehicles on a beach, and small children who move quickly present a special hazard. Exercise caution, especially when backing up. Install and use a back-up "beeper."

BOATS

The type of boat needed depends on its intended function. You might need a boat for:

- rescues within the swimming area
- patrolling outside the supervised swimming area or beyond the surfline
- daily checks and maintenance of the area and related equipment
- search operations
- assistance to other boats (if using a power boat).

The size of the boat and motor varies according to the area supervised. Inflatable rescue boats (IRB) with rigid hulls are ideal.

A power boat is desirable for rescuing other craft. Staff the rescue boat with two persons knowledgeable in rescue, firefighting, towing, navigation, radio operation, and under water search. Rescue boats should carry radio equipment to communicate the victim's exact location and to summon additional assistance if required.

The following equipment is desirable in the rescue boat:

- buoyant aid and line
- first aid kit
- blanket
- anchor and line
- mask, fins, snorkel, and scuba gear (if appropriate)
- personal flotation devices
- bailing apparatus
- extra oar, paddle, and gasoline (for motors)
- communication device(s)

Operating power vessels requires technical knowledge and skill for which training is necessary. Procedures for routine operation and rescue should be in accordance with all applicable regulations and small craft safety principles. (See *Boat Rescues* in Chapter 5.)

a) At shore.

Rescue boats often are placed at the water's edge. During the hours in which patrons are using the area, pull the boat onto the beach just far enough to keep it in position. Point the bow toward the water keeping oars or motor in ready position. After hours, pull the boat well ashore, secure it, and remove and safely store rescue equipment overnight.

b) At docks.

When the boat is moored ready for emergencies, secure it with a knot which is easily untied (chain knot, loop knot, or clove hitch). After hours, tie the boat securely and remove rescue equipment to a secure storage place.

Make the public aware that the rescue boat is for rescue purposes only; if they see it in use, they must remain clear. Alert patrons by printing the word "RESCUE" on both sides of the craft in bright safety yellow or orange.

Fibreglass and aluminum are popular materials for small rescue craft. Increasingly popular are inflatable rescue boats. These craft are flexible, very stable, and easily stored during offseason. Fast enough to provide effective small craft supervision, they are also highly manoeuvrable for personal rescue work.

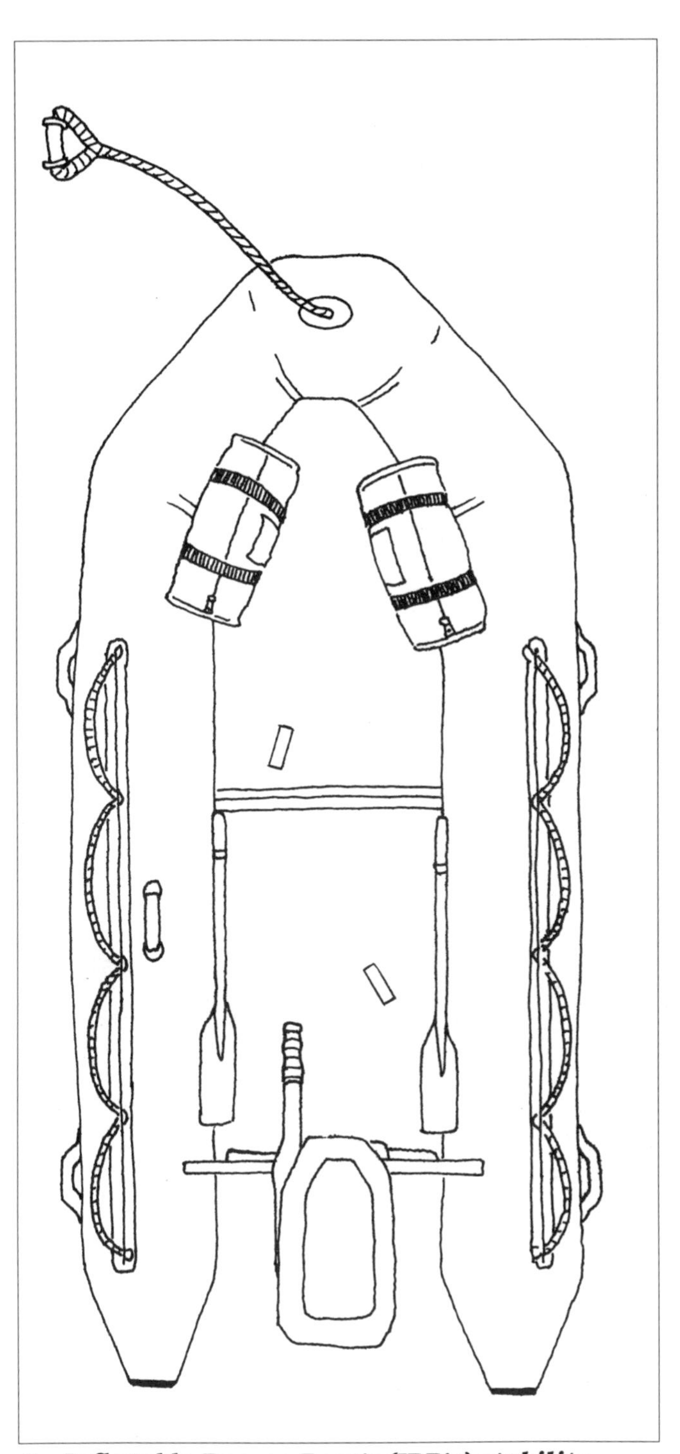

An Inflatable Rescue Boat's (IRB's) stability, speed, light weight and low freeboard, make it an effective rescue craft.

The advantages of a jet boat over more conventional craft are that they:

- are capable of entrance and exit through very rough surf conditions
- can operate within the surf zone
- are highly manoeuvrable, that is, fast acceleration and deceleration and can make turns of 180 degrees in their own wakes
- have smooth bottoms with no propeller, making them safer in shallow waters

Some significant limitations of jet boats, are that they:

- have no back-up propulsion system in case of engine failure
- maintain less stable positioning
- have less room on board for rescued individuals
- have a flat bottom which makes maintaining a steady course in rough seas difficult

PADDLEBOARDS

In medium and light waves the paddleboard is a fast and efficient method for reaching a swimmer in trouble. You can travel a great distance on a paddleboard with minimum fatigue. It is easily carried on land, launched, and manoeuvred. The paddleboard's buoyancy can support several victims and can provide flotation for effective artificial respiration in deep water. Both rescuer and victim can ride a paddleboard to shore.

Keep paddleboards close to the water during hours of operation. Move portable stands or blocks for the boards as tides change. In calm conditions, a lifeguard can patrol from the paddleboard.

Check paddleboards daily for required repairs.

See *Paddleboard Rescues* in Chapter 5.

RESCUE CANS AND RESCUE TUBES

Rescue cans and tubes are effective rescue aids which provide buoyant support both in calm water and in rough surf. Refer to Chapter 4, *Lifeguarding Skills and Procedures*, for information on these valuable pieces of equipment.

SKIN DIVING EQUIPMENT

Masks, fins, and snorkels allow lifeguards to perform water searches and underwater inspections of rafts, anchor lines, and bottom conditions even in murky water.

a) Masks.

Desirable facemask features include:

- Sufficient flexibility to fit face contours comfortably yet provide a water-tight seal.
- Shatterproof glass lens attached by a removable metal band.
- Head straps easily adjustable with firmly secured strap clamps.
- Solid nose piece without purge holes.

b) Snorkel.

J-shaped open tubes are popular. Although the design is a matter of individual preference, select one with the following features:

- Comfortable, properly fitting mouthpiece.
- Forms a right angle with the water surface when you swim face-down.
- Open tube without one-way valves (which are not recommended because they may jam and leak).
- Easily cleared in one breath by blasting or displacement method.

c) Fins.

Consider the fit when selecting fins. If they are too tight, your feet will cramp; if they are too loose, your feet will chafe and blister.

Fins are available in two designs. Full foot-pocket types with moderately stiff blades protect the feet from rocks and sharp objects. Open heel fins have adjustable foot straps to adapt to varying foot sizes. Because the blade is stiff, open heel fins can strain the leg muscles of inexperienced divers. The stiffer blade provides tremendous thrust. Choose buoyant fins which float if you lose them in the water.

REEL AND LINE

In other countries, the reel and line is mainly used during competitions rather than rescues. In Canada, the reel and line is used infrequently. Its chief advantage is that it protects the rescuer and assists the lifeguard during the return to shore. Because Canadian beaches are frequently staffed by a minimal number of lifeguards, the reel and line is impractical. At least two people are needed to move the reel into position.

STORAGE AND LOCATION OF EQUIPMENT

Store rescue equipment in an easily accessible place because each second that passes while fetching stretchers, blankets, resuscitators, and spineboards is critical. Use the same area to neatly store regular waterfront equipment and tools; only experienced personnel handle emergency equipment. Keep combustible materials and products and firefighting equipment in a separate storage area built with fireproof material.

Conduct daily inspections of all rescue equipment and replace or repair items that are not in first-class condition. Written reports indicating the completion of inspections are vital if subsequent legal action results from equipment failure during a rescue.

Daily Tasks of a Waterfront Lifeguard

There are daily jobs to do routinely at a beach or waterfront. Use the following checklist for these daily duties.

- **Water tests**
  - ❑ Temperature
  - ❑ Bacterial counts (as required)
  - ❑ Water clarity
  - ❑ Visible pollution
  - ❑ Bottom conditions
  - ❑ Currents/surf conditions
- **Equipment checks**
  - ❑ Rescue cans and tubes
  - ❑ Binoculars
  - ❑ Skin and scuba gear
  - ❑ Resuscitators
  - ❑ Spineboards
  - ❑ Stretcher
  - ❑ Public address system
  - ❑ Radios, telephones
  - ❑ Whistles, sirens, megaphones
  - ❑ Paddleboards
  - ❑ Boats and motors
  - ❑ First aid supplies
- **Maintenance**
  - ❑ Clean the beach, docks, rafts.
  - ❑ Check security of floatlines and markers.
  - ❑ Check construction, equipment, and tidiness of lifeguard stations and towers.
  - ❑ Put out/take in appropriate flags.
  - ❑ Clean and disinfect change houses.
  - ❑ Place found articles in "Lost and Found."
  - ❑ Check fire extinguishers.
  - ❑ Post, change, take in signs.
  - ❑ Check lights in buildings.
  - ❑ Inspect boats and motors.
  - ❑ Inspect vehicles.

CAMP PROGRAMS

Summer camps offer a variety of aquatic programs and activities, many of which take place in a limited area. Because resident camp owners frequently are held to a higher standard of care than operators of public beaches, the organization, administration, and training of camp aquatic staff must be adapted to include these extra demands.

GUIDELINES FOR CAMP WATERFRONTS

Planning for a summer camp waterfront requires special consideration. Swimming can include both a recreational and an instructional program; therefore, design structures to meet both needs. A boating program requires docking and mooring areas for rescue craft, sailboats, sailboards, canoes, rowboats, and other equipment. Also include facilities and areas for land instruction.

The purpose of the program should be reflected in the design of the waterfront. For example, if one of the goals is to provide every camper with an opportunity to participate in all aquatic activities, the waterfront layout must provide adequate space, varying water depths, and the appropriate equipment to meet this goal.

Camp waterfronts frequently provide only one entrance or a single entrance for each specific activity, for example: one for swimmers, another for canoeists, and another for sailors.

Camps should design their waterfront areas to accommodate unskilled sailors and canoeists who may have difficulty handling their craft. Dock or moor sailboats on the leeward side of the swimming area. Since canoes and kayaks are usually stored on racks or on docks at the shore, place them further downwind from the sailing docks or moorings.

Camps should have policies governing the campers' use of equipment. For example, the person in charge of waterskiing will decide when a camper is too tired to attempt another turn, or the person in charge of sailing will be responsible for approving the use of a boat in need of minor repairs.

Camps will also have a system to determine which activities are open to campers with injuries; a medical log records each injury and participation limitations in the programs.

Camp staff working as lifeguards should begin each season with a facility analysis of hazards and risks. (See *Assessment and Planning* and *Assessing Hazards and Risks* in Chapter 2.) All camps are expected to meet the following criteria:

a) Emergency procedures.

- A siren, bell, horn, or similar device specifically for emergencies must be in place. The emergency signal calls campers and staff to gather in a central location. The same device can be used to initiate a missing person search.
- Written instructions for emergencies must be prepared and distributed to all staff. Rehearsals are held to ensure each person knows his or her role in the emergency.
- In many camps, a method is required to signal all boaters and boardsailors to return to shore immediately. Often a flag is used for this purpose.

b) Waterfront equipment.

- Safety and rescue equipment must meet or exceed government regulations where such regulations exist.
- Transport Canada Small Vessel Regulations are followed regarding equipment and procedures for all small craft.
- A rescue craft must be provided for use in emergencies. A suitably equipped small power boat must be available at all times when boating activities are in progress.

c) Rules.

- Specific safety rules are established for each aquatic activity. Campers know these rules. Staff have the same rules and expectations as campers.
- Do not permit swimming and boating after dark. Define areas for each water activity.
- Use a check-in and check-out system. The staff in charge must know how many participants are in or on the water at all times.
- Individuals unable to swim the distance defined for a boating activity must wear a PFD at all times in the boat.
- Boardsailors must wear a PFD.

d) Staff.

- Staff must hold the qualifications required by government regulations. Where no government regulations are in place, camp leaders should hold relevant certifications in the activity. For example, swim staff should hold certifications from the Canadian Red Cross Society, or YMCA, and from the Royal Life Saving Society Canada.
- At least two staff members must be on duty when people are swimming; the number of staff is increased in proportion to the number of swimmers.
- The waterfront director must be experienced in the activities offered as well as in the leadership requirements for each activity.

e) Program organization.

- Restrict activities to specific areas.
- Screen campers for swimming ability before they participate in waterfront activities. The required level of swimming ability varies with the demands of the activity. For example, campers taking canoe trips may be required to swim 500 m but campers canoeing in the designated area at camp may be required to swim 200 m.
- Familiarize campers with the use and feel of their PFD before participation in any boating activity.
- All staff and campers practice a boating capsize procedure prior to participation in boating programs. In canoeing, a "dump" test is required of participants. In kayaking, a "wet exit" is required. In sailing, the capsize procedure depends upon the craft. In fast water programs, the ability to proceed to safety after capsizing is required.
- For long distance swims, each swimmer must be accompanied by a suitable boat equipped with a reaching and throwing aid, bailer, spare oars, and at least two qualified staff members.

RULES FOR GROUPS USING RESIDENT CAMPS

Camps which contract out their facilities to groups such as schools, organizations, and youth groups must establish rules for the use of the waterfront area and equipment. If you are a lifeguard with one of these groups, ascertain the rules and explain them fully to your people. This information should be in writing and posted in one or more locations:

- Specific hazards of the waterfront area.
- Camp emergency procedures.
- Behaviour expected of all participants.
- Supervision required before use of the waterfront or equipment is permitted.
- When and where swimming is permitted.
- How to enter the water, e.g., use of buddy system or other check-in method; entry at a specific spot; no dive entry from shore or docks into shallow water which can result in a diver with a broken neck or spine; walk on docks and rafts.
- Rules for the use of canoes, boats, kayaks, and sailboards, including use of PFDs or lifejackets.
- Requirements for specific clothing for each activity. For example, sneakers for sailors and boardsailors.
- Risks of hypothermia and what to do if you accidentally find yourself in cold water.

RIVER RECREATION

Popular river activities include canoeing and kayaking by skilled club members, canoeing by amateurs who have no knowledge of the craft, tubing or riding an inner tube down river with and without other participants, white water rafting, "crazy boat" races, and other special events. Commercial operators organize many of these activities, others are individual casual pursuits.

If you are involved in any river activities, use the assessment model outlined in *Assessing Hazards and Risks* in Chapter 2.

a) Determine risks.

Consider:

- Currents, eddies, whirlpools
- Obstacles and underwater hazards
- Capsize and separation from the boat or tube
- Injury while in the water
- Loss of propeller, paddle, or rudder

b) Eliminate risks.

Determine which risks can be eliminated through training and equipment:

- Helmets or PFDs to be worn by participants.
- Use only suitable sections of rivers for specific activities.
- Educate participants in techniques and judgments required.
- Practice rescues with participants.
- Prohibit participants who have capsized from returning to the activity if they are cold and/or exhausted.
- Do not allow participants to modify a craft where buoyancy, stability, and strength are reduced by the adjustments.

c) Control risks.

Regulate the activity:

- Establish rules for the activity. Specify which craft, tubes, or rafts are permitted.
- Require people to cooperate with others. Demand that participants must assist if they see others in difficulty.
- Locate safety equipment, especially throw bags, in key areas in boats, on rafts and on shore.
- Allow, or recommend that an activity be allowed only in safe temperatures. This is especially important in river rafting and fast-water kayaking.
- Cancel an activity if the weather becomes unsuitable.
- Permit certain activities only at specific times in the year or day, thereby maximizing supervision and assistance and avoiding environmental hazards.
- Establish emergency procedures and advise all participants.

Daily Report for Waterfronts or Beaches

Location . . . . Date . . . .

Weather conditions: am . . . . pm . . . .

Visibility . . . .

Air temperature . . . . Wind speed & direction . . . .

Water conditions: Height of waves . . . .

Temperature . . . . . . Current . . . .

Attendance: Beach - max. am . . . . min. am . . . . max. pm . . . . min. pm . . . .

Water - max. am . . . . min. am . . . . max. pm . . . . min. pm . . . .

Areas open . . . .

Towers open . . . .

Cars . . . .

Buses . . . .

Offshore boat traffic: heavy . . . . medium . . . . light . . . . negligible . . . .

Personnel on duty . . . .

Personnel called in . . . .

Equipment checks . . . .

Drills completed . . . .

Swimming rescues . . . .

Boat rescues . . . .

False alarms . . . .

Major first aid . . . .

Minor first aid . . . .

Lost persons . . . .

Repairs or equipment required . . . .

Signature . . . .

TEST YOURSELF

1. *Develop a list of questions and interview an experienced beach guard at the beach or waterfront. Construct the list of questions as if you were going to work at that beach. At the conclusion of the interview, refer to* Beach Organization *and* Daily Tasks of a Waterfront Lifeguard *in Chapter 12. Do you now have a more practical understanding of these items?*
2. *Visit a supervised beach or waterfront. Ask to shadow guard with an experienced lifeguard. Follow him or her throughout the day; when possible, ask the guard to point out hazardous features or conditions.*
3. *Enroll in a small craft course to learn the fundamentals of boating and sailing.*
4. *Visit an unsupervised pond, waterfront, river, beach, or conservation area. Draw the plan for setting up a safe swimming area there. Be sure to include in your plans a list of things you would do:*
   - *prior to opening the area*
   - *to mark the swimming area*
   - *to best protect the natural environment*
   - *to ensure you have enough lifeguards and equipment*
5. *If there is a popular, but unsupervised, swimming spot in your local area, write up a plan to make it safer. Approach your local council with your suggestions.*
6. *Main Street School has hired you as the lifeguard to supervise its students during an outdoor education experience at a resident camp. Write the questions you need to ask the camp's waterfront director prior to your arrival.*
7. *Draw a diagram of an ideal camp waterfront which includes a swim area (0 - 4.0 m in depth) 40 canoes, 12 kayaks, 16 sailboats, and 12 sailboards. Indicate the separate activity areas and the location of safety equipment required for each area. The waterfront accommodates 200 campers in summer; however, you are lifeguarding a school group of 50 students. What arrangements will you make with teachers to share the supervision? What qualifications will the teachers need for each area?*

Chapter 13

Waterpark Operation and Safety

Chapter Focus

Waterparks are different. As in other aquatic environments, novice and non-swimmers frequently find themselves in difficulty when they surpass their limits. However, the unique attractions of waterparks such as slides, wave pools, and river rides, all give rise to unique lifeguarding challenges in both supervision and rescue procedures.

This chapter highlights the characteristics of waterparks which have lifeguarding implications and outlines appropriate lifeguarding procedures for prevention, recognition, and rescue.

Think About the Reactions of a New Waterpark Lifeguard

Oh-oh, this isn't going to be like a pool at all!

How high is that slide? How fast do they travel on that one?

How big can they make the waves? How many people are in that wave pool? Will I recognize a problem if there is one?

Now, what did the supervisor mean by saying that things happen all the time? What did he mean that we would "freeze" at first?

Normally you watch for movement, but here everything is moving? And the look on their faces! But many of them have that look when they arrive in the catch pool....

And the water is always moving! What if a little kid gets in trouble in one of these currents? Will I be quick enough? Time factors seem so stressful. The supervisor said it, "You have to be quick because there is another rider coming." I hope that dispatcher won't be too fast and cause accidents.

What a pace... Rotation again, has it already been half an hour? So this is what they meant, "You know that you'll do a rescue everyday." And they were right – it is a minor event as long as you're quick – otherwise it's trouble.

The season seems all wrong – big groups at the beginning, small groups at the end. And the school groups: I don't understand the behaviour of some of them.

INTRODUCTION TO WATERPARKS

WATERPARK CHARACTERISTICS

A waterpark is an outdoor or indoor recreational park featuring a variety of activities with aquatic apparatus. Such attractions include wave pools, water slides, river rides, overhead chariot rides and rope swings, water craft, swimming pools, and beaches.

The lifeguarding experience at waterparks is different from that at wading pools, swimming pools, or beaches. Waterparks attract large numbers of people who move among the specialized waterpark attractions. Greater numbers of lifeguards and attendants are required to operate waterparks than are required at a traditional aquatic facility. Waterpark programming is oriented to providing entertainment.

The impact of these characteristics will be apparent in the difference in lifeguard duties, the knowledge and understanding lifeguards need about their park, and the direct and constant involvement they will have with patrons in guiding their activities. Waterpark amenities and equipment continue to evolve and improve, but lifeguards may find the need to compensate for older waterpark rides which may lack the safety factors increasingly incorporated in newer equipment.

THE ROLE OF THE WATERPARK LIFEGUARD

Waterpark lifeguards need both knowledge of the operation and potential difficulties associated with each attraction, as well as the skills and judgment to prevent accidents and perform rescues in the waterpark environment. Since waterpark lifeguards are often directly involved in the operation of the equipment, the successful prevention of accidents is in their hands.

The number of visitors to a waterpark and the variety of activities featured demand lifeguards who are skilled, competent, and knowledgeable. A professional attitude in the performance of all tasks, including the rescue and the care of persons needing assistance, is essential.

WHY THINGS GO WRONG

The causes of waterpark accidents can be divided into four categories:

a) **Equipment.**
- design
- construction
- inspection
- maintenance

b) **Management policies.**
- operational philosophy
- established rules and regulations
- follow-up on these rules and regulations

c) **Personnel.**
- application or enforcement of waterpark rules and regulations
- instructions given to patrons

d) **Patrons.**
- knowledge of waterpark rules and regulations
- willingness to abide by the rules and regulations
- physical ability
- behavioural or limiting factors such as use of alcohol/drugs

(From *Lifeguarding in the Waterparks*, by Richard Huint.)

WATERPARK EQUIPMENT

Waterpark equipment includes water slides, river rides, wave pools, activity basins, and specialty attractions. Each attraction requires operating knowledge, awareness of risks, lifeguarding strategies, and rescue procedures. Managers, operators, lifeguards, and attendants must heed the specific recommendations based on the manufacturers' tests of their equipment. Lifeguards need to remain current with the standards used by the waterpark industry through training programs and conferences, and to adapt their procedures as necessary to provide maximum pleasure and security for their patrons.

Checklist for Developing Waterpark Safety Rules

- Use limits
  - ❑ Age
  - ❑ Height
  - ❑ Weight
  - ❑ Medical history
  - ❑ Physical condition
  - ❑ Doctor's care
  - ❑ Prosthetic devices
  - ❑ Limitations due of use of drugs (prescription or non-prescription) or alcohol
- Attire
  - ❑ Clothing
  - ❑ Jewellery
  - ❑ Eyeglasses
- Special warnings
  - ❑ Phobias
  - ❑ Elements of surprise
  - ❑ Ride experience
  - ❑ Exhaustion/speed
  - ❑ Relative degree of difficulty
- Transport device
  - ❑ Tubes
  - ❑ Rafts
  - ❑ Sleds
  - ❑ Mats
  - ❑ Other
- Riding posture
  - ❑ Head first
  - ❑ Feet first
  - ❑ Prone
  - ❑ Supine
  - ❑ Seated
- Rider conduct
  - ❑ Twisting
  - ❑ Tossing about
  - ❑ Changing position
  - ❑ Trains (multiple riders)
  - ❑ Horseplay
- Entry techniques
  - ❑ Diving
  - ❑ Running
  - ❑ Swinging
  - ❑ Pushing off
- Entry and exit regulations
  - ❑ Entry and exit stipulations
  - ❑ Points of authorized entry/exit
  - ❑ Water depth at exit
- General
  - ❑ Special rules reflecting the unique aspects of the attraction/apparatus
  - ❑ Instruct - "Please follow the directions of lifeguards and attendants."
  - ❑ Warn - "Failure to follow rules and instructions can result in serious injury."

(From *Considerations for Operating Safety*, published by the World Waterpark Association, 1989.)

MOVING WATER AND MOVING RIDERS

An understanding of the movement of both riders and moving water may help lifeguards anticipate potential difficulties. If, for example, a rider does not follow the path created by the designer of the ride, the lifeguard knows how to overcome the difficulty or how to adapt the operation to prevent injuries.

a) Water flow.

Friction is a force which opposes movement. In waterpark attractions, friction can be either beneficial or harmful depending on where and when it occurs. Two types of friction occur on water slides and in river rides: sliding friction occurs when one surface passes over another. Smooth surfaces offer less resistance than rough ones. Viscous friction occurs when an object passes through a fluid. Viscous friction increases as surface area increases. Viscous friction increases with the square of the velocity; this means that the faster a rider moves through the water, the greater the force resisting the movement.

The volume of water flowing in the slide or the river also affects the rider's speed.

When the flow is properly set, viscous friction limits and controls rider speed as the rider moves through the course of the attraction. Insufficient water on the slide acts as a lubricant dangerously increasing riding speed. Lifeguards must always watch the flow of water and make adjustments when necessary. Excess speed resulting from an inadequate volume of water is a hazard to avoid.

b) Acceleration through a curve.

Movement through a curve accelerates a rider. This property of angular motion can lead to difficulties if the flow of water is not well controlled. A rider moving through a curve accelerates and moves beyond the flow of the water. Here, sliding friction slows the rider and can cause skin burns and injuries if the rider's speed is sufficiently slowed to cause a fall from the embankment of the slide to the bottom of the flume.

c) Kinetic energy.

Kinetic energy results from movement (and is calculated using the formula: K.E. = 0.5 mv^2 in which m = mass and v = velocity). Calculations will show that the kinetic energy of a rider weighing 80 kg is twice that of a 40 kg rider travelling at the same speed. Similarly, the kinetic energy of a rider travelling at 20 km/h is four times that of a rider travelling at 10 km/h when their weight is equal.

Kinetic energy must be removed from the moving system to stop the rider. This must be done progressively to stop the rider safely. Since hydrostatic braking is used in catch pools and in run-out channels, the correct water levels in both must be maintained to stop the riders properly. Should a rider collide with either the structure or another rider, the severity of the injury is likely to be proportional to the kinetic energy involved.

d) Somersaulting riders.

Riders may somersault as they arrive in a catch pool or run-out channel either because of their riding position (if they are heavy in the upper body), or because of the position of their feet when they first make contact with the water. A sudden increase in viscous friction causes a rapid deceleration. With the rider's feet acting as the fulcrum and the body acting as the lever, the kinetic energy causes the rider to somersault; injuries can result. Prevent this by controlling the water level in the exit zone and by ensuring that riders adopt a safe riding position.

e) Currents.

Flowing water develops a variety of currents and counter-currents which affect riders and bathers. Three principle currents occur in water slides and river rides: the main current of water passing through a basin or a flume; the hydraulic current; and the vortex current.

In the basins of a Stop-and-Go river ride, especially if they are long, and in water slide catch pools, the three currents can affect riders. The hydraulic's effect occurs on entry into the basin. The vortex affects riders as a counter-current which can impede their progress, while the forward motion of the main current draws them in its direction.

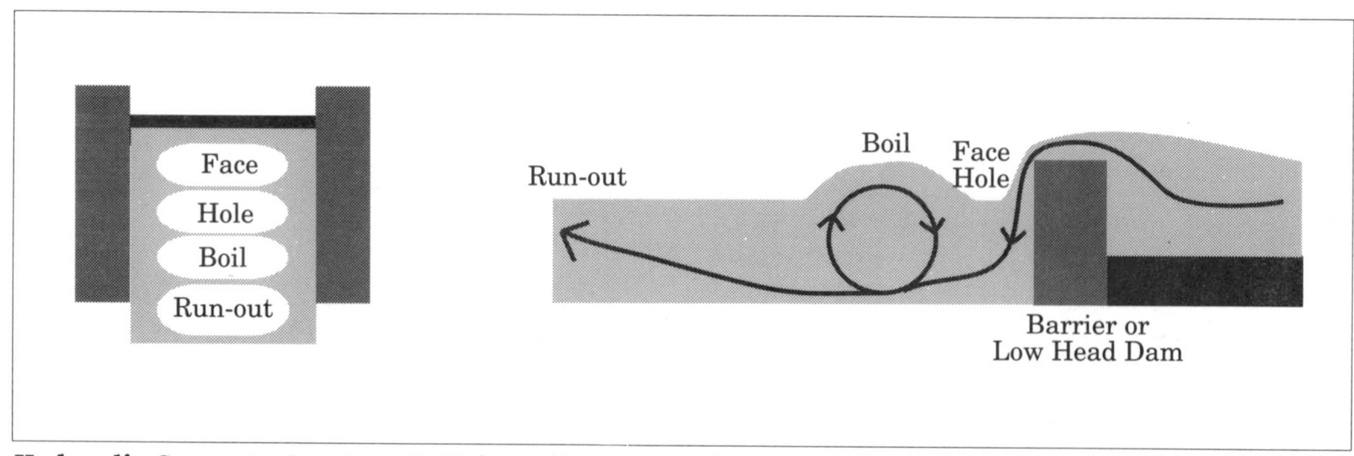

Hydraulic Current.* *Courtesy R. Huint, Lifeguarding in the Waterparks © 1990, Aqualude Inc.

- **Hydraulic current**

  A hydraulic current occurs when water flows over a barrier. It is characterized by a "hole" as the water plunges over the barrier down to the bottom of the basin and the return flow or "boil" as it comes back to the surface. The water flows out in the run-out zone of the current. Both the volume of water and the distance it has fallen after passing over the barrier affect the strength of the hydraulic current.

  Riding rafts or tubes can be overturned as they encounter the "hole" and the return "boil." Riders who have been ejected from these riding vehicles can be held under water by the boil if it is strong enough.

- **Vortex current**

  A vortex current occurs when water changes direction as it enters a basin or an open zone in a slide. The greater the change of direction, the more evident the effect of the vortex current. The strength of the vortex increases as the volume of flowing water increases. A barrier in a basin where a vortex current occurs strengthens the vortex current. This is a counter-current to the main flow.

- **Venturi effect**

  This effect develops as water slows down before a constriction and accelerates after it has passed through. The acceleration of the water accelerates the rider. This is typical in basins of a Stop-and-Go river. If there is a curve soon after, the acceleration is more pronounced and can lead to the loss of rider control or even an ejection from the structure.

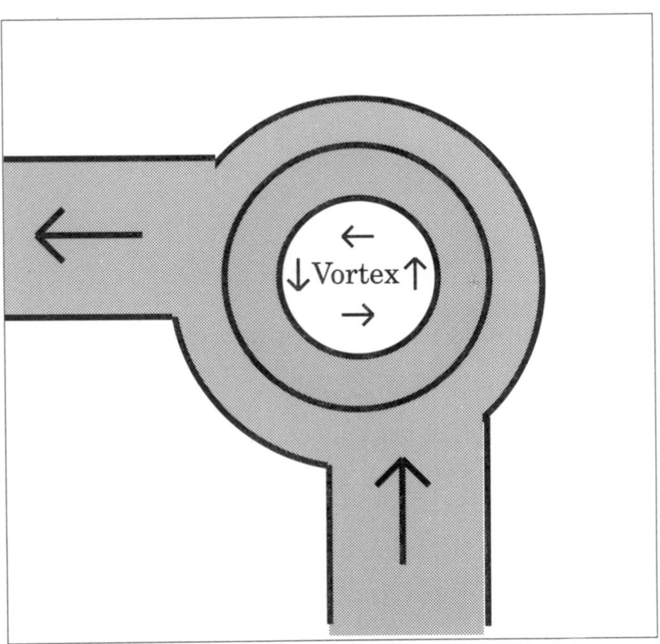

Vortex Current. Courtesy R. Huint, Lifeguarding in the Waterparks © 1990, Aqualude Inc.

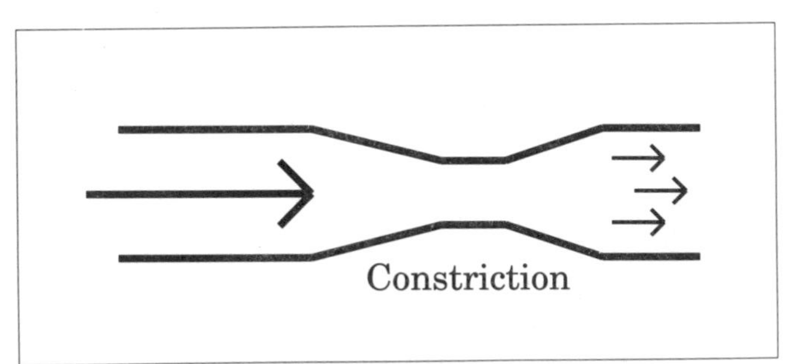

Venturi Effect: A constriction in the path of a moving fluid causes a decrease in the pressure of the flow, but it also causes an increase in the speed of the moving fluid. Courtesy R. Huint, Lifeguarding in the Waterparks © 1990, Aqualude Inc.

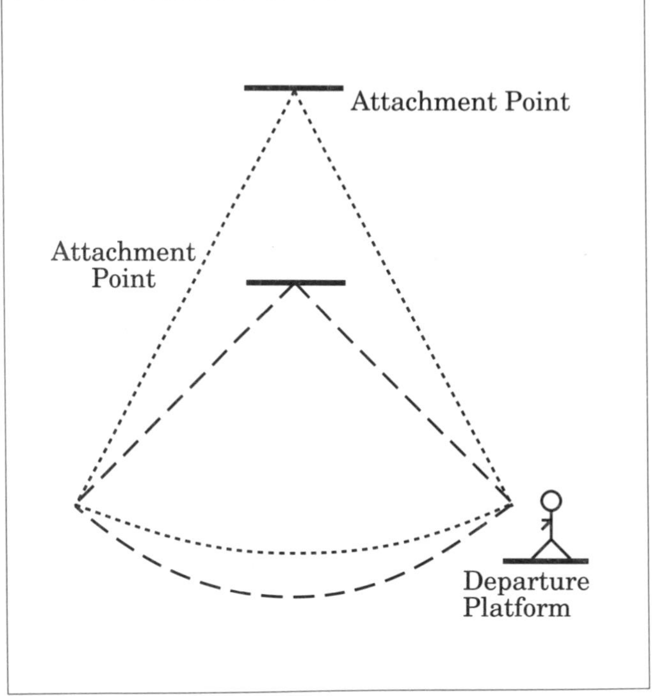

Pendulum Adjustment: The diagram shows that by raising the point where the swing is attached, the vertical distance through which the rider will pass while holding the swing is reduced. This also will reduce the shock of the force which the rider will encounter. Courtesy R. Huint, Lifeguarding in the Waterparks © 1990, Aqualude Inc.

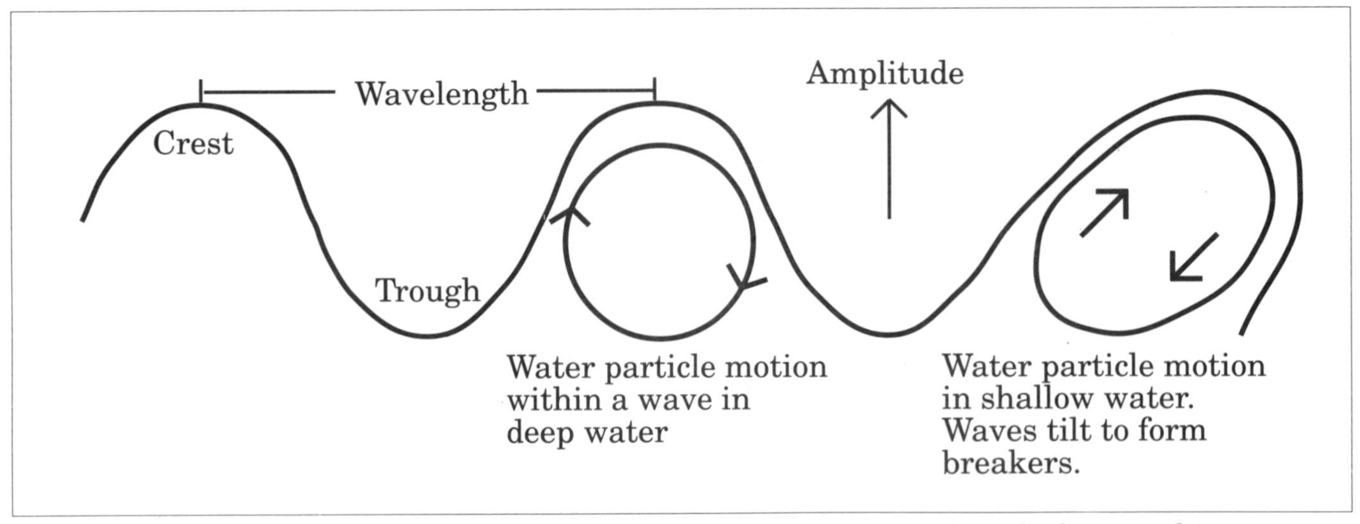

Waves: As the wave enters shallow water, wave speed decreases, wavelength shortens, but amplitude increases. In wave pools where the configuration of the bottom has been varied to create special effects in the passing waves, these factors will be affected. Courtesy R. Huint, Lifeguarding in the Waterparks © 1990, Aqualude Inc.

f) Wave motion.

In a wave pool, the motion of the waves is different in the deep end from that in the shallow end because of the friction between the wave and the bottom of the pool in the shallow end. The fan-shaped beach of the wave pool dissipates the energy of the waves by spreading it out. This assures that no reflected waves will return to affect bathers in the pool.

g) Pendulum.

The principle of the pendulum is the basis of the Tarzan swing. The force of a pendulum provides both control and a more pleasant ride. The force of the swing is directed to a point of equilibrium and is affected by the vertical distance through which the rider passes while holding the swing. If the vertical distance is great, the force exerted on the rider's hands, wrists, arms, elbows, and shoulders is great. To minimize the strain on the body, keep the vertical distance to a minimum by raising the point of attachment of the swing as high as possible.

WATER SLIDES

TYPES OF WATER SLIDES

Several types of water slides are in use. Each type is operated according to its specific requirements to maintain maximum safety conditions.

Slides can be categorized as moderate or high speed slides, drop-off slides, free fall slides, tube, mat, or sled slides, and "kiddie" slides.

a) Moderate speed slides.

Moderate speed slides have a gentle slope and riding speed is not especially fast. Often, they are called Serpentine slides or "Twisters." These slides end in catch pools which are both deep enough and wide enough to allow riders to stop gently and safely. They can be operated with several riders at a time in the flume if there is sufficient space and time between riders to avoid collisions during the ride and in the catch pool.

b) High speed slides.

High speed slides are straight and shorter than the moderate speed slides. Often, they are designed to give riders the feeling of "zero gravity" as they pass from one level to another during the ride. "Fast" refers to speeds of 30 km/h or more. Riders may attain speeds of 60 km/h on some slides. High speed slides end in long, narrow run-out channels in which riders glide to a smooth stop. Riders are limited to one at a time in the flume.

c) **Drop-off slides.**

Drop-off slides feature a fall into a deep water basin at the end of the ride. Riders are limited to one at a time in the flume.

d) **Free fall slides.**

Free fall slides give the rider the perception of a vertical free fall through open space during the descent part of the ride. They end in long, narrow run-out channels for smooth stops. Riders are limited to one at a time in the flume.

e) **"Kiddie" slides.**

"Kiddie" slides, designed for little children, are gentle, short, and slow, and end in a catch pool. Some "Kiddie" slides are designed to permit a parent and child combination in the flume.

LIFEGUARDING WATER SLIDES

Before slides open daily to the public, lifeguards inspect the structures for possible damage and ensure that the correct flow of water has been set. Throughout the day, check the water flow and make corrections if riders are sliding too fast or too slowly.

To operate water slides, policies must be established concerning:

- rider eligibility – age, height, weight or medical restrictions (based on equipment manufacturer's guidelines or current industry safety standards)
- riding position
- dispatch timing and control
- exit zone control

a) **Positioning.**

Attendants control the dispatch zone and a lifeguard is stationed at the exit zone of all slides. Where more than two slides exit into a common catch basin, two lifeguards are posted to ensure back-up and ride control should an accident occur. When possible, lifeguards are also placed at strategic locations where they can supervise the course of several slides.

b) **Dispatch zone.**

The attendant at the dispatch zone controls the timing of riders to prevent collisions along the course of the descent and in the catch pools and run-out channels. The safest way to operate water slides is to limit dispatch to one rider at a time.

Moderate speed slides can be operated with more than one rider at a time in the flume if there is sufficient space and time between riders to ensure that no collisions will occur either during the ride or in the catch pool at the end. Riders in high speed or free fall slides are dispatched only when the exit zone guard signals the "all-clear." Sliding with another person is dangerous and should only be permitted in some "kiddie" slides where the design of the equipment is adequate.

Attendants enforce restrictions and explain to patrons how to ride and the correct positions for departure. Riding positions are generally restricted to sitting or lying on the back, feet-first. Although on some slides, riders are required to use a mat in a prone head-first position, this is potentially dangerous if the slide is not designed for this.

Photo: Richard Huint

c) Exit zone.

Lifeguards at the exit zone check that riders have not changed positions during their descent. Riders must leave the exit zone comfortably but quickly, and by the correct pathway (not by crossing other run-out channels). Ask riders waiting for friends to stand back from the immediate area in a safety zone around the exit identified with a rope or a coloured line painted on the deck.

In catch pools, lifeguards are stationed on the top step of the exit to allow them to respond quickly when needed.

In both run-out channels and catch pools, riders can be spatially disoriented when they arrive. An awkward descent with changes in riding position can cause difficulties in the exit zone when riders find themselves in unusual positions.

Often, novice and non-swimmers find themselves in difficulty even in shallow catch pools because they arrive in a sitting position which leads to submersion as they enter the water. In run-out channels, friction is often the cause of discomfort because of the high speed of the ride.

RESCUE TECHNIQUES FOR WATER SLIDES

The most common accidents around water slides are slips and falls because of quick or careless manoeuvres made by patrons. The walkways, stairs, entrance, and exit zones should be protected with non-skid surfaces and lifeguards should direct patrons to walk in these areas.

Rescue techniques for water slides are simple adaptations of those used in pools and beaches. Typically, rescues are necessary in two areas – the exit zone (catch pool or run-out channel), and in the slide itself (most probably in the flume of a moderate speed slide).

a) Rescues in a catch pool.

Rescuers working in a catch pool should remember that, until the dispatcher has been advised of the emergency, riders will continue to arrive. The victim must be moved out of the way of subsequent riders to avoid collision and further injury. Another unique factor is the strength of the currents within the basin. Depending on the incident, lifeguards may have to call for the stoppage of the flow of water.

Lifeguards may frequently have to assist novice or non-swimmers as they submerge

Water Slide Restrictions

- Water slides are not recommended:
  - For patrons knowing or suspecting that they suffer from a chronic condition or handicap which could place them at risk of difficulty or injury.
  - For patrons who have had recent surgery.
  - During pregnancy.
  - For patrons with chronic back conditions.
  - For patrons with known heart conditions.
- T-shirts and bathing suits with metallic decorations are not permitted.
- Cut-off jeans are not permitted.
- Jewellery is not recommended.
- Eyeglasses should not be worn on water slides.

(From *Lifeguarding in the Waterparks*, Richard Huint.)

on arrival. A quick response will prevent this common occurrence from becoming a serious situation.

Where sliding mats, tubes, or sleds are used, riders can slip or tumble from the riding vehicle and suffer injuries or friction burns. Be ready to treat injuries resulting from a high speed tumble from riding sleds and the inverse arching of the lower back as a rider is propelled into deep water on a sliding mat. Control unused riding equipment to keep it from becoming a cause of slips and falls in the exit zone.

The major injuries which can occur on water slides include head or spinal injuries resulting from collisions within the course of the ride. These collisions can be between the rider and the structure or between two riders. In both cases, the victim arrives in the exit zone injured and possibly suffering an impaired level of consciousness. Because of the currents and the victim's position on arrival in the catch pool, immobilization using the upper arms (see *The Canadian Lifesaving Manual*) can be quickly applied and maintained. This technique allows the rescuer to manoeuvre the victim out of the principal current and to use the counter-current to hold the victim in a horizontal position while waiting for assistance.

Another type of serious accident which can occur on water slides is respiratory arrest caused by aspiration and laryngospasm. The rider arrives in the basin unconscious and not breathing.

b) Rescues in a run-out channel.

Lifeguards supervising a slide with a run-out channel, will have to adapt rescue techniques to the narrow space. As with the catch pools, the most difficult rescues will be for victims suffering from head or spinal injury who may have a reduced level of consciousness. If the victim must be placed on a spineboard, several lifeguards working together will lift the victim while the spineboard is slipped into place. The rescuer holding the head and neck directs the rescuer who is pushing the spineboard into place. Removal from the run-out channel is not difficult but should, with the other manoeuvres, be practiced regularly.

Inadequate space between riders causes collisions in the catch pool at the end of the ride.

c) Rescues in the slide.

For victims who have stopped within the slide, lifeguards must provide on-site care. Limited space within the flume makes such a rescue more difficult. Stop the flow of water to allow rescuers to reach the injured victim. Lifeguards and attendants should wear anti-skid shoes (with thin jogging socks for added comfort).

Be prepared to remove the victim from suitable sites along a water slide. Where no exit is possible (often the case on elevated structures), lifeguards descend within the flume itself. This can be done safely using the tread of the non-skid shoes for maximum grip. For a descent with a spineboard, four rescuers each take the corner of the board using the side wall of the slide for support. Practice this technique with a manikin to simulate the weight and the balance of a person. (Such a manikin can be made with a long block of foam rubber in a plastic bag. The foam is filled with water for weight and its length can be made to represent a person on a spineboard.)

RIVER RIDES

River rides are wider than regular water slides, require a greater volume of water to operate, and are used with riding tubes or rafts. All four types of river rides are popular, high-capacity attractions.

CONTINUOUS RIVERS

Continuous rivers, similar to moderate speed slides, operate with the same dispatch timing and control permitting the distribution of riders within its course. Riding tubes or rafts are used. When multiple-rider rafts are used, riders wear helmets, especially on rivers built with bumps to create the effects of river rafting. These rivers are similar to the moderate speed slides in lifeguarding strategies, potential difficulties, and rescue techniques.

Lifeguards supervise riders over the course of the river and at arrival in the basin. Additional, usually less qualified attendants, supervise equipment exchange and storage.

STOP-AND-GO RIVERS

Stop-and-Go rivers consist of a series of chutes and basins through which riders pass, usually in a riding tube. Riders are dispatched one at a time to allow them to be distributed throughout the course of the river. Chains of riders are not permitted because of potential collisions and pile-ups.

As in moderate speed slides and the continuous rivers, lifeguards are stationed in strategic locations to supervise the river, the basins, and the exit zone. Additional attendants are stationed to help riders at basins where hydraulic currents can cause spills and vortex currents can impede continuous movement.

Riders injured in collisions with other riders or with the structure usually do not make it to the exit zone, but are found in the basins. Lifeguards provide on-site treatment to victims and remove victims at the most convenient location. Elevated structures are designed with stairways; however, if lifeguards are rescuing with a spineboard or stretcher, the water must be stopped while the lifeguards descend relying on anti-skid shoes and the structure itself for support.

A technique for controlling the flow of water in a basin assists in the rescue: People (usually arriving riders), deflect the water by standing between the victim and the water arriving in the basin.

SLOW RIVERS

Slow rivers provide a long and lazy cruise in a riding tube, often a distance of 300 m to 450 m with a depth of approximately one metre and a current flowing at approximately five to eight kilometres per hour. These rivers are high capacity and low risk attractions; nevertheless, they must be closely supervised.

Riders enter and exit from stairways at designated access points. Riding tubes are available at the entrance/exit zones and float freely in the river. At busy times, riders are limited to a single trip around the river. A barrier is usually stretched across the river to indicate the limit of the ride. Do not permit entrance and exit from areas other than those designated. Decorative landscaping and fencing guide riders to entry/exit areas.

Lifeguards supervise at entry/exit points and also patrol the river providing continuous supervision. Lifeguards stop any inappropriate or disruptive behaviours such as riders jumping in and out of the river, tipping other tubes, wrestling, duelling, tumbling each other, and racing their tubes. Not only do these activities disturb other riders, they can lead to injuries.

Rescue techniques are the same as in any shallow water basin or pool.

ACTIVITY RIVERS

Activity rivers are similar in construction to slow rivers with the addition of waves and zones or basins which include activities such as volleyball and overhead sprinkling. Lifeguards provide additional supervision in the activity zones. As in wave pools, waves are deactivated for all water rescues.

WAVE POOLS

Wave pools differ from the traditional or the leisure swimming pool most obviously because of their artificially induced waves. Another difference is that people do not come to a wave pool to swim – they come to enjoy the waves.

A wave pool is the beach away from the beach. This is evident on both the busiest and the quietest days. Bathers are generally grouped in two zones; the first, in waist-deep water where the waves break, the second along the fan-shaped beach where the waves wash "ashore." Few patrons go to the deep end of wave pools. In wave pools equipped with riding tubes and air mattresses, patrons are more evenly distributed because they ride the waves rather than play in them.

OPERATIONS

Waves are created by a computer-controlled wave generator, which can be a mechanical instrument with moving "wall" panels, a pressurized air system using the principle of water displacement, or a water pressure system using large tanks and high capacity pumps.

Wave generators can produce parallel waves, skewed waves which travel diagonally across the pool, or diamond shaped waves. Various wave sizes can be created, some as high as two metres. Automatic Wave-Stop buttons built into the electrical circuitry are placed, ideally, at each lifeguard station. Wave-Stop buttons override the computer program and produce calm water within seconds.

Many operators limit wave size to 30 cm to 75 cm and keep wave patterns simple. For example, unidirectional parallel waves are predictable and safer than either the skewed or diamond waves whose lateral movement can push patrons into the walls.

Entrance to a wave pool is limited to the beach end. Wave pools are fenced off around the sides to limit entry. Such fencing should provide a passageway wide enough to allow lifeguards to walk comfortably along the sides of the pool. Signs remind bathers that ladders are for exit only.

The waves are usually operated in cycles punctuated by pauses built into the program. Playing in a wave pool is tiring; the pause allows bathers to rest. When a wave pool becomes very crowded, shortening the wave cycle or stopping the waves encourages many people to leave the water. This intermission reduces the risk to weak or tired bathers, and provides lifeguards with temporary relief from the demanding supervision of a full wave pool during the wave cycle.

Some parks use a bell or a horn to signal the resumption of the wave cycle. This may result in accidents from patrons running to the wave pool from every direction in the park. If this occurs, avoid this practice.

Lines painted on the bottom of the pool dividing it into zones encourage bathers to keep their distance from the walls to avoid injury. Signs posted also remind bathers to keep clear of the walls. A line divides the shallow and the deep zones. Another line limits bathers from passing too close to the wave generator. A suspended cable with signs indicating that bathers should not pass, hangs above the line painted on the pool bottom.

Encourage novice and non-swimmers to use lifejackets or PFDs (personal flotation devices) which should be available in the park. These are either free or are available for a nominal deposit at a control center. Do not permit bathers to wear T-shirts or other clothing in the pool because of the strain they place on

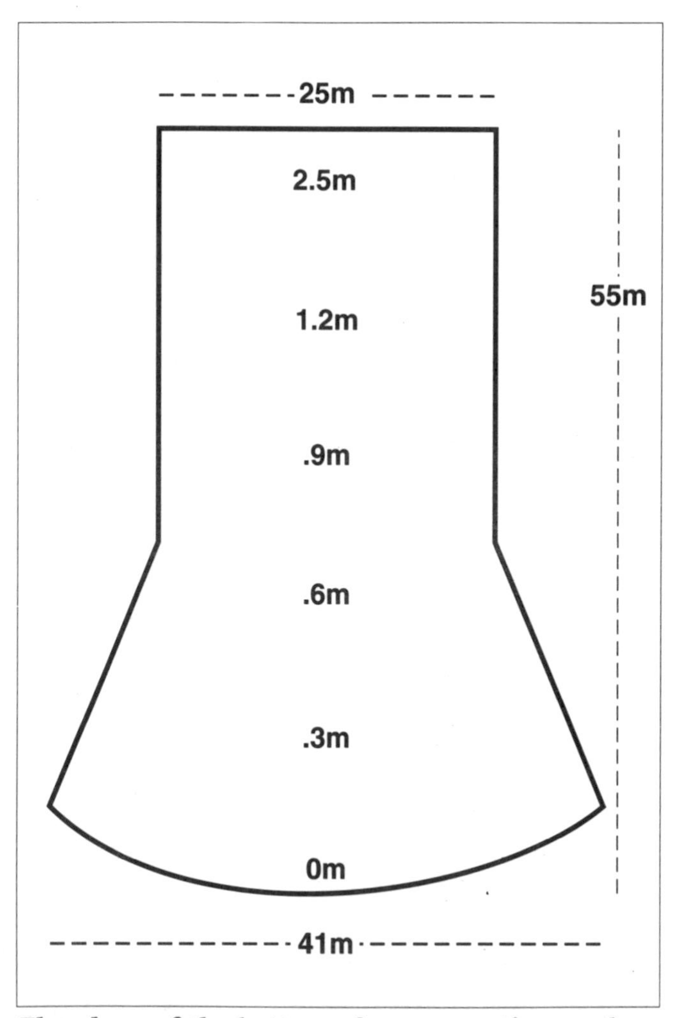

The slope of the bottom of a wave-action pool causes the waves to break. The fan-shaped "beach" end of the pool allows the waves to dissipate.

weak or non-swimmers. Eyeglasses and objects around the neck are a source of possible injury. Permit eyeglasses if they are securely tied. Coin and key containers should be wrapped around the bathers' wrists.

Some waterpark operators permit, as a demonstration or as a regular activity, sports such as surfing or kayaking. When these activities occur, bathers are asked to leave the pool to the participants who are strictly supervised.

LIFEGUARDING THE WAVE POOL

a) Positioning.

Teamwork is an essential element in lifeguarding a wave pool. A strategy of overlapping zones is generally used and lifeguards are added as more bathers arrive. (Refer to any applicable government regulations or standards concerning lifeguard/bather ratios.)

Special towers are being developed for wave pools and lifeguards generally stand during the wave cycle. These new towers feature quick descent steps, overhead protection from the sun, and automatic Wave-Stop controls.

Lifeguard towers in the shallow zone provide a good vantage point in an area which becomes crowded. They also serve as a point of reference for bathers who always know where the shallow water lifeguard is (not possible when a lifeguard patrols this zone on foot).

b) Evacuation.

Establish a policy for the evacuation of the wave pool. Where clearing the pool may be standard procedure for major rescues in traditional pools, it may not always be the best strategy in a crowded wave pool. Much depends on the reason for the evacuation.

Most rescues can be effected with local crowd control (during which most bathers are never aware that a rescue is being carried out), whereas an evacuation would draw attention and a more detailed crowd control operation would become necessary.

When evacuation is necessary, (e.g., an approaching thunder storm), stop the waves to draw the attention of bathers. Then signal and supervise the evacuation.

c) Potential difficulties.

Most frequently novice or non-swimmers are overcome by waves in deep water, especially at the beginning of the cycle. Small children sitting in shallow water also find themselves in difficulty when waves tumble them at the beach or when the return flow of water carries them into deeper water.

Wave Pool Restrictions

- Wave pools are not recommended:
  - For patrons knowing or suspecting that they suffer from a chronic condition or handicap which could place them at risk of difficulty or injury.
  - For patrons who have had recent surgery.
  - During pregnancy.
  - For patrons with chronic back conditions.
  - For patrons with known heart conditions.
- T-shirts, sweatshirts, and similar items are not permitted.
- Jewellery is not recommended.
- Eyeglasses are not permitted in the deep end. They must be securely tied if worn in the shallow end.

(From *Lifeguarding in the Waterparks*, Richard Huint.)

Collisions are also a common hazard. Collisions occur between bathers, between bathers and the walls or the bottom of the pool, and between bathers and the waves.

Prevent bather-to-bather collisions by not permitting bathers to hold on to each other in the deep zone where the waves cause these accidents. Restrict parents who are holding little children to the shallow zone.

Prevent collisions with the structure by ensuring that bathers maintain a safe distance from the walls of the pool, and that they do not body surf or dive in shallow water.

Limit the size of the waves to avoid injuries resulting from collisions between bathers and waves. (People with previous injuries or recent surgery have been injured even by small waves.)

In wave pools where riding tubes and air mattresses are used, the lifeguards' line of sight can be restricted as the pool becomes a sea of flotation equipment. Divide the wave pool into two sections: one limited to bathers, the other to riders on flotation devices, and/or control the number of flotation devices.

d) Rescues in wave pools.

Stop the waves for all water rescues, and use standard rescue techniques. Once a problem is identified signal other guards and descend from the tower. Slip in at the ladder or use a stride entry from the deck into deep water. Never enter the water directly from an elevated tower: wave pools are not deep enough.

Because wave pools become very crowded, use a soft rescue aid to protect bathers. Do not wear anything which could be tightened around your neck, especially whistle lanyards.

Remove the victim from the beach end, or by a ladder with one lifeguard in the water with the victim and another guard on deck. Provide on-site treatment, transport by wheel chair or a portable stretcher to the first aid center, or await the arrival of an ambulance.

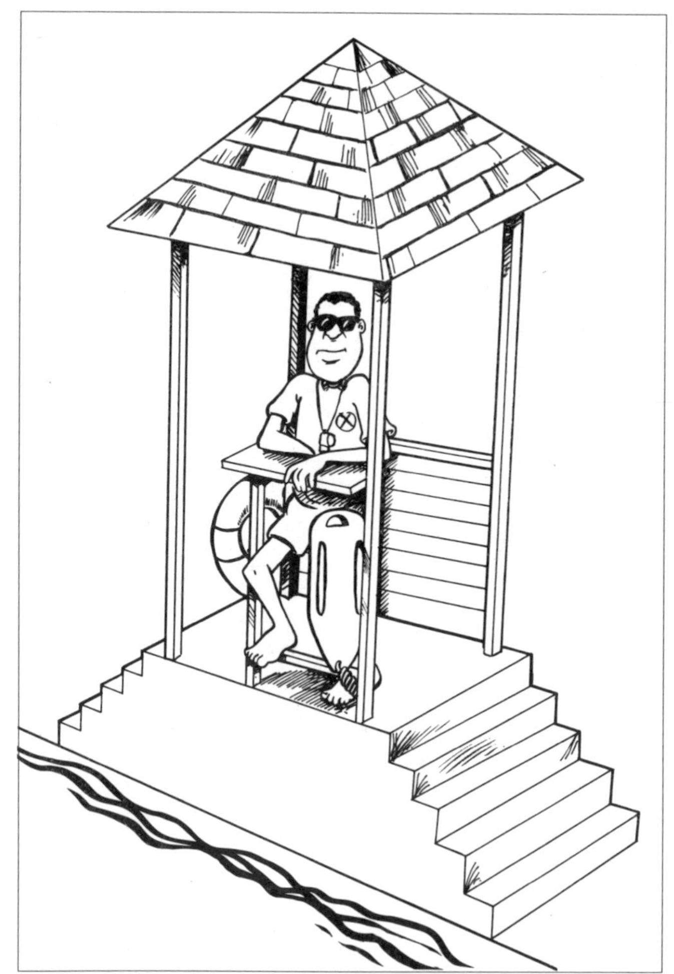

This tower provides easy side access, sun protection, and footrail for standing.

ACTIVITY BASINS AND SPECIAL ATTRACTIONS

ACTIVITY BASINS

Activity basins are shallow water basins where many types of attractions amuse both young and old alike. Among the most popular are floating logs and lily pads, various swings, overhead shower structures, volleyball, and water pistols. Activity basin equipment should be operated according to the manufacturer's instructions. Lifeguards should be wary of patrons who want to adapt the rules to invent new games which may be inappropriate for the equipment or the area. Particular attention should be given to preventing the most frequent shallow water injuries caused by slips and falls, pushes, or head-first dives.

Riders who perform acrobatics risk injury.

SPECIAL ATTRACTIONS

Special attractions continue to be developed for waterparks. Many are successful and safe only when adequately supervised. Lifeguards need to evaluate these new structures and attractions and make recommendations on the purchase of such items.

TARZAN SWINGS AND CABLE CHARIOT RIDES

Tarzan swings and cable chariot rides require close supervision. Restrict their use to patrons who can swim since riders must fall into deep water.

Riders leave in a feet-first position with their elbows bent to absorb the shock of the departure. Riders who leave in a position which directs the body weight to the hands and shoulders risk injury. Those who perform acrobatic manoeuvres in the air can make an unpredictable entry into the water, causing ruptured ear drums and shoulder dislocations. Be ready to rescue novice or non-swimmers who insist on riding despite their lack of swimming skills.

TEST YOURSELF

1. *Arrange for a tour of a waterpark facility. Try to identify patron traffic patterns among the various attractions.*
2. *Develop a list of questions and interview an experienced waterpark lifeguard. Construct the list of questions as if you were going to work at the waterpark.*
3. *Visit a waterpark and ask to shadow guard with an experienced lifeguard. Follow him or her throughout the day; when possible, ask the guard to point out hazardous conditions or features.*
4. *Visit a waterpark as an ordinary patron. Try all the attractions and use the equipment. Make notes which you could use in a presentation about your experience to a group of lifeguard candidates on an NLS course.*

Index